Geography of
RUSSIA

Geography
of
RUSSIA

N. T. Mirov, M.S., Ph.D.

LECTURER IN GEOGRAPHY
UNIVERSITY OF CALIFORNIA
BERKELEY

JOHN WILEY & SONS, INC., NEW YORK

CHAPMAN & HALL, LTD., LONDON

"Plus ça change, plus c'est la même chose."

Preface

Although it is my hope that this book will be read with pleasure and profit by the interested layman, I have had the college student primarily in mind while writing it. It is meant to be inclusive without becoming encyclopedic, and factual without losing the interest of the reader, for I have tried to steer a course between the extensive coverage of L. S. Berg's monumental volume and the exclusively popular styles of some of the less scholarly authors. The physical aspects of Russian geography have been treated to the exclusion of the economic, since the scarcity of available data precludes an adequate discussion of this feature.

I have also attempted to keep the American reader in mind as I wrote, and for that reason considerable thought has been given to the selection of detail, for example, of the flora and fauna of Russia, that would appeal to an American audience.

Many statements in Russian geography books, too well known among Russian readers to require an explanation, are meaningless to English-speaking readers, and in order to clarify statements of this kind, I have included numerous explanatory footnotes. Just as an American geographer, writing for a Russian audience, would need to supply explanations for such terms as "Grand Canyon" or "Great Basin," I have tried to provide similar incidental and background information for Russian geographic features. Also in deference to the American reader, I have placed more emphasis on the peripheral regions of Russia, such as islands near the northeastern coast of Siberia, and the peninsula of Kamchatka, that lie close to North America.

As L. S. Berg has said, Russia is not merely a different country; it is a different planet. Recently, with the political dissension that has arisen between Russia and the rest of the world, that country has become even more remote. Added to the problems of language difficulties and insufficient geographic information, this makes the writing of a physical geography of Russia a formidable task indeed. Preferably, the writer of such a book should be thoroughly aware of the subtle undercurrents that may escape the attention of a stranger to Russia; yet, on the other hand, he should also be acquainted with the American environment so that he will know what is of interest to the American reader. Furthermore, he should be familiar enough with the scientific language of Russia to be able to translate it exactly into scientific English.

Because, as a native of Russia and later as a citizen of the United States, I have worked in scientific fields in both countries, I have undertaken the writing of a physical geography of Russia, hoping to interpret the geographic features of the country perhaps more accurately than a literal translator might be able to.

In preparing the book, I have relied not only upon my own knowledge of Russia but also upon several Russian textbooks on physical geography, notably *Geographical Zones of the USSR* and *Priroda USSR* (Nature of the USSR), both by L. S. Berg, and three books entitled *Physical Geography of the USSR*, by N. N. Baransky, B. F. Dobrynin, and S. P. Suslov. The last two volumes were written for university courses in the physical geography of Russia.

Besides these general books on physical geography, I used numerous studies of regional geography, such as Professor S. V. Kalesnik's *Northern Caucasus and the Lower Don*, published by the Russian Academy of Sciences in 1946, and many Russian publications on the subject which were available in American libraries. Of special value were the *Bulletins of the Russian Geographic Society* and several other Russian periodicals. I also consulted original works on the geography of Russia written in English and published in British and American magazines.

The chief source of cartographic information was *The Great Soviet Atlas of the World*, Parts I and II, Part II being available in microfilm in some American libraries. In addition, the more recent *Geographic Atlas of U.S.S.R. for High Schools* was frequently consulted. Several maps have been adapted from the above-mentioned works. Climatic data were taken chiefly from A. V. Vosnessenski's text accompanying "The Climatic Map of U.S.S.R." in *Bulletins of Agricultural Meteorology*, No. 21, Leningrad, 1930. *Animal Geography*, by N. A. Bobrinski, L. A. Zenkevitch, and I. A. Birstein (1946), was consulted frequently in describing regional faunas.

In transliteration of Russian geographic names, I followed as closely as possible the spellings used on the map of Russia entitled "Union of Soviet Socialist Republics," complied and drawn in the Cartographic Section of the National Geographic Society for the *National Geo-*

graphic Magazine in 1944.   Many of the Russian geographic names appearing in the text are accompanied with English equivalents.   The reader is urged, however, to become acquainted with the Russian alphabet and to familiarize himself with the intricacies of Russian grammar in order to recognize word roots as they appear in different grammatical forms of Russian geographical names.   Sometimes the book includes brief biographical data on persons after whom geographic features are named.

Since the establishment of the Soviet government, the names of many mountains, islands, regions, and peoples have been changed, although all rivers have retained their original designations.   Occasionally, a geographic name has been changed several times.   In this book the latest geographic names are usually given, sometimes supplemented with the old ones.

I wish to express my thanks to Dr. Carl O. Sauer, Chairman of the Geography Department, University of California, without whose influence the book could never have been written.   Acknowledgments are also due to Dr. John B. Leighly, who read the chapter on climate, and to Mr. B. L. Gordon, who read the entire manuscript.

During the preparation of the book, I often consulted members of the departments of geography, botany, zoology, and Oriental languages of the University of California.   Their assistance is greatly appreciated.

N. T. Mirov

Berkeley, California
December 21, 1950

Contents

Part 1

General Picture
of the Country

Chapter 1

Location

The Union of Soviet Socialist Republics (USSR), sometimes called the Soviet Union, Soviet Russia, or simply Russia, is located in the eastern part of Europe, in northern Asia, in the western part of Central Asia, and in a part of western Asia (Caucasus). The area of the country is about 8.6 million square miles, or about one-sixth of the earth's land surface, excluding Antarctica. The distance from Mys (Cape) Cheliuskin in the Arctic, at 77°44′ latitude N, to Fort Kushka on the Afghanistan border, at about 35° latitude N, is about 3000 miles. From the westernmost point in the country, near Königsberg, at 20° longitude E, to Mys Dezhneva * (East Cape), at 170° longitude W, is approximately 7000 miles.

The boundary line totals about 37,500 miles, and most of it follows the shoreline of the Arctic and the Pacific oceans. Although the southernmost point of the Soviet Union, Kushka, is found on about the same latitude as Albuquerque, New Mexico, or Amarillo, Texas, most of the country, with the exception of the Caucasus and Central Asia, is located above the 45th parallel, or, roughly, north of the line formed by Montreal, Minneapolis, and Portland, Oregon. Moscow, the capital of the Soviet Union, is located somewhat north of Edmonton, Canada, and Leningrad at the same latitude as Seward, Alaska. A comparison of the location of Russian cities with those of western Europe, however, is not so startling. Leningrad, Stockholm, and Oslo are located on the same latitude. Moscow is at the latitude of Glasgow, and the location of Tashkent, the capital of the Uzbek Soviet Socialist Republic of Middle Asia, may be compared with that of Barcelona, Spain. Chita, which is located in the Transbaikal Province of Eastern Siberia, lies approximately on the same latitude as London. Irkutsk, the main city of Eastern Siberia, and Berlin are located almost on the same parallel.

A cursory glance at the map of Russia reveals several important geographic features: The country as a whole is located in the cold,

---

* Named after Semen Dezhnev, who first sailed through the strait between Asia and America in 1648.

northern part of the Old World and more in Asia than in Europe. It occupies a large, uninterrupted stretch of land. The Soviet Union is the former Russian Empire, whose colonies were contiguous to the mother country rather than separated from it by the seas.* The distances between the different centers of the country are very great. From Moscow to Vladivostok is 5793 miles. These factors—cold climate, great distances, a large continuous area, and domination of the northern part of Asia—have had an important influence upon the development of the country.

The western boundary of the Soviet Union begins on the shores of the Barents Sea not far from Petsamo (or Pechenga), and for a short distance of about 100 miles it touches Norway. Farther south the international boundary lies between Russia and Finland. After World War II, the Soviet Union acquired from Finland the Petsamo Province in the north and some territory farther south. Both areas have become part of the Murmansk Province. Another area, northeast and southwest of Lake Ladoga, acquired from Finland, was incorporated with the Karelo-Finnish Soviet Socialist Republic and with the Leningrad Province. The three Baltic Republics, Estonia, Latvia, and Lithuania, which had withdrawn from Russia in 1917, became in 1940 a part of the USSR, so that the 1950 international boundary of the Soviet Union follows the shores of the Baltic Sea and includes several nearby islands.

At the end of World War II, the Soviet Union obtained from Germany a part of East Prussia, including Königsberg, whereas the rest of the region became a part of Poland. The Königsberg region did not become a part of nearby Lithuania but was incorporated with Russia proper (i.e., with RSFSR). The eastern part of Poland, extending from the Lithuanian border to the former boundary of Czechoslovakia, was incorporated into the Soviet Union; the northern part of this section became attached to the Belorussian Soviet Socialist Republic, and the southern (larger) part merged with the Ukrainian Soviet Socialist Republic. Carpatho-Ukraine had been ceded to the USSR by Czechoslovakia in 1945, and the Soviet Union won from Romania northern Bukovina and regained Bessarabia.

Thus the 1950 boundary, as it leaves the shores of the Baltic Sea near Danzig Bay, runs first between the Soviet Union and Poland, and then it crosses the Carpathian Mountains and touches borders of the

---

* Russia never had been interested in establishing an overseas empire in spite of the fact that Russian explorers discovered such remote corners of the earth as Alaska and Bikini.

new neighbors, Czechoslovakia and Hungary. Then the line crosses the Carpathian Mountains again and follows the River Prut, separating the USSR from Romania.

The boundary reaches the Black Sea at the mouth of the Danube. After crossing the Black Sea, the boundary continues along the Armenian Plateau, where the USSR borders upon Turkey. The Turkish regions of Kars and of Ardahan were taken from Turkey by Russia during the war of 1877–1878 and were returned in 1921.

Then the boundary line runs between the USSR and Iran. It reaches the Caspian Sea at Astara. Between 1723 and 1732 the southern shores of the Caspian Sea were occupied by Russia. The 1950 boundary crosses the southern part of the Caspian Sea and continues from the mouth of the River Atrek up to the Kopet Dagh Mountains. The next neighbor of the USSR to the east is Afghanistan. The northeastern part of Afghanistan (Vakhan) is shaped like a panhandle; it is only about 10 miles wide in its narrowest place. This country has served as a buffer between Russia and India. India itself does not actually adjoin the Soviet Union.

This region,* where Russia extends almost to Pakistan and touches the Chinese province of Sinkiang, is mountainous and very rugged. The international boundary line, although very precisely determined and carefully maintained, still cannot be considered permanently settled, and there will probably be some frontier readjustments in the future. The region shown on Map 1 is a very sensitive area politically.

The Soviet-Sinkiang boundary turns north along the western slopes of the Mustagh-Ata Range and then northeast along the border mountains toward the Altai system. Russians occupied the Kulja region of Chinese Turkestan (or Sinkiang) during the Moslem revolt of 1871–1881. A Russian occupation of part of Sinkiang took place from 1934 to 1943, when a Russian army garrison was stationed as far inland as Hami.

After passing the region of Dzungaria (nominally a part of Sinkiang), the boundary next extends for a very long distance between the Soviet Union and Outer Mongolia. In this region, in the upper reaches of the Yenisei, the USSR in 1945 annexed a region formerly known as the Uriankhai Territory but later renamed the Tannu Tuva People's Republic. Now it is called the Tuva Autonomous Region.

---

* The region of Chitral (a part of Pakistan) and the former Gilgit Agency, a part of Kashmir, administered by the British. It is not clear what the future status of Kashmir will be—whether it will become a part of Pakistan, a part of India, or an independent state.

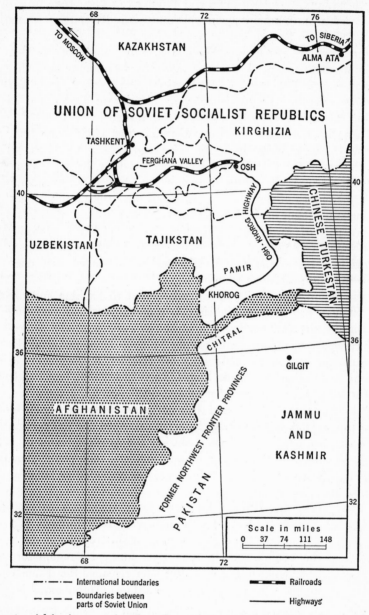

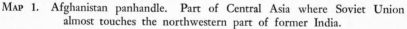

MAP 1.   Afghanistan panhandle.   Part of Central Asia where Soviet Union
almost touches the northwestern part of former India.

The boundary line runs south of the Tuva Region, along the Tannu Ola Mountains, and farther east along the mountain chains dividing the province of Transbaikal from the northeastern part of Mongolia. Starting near the town of Manchouli or Lupin (or Manchuria) the boundary lies between the Soviet Union and Manchuria (a part of China); it follows the River Argun to its confluence with the Shilka and then extends down the Amur to its tributary the Ussuri. Next it leaves the Amur and goes (southward) up the Ussuri, crosses Lake Khanka, and reaches the Pacific in Posiet Bay. Near the ocean for a short distance (along the River Tumen) the USSR borders Korea.

After World War II, the USSR obtained (in 1945) from Japan the southern half of the island of Sakhalin (which originally had been Japanese, then Russian; in 1905 its southern part had been won by Japan from Russia) and the chain of Kuril Islands, which stretches from Japan to the Russian peninsula of Kamchatka. These islands were discovered in 1643 by Maarten De Vries and came under Russian rule in 1711; in 1875 they were given to Japan in exchange for the southern part of Sakhalin. The 1950 boundary line between the USSR and Japan goes through La Pérouse Strait (between the islands of Sakhalin and Hokkaido) and through Nemuro Strait (between Hokkaido and the Kuril Islands). Then the boundary continues northward along the eastern shores of the Kamchatka Peninsula and includes the Commander Islands (chief of which are Bering and Medny), named after Commander Vitus Bering, who landed and died in 1741 on the island that bears his surname.

The boundary between the United States and the Soviet Union goes through Bering Strait between the two Diomede Islands. Big Diomede is Russian; Little Diomede is American. The distance between the two islands is about 3 miles. The width of Bering Strait in its narrowest place is 55 miles. According to the Russian maps, the Soviet boundary after passing through Bering Strait to the Arctic extends up to the North Pole, and from there it turns southward, passing between the Norwegian island Kvitöya (east of Spitsbergen) and the Russian island Victoria (west of Franz Josef Land).

Within these boundaries the country may be conveniently subdivided into the following major parts. This subdivision is very general, and in many instances the boundaries between the different areas are not well defined: (1) European Russia, (2) the Caucasus, (3) Western Siberia, (4) Eastern Siberia, (5) the Far East, and (6) Middle Asia. Middle Asia is the term applied by Russian geographers to

Soviet Central Asia, the latter name being reserved for the area south of the Russian border.* Soviet Middle Asia is understood to include the mountainous and desert section of the USSR bordering Chinese Turkestan, Afghanistan, and Iran; in the west it borders the Caspian Sea, and in the east it touches the Altai. In the north, Middle Asia merges gradually into the Western Siberian steppe.

The Soviet Union is composed of sixteen member republics: Russia, Ukraine, Belorussia, Karelia, Estonia, Latvia, Lithuania, Moldavia, Azerbaijan, Georgia, Armenia, Turkmenia, Uzbekistan, Tajikstan, Kirghizia, and Kazakhstan. Of the total area of the Soviet Union (8.6 million square miles), Russia proper occupies 6.5 million square miles. The dry prairies, semideserts, and wastelands of Kazakhstan occupy 1.1 million square miles. The rest of the territory (i.e., 1 million square miles) is occupied by the other fourteen republics. Thus, Russia proper (whose full name is the Russian Soviet Federated Socialist Republic) is the largest in the area. It occupies most of the northern part of eastern Europe, together with considerable areas near the Caucasus. Recently acquired territory in East Prussia, and the Crimean Peninsula, as well as the whole of Siberia, are also a part of Russia proper. Within the Russian Republic are located several autonomous republics: the Tatar, Bashkir, Komi, Mari, Mordovian, Udmurt, and Chuvash in eastern Europe, and two large autonomous republics in Siberia—the Yakut Republic, located along the River Lena, and the Buriat-Mongol Republic, situated near Lake Baikal.

The smaller minorities form so-called autonomous regions, such as the Daghestan Autonomous Region in the Caucasus and the Oirot Autonomous Region of the Altai Mountains. Still smaller minorities, such as all Paleo-Asiatic peoples of Siberia, form national districts which are not unlike the Indian reservations of the United States. The rest of the member republics, excluding Kazakhstan, are relatively small. They are located on the periphery of the Soviet Union, and most of them thus border upon some foreign country. The Russian Republic itself has no direct physical contact with western Europe, save in the Königsberg region of East Prussia. The Asiatic part of the Russian Republic touches China and Korea.

On the north, the Soviet Union borders the Arctic Ocean; on the east, it fronts on the waters of the Pacific; and on the west and south, European Russia has access to the seas that comprise parts of the Atlantic.

* Humboldt even included part of the Ural Mountains in Central Asia.

TABLE 1.   COMPOSITION OF SOVIET UNION BY MEMBER REPUBLICS

(From the *Great Soviet Encyclopedia*, 1948 supplement, Union of Soviet Socialist Republics, Moscow, 1948)

Member Republic	Location	Area in Thousands of Square Miles
Russia	Northern part of eastern Europe, all Siberia, Crimea, North Caucasus, Königsberg area of East Prussia	6534.0
Ukraine	Southern part of eastern Europe and Carpathian region	222.5
Belorussia	Western part of eastern Europe	77.5
Karelia [1]	Northwestern part of eastern Europe	69.2
Estonia	Baltic coast	17.9
Latvia	Baltic coast	24.9
Lithuania	Near Poland	25.2
Moldavia	Near Romania	13.1
Azerbaijan	Along Caspian coast of the Caucasus	33.2
Georgia	Near Black Sea coast of the Caucasus	29.5
Armenia	Southeast Caucasus	11.6
Turkmenia	East of the Caspian Sea	187.1
Uzbekistan	Foothills and lowlands of Middle Asia	157.3
Tajikstan	Mountains of Middle Asia	55.0
Kirghizia	Mountains of Middle Asia	76.0
Kazakhstan	Prairies and semideserts between Western Siberia and Middle Asia	1064.0

[1] The Karelo-Finnish Republic.

In the European part of the Soviet Arctic are several groups of islands: Franz Josef Land, an archipelago of some 800 islands; the Islands of Novaia Zemlia, consisting of two large islands separated by a narrow strait; and Kolguev Island, located between Novaia Zemlia and the mainland.   The following large islands are located in the Asiatic part of the Soviet Arctic: Severnaia Zemlia (North Land) consists of four large islands and several small ones.   The New Siberian Islands, located in the Arctic between the Yana and the Indigirka rivers, consist of three groups: (1) the De Long Islands—Bennett, Jeanette, Henrietta, Zhohov, and Vilkitski; (2) the New Siberian Islands proper, consisting of four large islands and an extensive shoal seen only at low water—Zemlia Bunge; and (3) the Liakhov Islands, located between the New Siberian group and the mainland.   Wrangel Island is the easternmost island of the Soviet Arctic.

All the islands of the Russian Arctic are located on the underwater shelf of the Eurasian continent.   In the vicinity of Franz Josef Land the width of this shelf is over 900 miles.   Farther east it is narrower, being, north of the Yenisei, about 600 miles. Depths on the shelf do not exceed 650 feet, whereas the depth of the Arctic north of the shelf reaches 16,000 feet and even more.

The mainland protrudes into the Arctic in several places, forming the Kola and Kanin peninsulas in the European part and the Yamal and Taimyr peninsulas in the Asiatic part of the ocean. In the extreme east of the Arctic lies the Chukotski (i.e., of the Chukchi) Peninsula. The islands and the peninsulas separate the Arctic into several seas—the Barents Sea, the Kara Sea, and the Siberian Polar Sea.

The Barents Sea is located between the European mainland, Franz Josef Land, and Novaia Zemlia. It is named after a Dutch mariner of the sixteenth century who sailed the Arctic seas and who died on his way from Novaia Zemlia to the mainland. The eastern portion of the sea has two large bays: Cheshskaia Guba (Bay), which is protected from the west by the Kanin Peninsula, and Pechorskaia Guba, which is separated from the Cheshskaia Guba by the lowland Malozemelskaia (i.e., Little Land) Tundra. The southern portion of the Barents Sea cuts deeply inland, forming a large body of water known as the White Sea (Beloe More). The western shores of the Barents Sea are rocky and abrupt, with numerous fiords; the eastern shores are low, with many islands and banks. The warm currents of the Gulf Stream keep the western part of the sea from freezing, thus permitting year-round navigation.

The White Sea may be divided into three sections: (1) the northern part with Mezen Bay, (2) the Gorlo (throat), a narrow strait that connects the northern part with (3) the inner part of the White Sea, with its three large bays—Kandalaksha Guba, Onega Guba, and Dvina Guba. The Solovets(ki) Islands are located in the Onega Bay. The White Sea, as well as the Barents Sea, is rather shallow, except for the deep Kandalaksha Bay. Its water contains less salt than the Barents Sea, and it is covered with ice from the fall to the early summer.

The Kara Sea (Karskoie More) lies east of the Barents Sea and is connected with it by means of three straits: Matochkin Shar, between the two islands of Novaia Zemlia; the Kara Gate (Karskie Vorota), between the Southern Island and the island of Vaigach; and Yugorski Shar (passage), between Vaigach and the mainland. The name Yugorski Shar is of great historical significance as it relates to the early sailing of Russian explorers to the Ugrian land of Western Siberia. The shores at the southern end of the Kara Sea are generally low. On the west they take the form of low cliffs; farther east they are flat and sandy. The coast line is deeply cut, forming numerous bays and estuaries. The Kara Sea is not very deep, exceeding 300 feet only near Novaia Zemlia, where there are depths of more than 600 feet. A great deal of warm water flows into the Kara Sea in summer from the two great Siberian rivers, the Ob and the Yenisei. The warm fresh water spreads on the surface of the sea, forming a layer 30 to 60 feet deep. In summer this layer prevents the warming up of the deeper layers of sea water. In winter when the rivers are frozen and no fresh water is brought to the sea, the salt water is exposed to the low temperatures and is considerably cooled.

Ice of the Kara Sea is not brought from the Arctic but is formed in the sea itself. In winters, when the weather is generally clear and cold and the radiation of heat from the water surface is great, enormous amounts of ice are formed. Summer, with its low temperature, drizzle, fog, and snow, is not very favorable for the melting of the accumulated ice. Only towards September in the southern part of the sea is the ice melted, crushed, and carried away by southwestern winds. Even in the middle of the twentieth century, in spite of the general warming of the Arctic and the assistance of modern technical improvements such as powerful icebreakers, airplanes, and radios, navigation across the Kara Sea still involves considerable difficulty.

The Taimyr Peninsula and its continuation, the archipelago of Severnaia Zemlia, with Vilkitski Strait between, separates the Kara Sea from the eastern part of the Arctic, broadly known as the Siberian Polar Sea. This sea can be subdivided into three distinct areas: (1) the Laptev Sea,* situated between the Taimyr Peninsula, Severnaia Zemlia in the west, and the New Siberian Islands in the east; (2) the East Siberian Sea, between the New Siberian Islands and Wrangel Island; and (3) the Chukchi Sea (Chukotskoe More in Russian) located farther east and extending to Bering Strait. Near the coast the Siberian Polar Sea is not very deep.

In the Laptev Sea depths of 65 to 130 feet extend from the coast for 280 to 340 miles and, in an area near the New Siberian Islands, for over 600 miles. Depths of 200 to 250 feet or greater are rare, except near the northeastern end of the Taimyr Peninsula, along Severnaia Zemlia, where the sea is from 650 to 1300 feet deep.

The East Siberian Sea is not more than 150 to 200 feet deep; in many extensive areas it is as shallow as 60 to 80 feet. In the southern and middle parts of the Chukchi Sea depths do not exceed 150 feet, ex-

* Named after two members of the second Bering expedition, 1733–1743, Khariton and Dmitri Laptev, both outstanding Arctic explorers.

cept in a deep channel that is located east of Herald Island and west
of the Herald Shoals (i.e., east of Wrangel Island). Through this
channel, cold water of the Arctic flows to the southern parts of the
sea. The summer inflow of warm water of several large Siberian
rivers has a considerable effect on the salinity of the East Siberian Sea.
Fresh water delivered by the Lena River may be detected as far as
300 miles from its mouth. In the Chukchi Sea there is a great deal
of warm water that is brought from the south through Bering Strait.

Ice is formed in the East Siberian Sea much faster than in the western
part of the Arctic; it is formed even in summer. Vilkitski Strait is
free of ice only during the most favorable summers. Generally, however, only a small ice-free channel near Cape Cheliuskin opens in August and September. The most difficult part of the East Siberian Sea
for navigation is that between the rivers Piasina and Khatanga in the
west and between Cape Shelagski and Cape Schmidt in the east. In
these two places there are no large rivers emptying into the Arctic,
and accordingly the ice pack is heavier and encountered more frequently than in the rest of the Arctic.

In those parts of the Arctic where salinity is high, as in the northern
parts of the Laptev Sea, the fauna is composed of high Arctic and
Atlantic-Arctic species, but near the coast the fauna is characterized
by species that can tolerate low salinity. Sea life here consists of few
species but of a great number of individuals within each of these
species.

The Pacific Ocean near the east coast of Soviet Asia forms the Bering Sea, the Okhotsk Sea, and the Sea of Japan. The southern part
of the east coast of Kamchatka and the newly acquired chain of Kuril
Islands border the Pacific itself.

The Bering Sea is separated from the Pacific by the Aleutian Islands
(USA) and their continuation, the Commander Islands (USSR). It
is connected with the Arctic by Bering Strait, named after the head
of the Russian expeditions of 1725–1743, sent by Peter the Great in
search of a passage between Asia and America. The passage, however,
apparently had been discovered at an earlier date by Semen Dezhnev
in 1648.*

* Cf. F. A. Golder, *Russian Expansion in the Pacific*, 1641–1850, Cleveland,
Ohio, 1914, 386 pp., Chapter 3. This book contains a critical examination of
Dezhnev's voyage, pp. 67–95. A more recent discussion may be found in L. S.
Berg's *Discovery of Kamchatka and Bering's Expedition* (in Russian), Academy
of Science of the USSR, Moscow-Leningrad, 1946, pp. 27–38; see also Bering's
portrait, p. 84.

The northeastern part of the Bering Sea is not very deep—about 650 feet. In the winter this portion is packed with floating ice. Near the Aleutian Islands the sea has depths of 13,000 feet. The very southern part is free of ice throughout the year. Because of the free inflow of water from the Pacific, the salinity of the Bering Sea is relatively high—from 32 to 34.5 parts per thousand, except near the large rivers, such as the Anadyr.

Bering Strait is rather shallow, not deeper than 200 feet, and, accordingly, the cold arctic water does not affect appreciably the thermal balance of the Bering Sea. Furthermore, arctic ice is not carried through the strait. In summer the whole Bering Sea is free of ice, but in the bays of the northwestern coast, such as Anadyr Bay, ice remains until June.

The Okhotsk Sea (Okhotskoie More) * lies between the Siberian mainland, the peninsula of Kamchatka, and the Kuril Islands. In the extreme south it touches the Japanese island of Hokkaido. The large island of Sakhalin is located in its southwestern part, close to the mainland. Also in the southwestern corner of the sea are the Shantar Islands, and in the northern part the group of Yamski Islands. The northern part of the sea cuts deeply into the mainland, forming Gizhiga Guba (Bay) and Penzhina Guba, separated by the Taigonos Peninsula. The coast line is generally formed by the abrupt slopes of mountain chains. Only the west coast of Kamchatka is flat and low.

The deepest part of the sea is located in its extreme southeastern end—10,667 feet. Although the Okhotsk Sea is located between the same latitudes as the Baltic and Black seas, it is typically an arctic body of water. Long winters with very low temperatures cause an enormous accumulation of ice. In winter (January-February) almost the entire area of the sea, except the very southern part, is covered with ice, which breaks during severe winter storms. The ice begins to melt in May, but navigation, even in favorable years, is not possible before July. Salinity of the Okhotsk Sea is lower than that of the Bering Sea (31 to 32.5 parts per thousand), especially in the southwestern portion, where great masses of fresh water are brought by the Amur River.

Tides are very pronounced in the Okhotsk Sea. In Gizhiga Bay they may be as high as 37 feet. In the summer in certain parts of the sea, such as in the north near St. Jonah Island,† cold water rises to the

* The name "Okhotsk Sea" is preferable to the commonly used "Sea of Okhotsk."
† See Map 32.

surface and causes moisture condensation from the air. Fogs here are almost continuous. The temperature of the surface water near St. Jonah Island at the beginning of August may be as low as 34 to 37°F.*

The Okhotsk Sea is very rich in salmon.

South of the Okhotsk Sea and separated from it by Sakhalin (USSR) and Hokkaido (Japan) islands lies the Sea of Japan. The northwestern coast of the sea belongs to the Soviet Union—the Maritime Province. The Sea of Japan is connected with the Okhotsk Sea by the long and shallow Tatar Strait (Tatarski Proliv), located between the mainland and Sakhalin Island, and La Pérouse Strait (about 200 feet deep) between Sakhalin and Hokkaido. The southern limit of winter floating ice is a line drawn from northern Korea to Hokkaido. In the Russian part of the sea the bays are covered with ice all winter. The northern part of the Tatar Strait is packed in winter with floating ice, and the estuary of the Amur freezes, permitting communication with Sakhalin over the ice.

The Sea of Japan is notorious for its typhoons, but these pass either through the middle of the sea or along the coast of Japan so that the Siberian coast is not affected by them. The Soviet Union owns no islands in the Sea of Japan, except some small ones near Vladivostok.

The depth of the Sea of Japan in the eastern part reaches 12,881 feet. Because of the excellent vertical circulation, the waters of the sea are well supplied with oxygen, thus permitting development of fauna to very considerable depths. Of interest is the abundance of kelp.

The coast line of the Sea of Japan parallels the Sikhote Alin range in a southwesterly direction, and it does not have many deep bays. Of importance are De Castri Bay † and Soviet Haven in Tatar Strait and Olga Bay farther south. Near Vladivostok the coast line turns west, cuts the mountains, and forms many sheltered coves and bays. The largest is Peter the Great Gulf. The important port of Vladivostok is located on the shores of one of its inlets. Posiet Bay is farther south near the Korean border.

The Baltic Sea and the Black Sea are parts of the Atlantic Ocean. The Baltic Sea is as remote from the Atlantic as Lake Superior. Its eastern extremities—the Gulf of Riga and Gulf of Finland—touch the shores of the Soviet Union. During the glacial period the depression occupied by the Baltic Sea was filled with ice and a great deal of glacial debris. The sea is noted for its shoals, sand banks, and submerged

---

* Author's personal observations.

† Named by La Pérouse after his contemporary, the Minister of the French Navy.

rocks. Near the coast of Finland it is dotted with numerous small islands.

The Gulf of Finland extends from west to east for about 250 miles. Generally the water is of low salinity, and near the mouth of the Neva it is almost fresh. The eastern part of the gulf freezes in winter, but the western part is free of ice.

The Gulf of Riga is separated from the Baltic Sea by four islands: Sarema (Özel), Khiuma (Dagö), Vormsi, and Muhu (Moon). The central part of the gulf freezes only during exceptionally severe winters.

The Black Sea is connected with the Mediterranean Sea through the Bosporus, the Sea of Marmora, and the Dardanelles. Its coasts extending from the mouth of the Danube eastward and then southward to Transcaucasia belong to the Soviet Union. The Crimean Peninsula is located at the northern end of the sea. Northeast of it lies the Azov Sea *—14,500 square miles. The Azov Sea is connected with the Black Sea by the 3-mile-wide Kerch Strait. The western and northern shores of the Black Sea are low, often abrupt. The southern coast of the Crimea and the Caucasian coast are mountainous. In the northwest the sea is shallow, but farther south it is considerably more than 6560 feet deep. Because of the lack of vertical circulation, the water 600 feet or more below the surface is lacking in oxygen and saturated with hydrogen sulphide. Accordingly no marine life exists below that depth in the Black Sea.

In the northern part of the sea ice may form near the coast, but it does not last long. The rest of the sea does not freeze. Generally speaking, the eastern part of the sea is warmer than the western part.

The Azov Sea is very shallow—not exceeding 50 feet in depth. It freezes in winter. Because of the large amount of fresh water flowing into it from the rivers Kuban and Don, water in the Azov Sea is much less saline than that in the Black Sea. The fishing industry is of considerable importance. Four times as much fish is caught in the Azov Sea as in the Black Sea.

The Caspian Sea is the largest salt-water lake in the world, occupying an area of 169,380 square miles. It is 760 miles long and 270 miles wide. Most of it is located within borders of the Soviet Union; only a small southern part of the sea belongs to Iran. As late as glacial times, the Caspian Sea connected with the Black Sea. At the end of the glacial period, when the Black Sea found an outlet to the Mediter-

* It is more correct to say Azov Sea than Sea of Azov.

ranean, the Caspian Sea was separated from the Black Sea and became a land-locked body of water. It lies 85 feet below sea level. Its northern portion is shallow, whereas the southern portion reaches depths of 3326 feet. In the north, where the climate is more severe and the salinity low, the waters are covered with ice in the winter. The rest of the sea is free of ice throughout the year.

Chapter 2

Geology and Topography

Essentially the tectonic structure of the area occupied by the Soviet Union consists of two large, ancient, continental platforms: the eastern European platform and the Siberian platform. The former is located under the eastern European plain except under the southern part; the latter lies under the Central Siberian Plateau and under some parts of the Baikal area in the Transbaikal region.

The ancient pre-Cambrian and sometimes Lower Paleozoic crystalline rocks, such as granite and gneiss, forming these platforms were subjected to an extensive folding during pre-Cambrian time. Later the ancient continent was leveled by erosion and underwent considerable tectonic changes; some parts sank, while others were elevated. Extensive areas remained as stable platforms. Occasionally the crystalline rocks appear on the surface, but generally they are covered with horizontal sedimentary deposits. In European Russia these surface crystalline rocks form the Baltic Shield in the northwest and the Azov-Podolia Shield in the south.

Closely associated with the structure of the Siberian platform are Lower Paleozoic (Caledonian) folds. Such folds are found in the Sayans and in the Transbaikal mountains of Eastern Siberia.

Between the two ancient continental platforms is a region of the Upper Paleozoic (Hercynian) folding. These Hercynian structures are the foundation of the Western Siberian lowlands; upon this foundation lie horizontal strata, deposited in Tertiary and Quaternary times. On the ancient platforms and on the Hercynian folds of Western Siberia and parts of Turkestan have developed extensive plains and lowlands. The Hercynian foldings formed the Urals; the mountains of Novaia Zemlia; the Altai system; and the mountains of Central Asia, except for the northern arcs of the Tien Shan system, which were formed during the Lower Paleozoic, and the Kopet Dagh system, which is of Tertiary origin. Hercynian foldings are also evident in the Donetz Heights, where they are covered with more recent deposits.

17

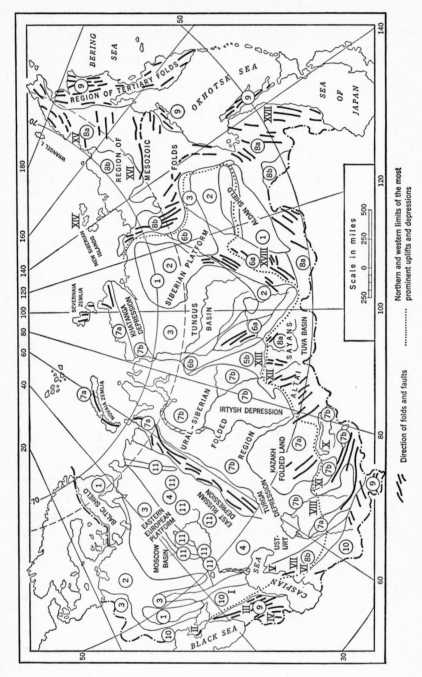

MAP 2. Tectonic Map of the Soviet Union. (*Modified, after Archangelski-Dobrynin.*)

A. Regions of pre-Cambrian folds.

    1. Pre-Cambrian rocks are found on or near the surface.
    2. Pre-Cambrian rocks are covered with younger, undisturbed or slightly disturbed deposits.
    3. Pre-Cambrian rocks are located deep beneath the surface.
    4. Either pre-Cambrian or Caledonian (Paleozoic) foldings (age of rocks unknown).

B. Regions of Paleozoic folds.

    5a. Caledonian-folds; rocks on the surface.
    5b. Same but rocks found deep beneath the surface.
    6a. Proterozoic or Cambrian folds; rocks on the surface.
    6b. Same but rocks found deep beneath the surface.
    7a. Hercynian folds; rocks on the surface.
    7b. Same but rocks are found deep beneath the surface.

C. Regions of Mesozoic folds.

    8a. Rocks are found on the surface.
    8b. Rocks are located deep beneath the surface.

D. Regions of Tertiary folds.

    9. Regions of Tertiary folds.
    10. Piedmont Tertiary depressions.
    11. Gentle folds of Mesozoic and Cainozoic age located on the East-European platform.

    I. Crimean-Caucasian depression.
    II. Crimean Mountains.
    III. Greater Caucasus.
    IV. Lesser Caucasus.
    V. Mangyshlak Mountains.
    VI. Greater Balkhan.
    VII. Tuarkyr.
    VIII. Syr-Darya depression.
    IX. Ferghana depression.

    X. Balkhash depression.
    XI. Chuia depression.
    XII. Kuznetsk Basin.
    XIII. Minussinsk Basin.
    XIV. Platform of De Long Islands.
    XV. Kolyma-Chukotsk folded land.
    XVI. Alazei-Yukaghir block.
    XVII. Maritime folded land.
    XVIII. Baikal Lower Paleozoic folds.

More recent than the Hercynian was the formation of the Mesozoic folded mountains along the Pacific coast of Siberia, ramifying both in the north and in the south. In the north the Cherski and the Verkhoyansk mountains are examples; in the south the Mesozoic folds are evident in the structure of the mountains of the Maritime Province, of the Amur region, and of southern Transbaikal. In European Russia the Crimean mountains, the main axis of the Caucasus, and the mountains of Mangyshlak (east of the Caspian Sea) and of western Turkmenia were formed also during the Mesozoic era.

The most recent Tertiary folded mountains are limited within the Soviet Union to the periphery of the country. This type of structure is found in the Carpathian Mountains, in the Caucasus, in the Kopet Dagh, in the Pamirs, on Sakhalin Island, in the mountains of the Kamchatka Peninsula, along the coast of the Okhotsk Sea, and in the Anadyr Mountains of extreme northeastern Siberia. In the northeastern corner of Siberia the mountain-forming processes are still continuing; earthquakes are frequent here, and volcanoes in Kamchatka and on the Kuril Islands are still active.

Baransky * estimates that only one-twentieth of the whole country is higher than 6560 feet above sea level. The highest peaks in Central Asia reach 23,000 to 24,000 feet. The rest of the country may be divided into two almost equal parts: the lowlands, which are not over 656 feet above sea level; and the highlands, areas situated from 656 to 6560 feet above sea level. The plains, which are predominantly low, are found in European Russia (a rather rolling country); they merge in the southeast into the Caspian lowland, where are located the lowest points of the Soviet Union. The Caspian Sea is 85 feet below sea level; the depression Batyr on the Mangyshlak Peninsula is 426.4 feet below sea level. Farther east stretches the Turan lowland, which in the north is connected with the enormous flat and monotonous Western Siberian lowland. On the west the Western Siberian lowland is separated from the eastern European lowland by the Ural Mountains, and in the north it merges into the north Siberian lowlands, which extend into Eastern Siberia above the 70th parallel; along the Lena, the Indigirka, and the Kolyma the low-lying terrain, however, extends farther south. Only on the Taimyr Peninsula and on the islands of the Arctic is the country more elevated. A small patch of plains is found in the region beyond the Carpathian Mountains; it belongs to the Danube lowlands.

* N. N. Baransky, *Physical Geography of the USSR*, 7th ed., Moscow, 1943, 100 pp.

East of the Yenisei the Western Siberian lowlands merge into the extensive Central Siberian Plateau. The country here still retains the character of plains; the mountains are not very high, are flat-topped, and originated mostly through erosion.

The northeastern part of Siberia, the country east of Lake Baikal, and the southern regions of the Soviet Union in Asia, including the Caucasus, are essentially mountainous regions.

As a whole the country has the appearance of a huge amphitheater, sloping from the northeast, east, and south to northwest, towards the Arctic.

During the ice age, the great Scandinavian glacier descended upon the Russian plains, moving, as it advanced, on both the eastern and western sides of the central Russian uplands. The slowly moving ice of the glacier left ample traces of its advance on the crystalline rocks of the Baltic Shield; it polished and furrowed the granite rocks, and it formed numerous lakes in the northwest of European Russia. It carried farther south many boulders and a great deal of debris and deposited these on the plains of Russia. The great ice mantle has advanced and retreated several times during the Quaternary period, and the streams fed by the glacier have brought forth large quantities of fluvioglacial material that has been deposited gradually, depending on the size and weight of the particles. Sand, being the heaviest of the materials, has been deposited in low places near the edge of the glacier, and silt has been carried farther south.

It is not certain whether the oldest of the three glaciations, the Mindel, was present in the Russian Plains; at least all signs of it, if they ever existed, have been completely obliterated there by the two following glaciations: the Riss and the Würm. The eastern European plains bear unmistakable evidence of these two great glaciations. The greater, which also extended farther south, was the Riss, although its moraine deposits have been eroded and obliterated by the streams of the Würm glaciation. The Würm glaciation has left the most evident traces of the three.

Western Siberia has had only one great glaciation; apparently this one corresponded to and was contemporary with the Riss glaciation of Europe. Because of the drier climate the Western Siberian glaciation did not extend so far south as the eastern European glaciation; nor was the thickness of the ice mantle so great as in European Russia. The ice mantle measured about 2300 feet, whereas in European Russia it was over 6500 feet thick.

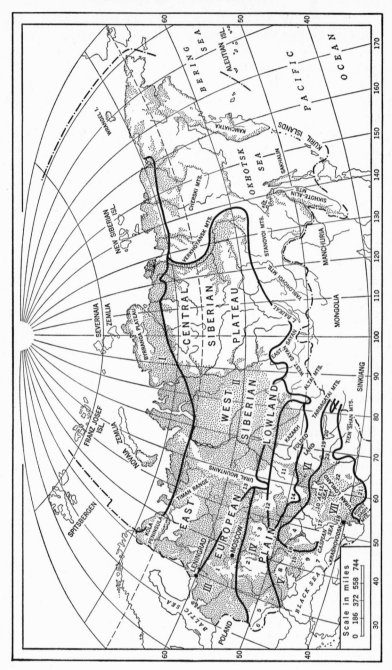

Map 3. Topographic Map of the Soviet Union. *(Partly after Vitkovich, Geography, 1949.)*

1. Valdai Hills.
2. Central Russian Upland.
3. Volga Heights.
4. Caspian Lowland (Caspian Depression).
5. Volhynia-Podolia Upland.
6. Carpathian Mountains.
7. Caucasus.
8. Donetz Heights.
9. Stavropol Plateau.
10. Ust Urt Plateau.
11. Turgai Tableland.
12. Obschii Syrt Plateau.

13. Ufa Plateau.
14. Mugodjar Mountains.
15. Manych Depression.
16. Ergeni Plateau.
17. Mangyshlak Mountains.
18. Kara-Boghaz-Gol Gulf.
19. Bet-Pack-Kala Desert.
20. Lake Balkhash.
21. Kara Kum Sands.
22. Kyzyl Kum Sands.
23. Muyun Kum Sands.

Heavy lines denote boundaries of the seven lowland regions.

I. Tundra region.
II. Taiga region.
III. Mixed forest region.
IV. Woodland region.

V. Prairie region.
VI. Semidesert region.
VII. Desert region.

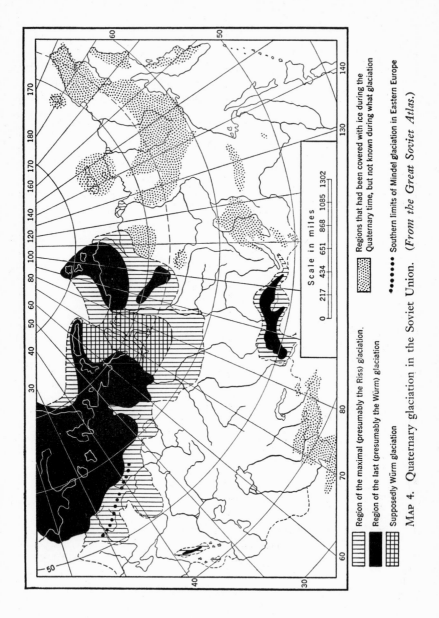

Region of the maximal (presumably the Riss) glaciation.

Region of the last (presumably the Würm) glaciation

Supposedly Würm glaciation

Regions that had been covered with ice during the Quaternary time, but not known during what glaciation

• • • • • • Southern limits of Mindel glaciation in Eastern Europe

Scale in miles

0   217   434   651   868   1085   1302

MAP 4. Quaternary glaciation in the Soviet Union. (*From the Great Soviet Atlas.*)

The Western Siberian glaciers were centered in the northern Ural and on the Taimyr Peninsula. From there they descended to the low-

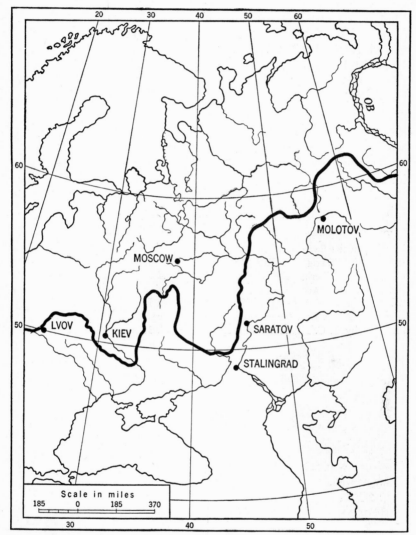

MAP 5. Southern limits of glaciation of eastern European plain. (*After Baransky.*)

lands. Whereas in European Russia the rivers rushed southward from under the retreating glaciers, in Western Siberia the rivers rushed towards the retreating ice sheet and on to the Kara Sea. The latter rivers, dammed by the ice, caused topographical changes that were different from those produced by the rivers of European Russia and that are evident even now in the form of depressions made by the meandering streams of blocked rivers. It is possible that part of the water flowed over the ice sheet, between the Ural and the Taimyr Peninsula. The Würm glaciation in Western Siberia was merely of a local character, having been restricted to the Ural Mountains west of the lowland and to the Altai system south of the lowlands.

In Eastern Siberia lack of moisture excluded any extensive glaciation during the ice age. Glaciation occurred only locally, and for the most part it was restricted to the mountains. But the climate of Eastern Siberia during that period was even more severe than in the twentieth century; extensive areas of the land were cooled to temperatures below freezing, and they have remained permanently frozen to the present time.*

In Middle Asia and in the Caucasus, glaciation was confined to the high mountains, where it still exists.

* *The Great Soviet Atlas* gives a somewhat different picture of the extent of glaciation in the Soviet Union. See Map 4. For a more complete discussion of glaciation in Siberia, see Richard Foster Flint and Herbert G. Dorsey, Jr., "Glaciation of Siberia," *Bulletin of the Geological Society of America*, Vol. 56, pp. 89–106, 1945. Also consult I. P. Gerasimov and K. K. Markov, "The Glacial Period in the Territory of the USSR," 462 pp. (in Russian with 20-page English summary), *Trans. Inst. Geog.*, Academy of Science of the USSR, Vol. 33, 1939; abstracted by C. C. Nikiforoff in *Geog. Rev.*, Vol. 31, pp. 343–345, 1941.

Chapter 3

Climate

The Soviet Union lies chiefly in the northern part of the Eurasian continent, and because of its geographic location the climate of the country is, as a whole, very severe. The severity is augmented by the sloping of Western Siberia towards the Arctic. The absence of mountains in the north (with the exception of northeastern Siberia) permits an unobstructed flow of cold air masses southward; on the other hand, high mountains and plateaux situated south of Asiatic Russia prevent penetration of warm tropical air from the Indian Ocean northward. Furthermore, the position of the country on the largest continent, with some parts located far from the oceans, makes the climate extremely continental.

Occupying an area extending from the Arctic Ocean to the borders of Afghanistan (35° latitude N) the Soviet Union, in its lowlands, possesses a gradation of climates ranging from cold to warm. On this general pattern, governed by the latitude, are superimposed two major climatic factors: the atmospheric conditions existing in the heart of the Eurasian continent and the influence of the Atlantic Ocean, which is strongest in the western part of the country and gradually decreases to the east.* The influence exerted by the Pacific upon the climate of the country is only local, being limited to a narrow strip along the Asiatic coast, to the Amur River area, and to the extreme northeastern part of Siberia. The Arctic exerts some mollifying effect on the coast of Siberia; farther inland the winters are colder than on the shores of the ocean.

Of primary importance, however, is the distribution of atmospheric pressure over the Eurasian continent. In the winter the northern part of Asia cools considerably, and very cold and thus very heavy air masses become established over the eastern part of Siberia and Mongolia. The presence of these heavy air masses manifests itself by a very high barometric pressure, which may reach 30.26 inches. In the region of the Siberian anticyclone, calm, sunny, and steadily cold weather predominates in winter. The heavy air masses exert a tre-

---

* In the Temperate Zone, the prevailing air masses move from the west.

27

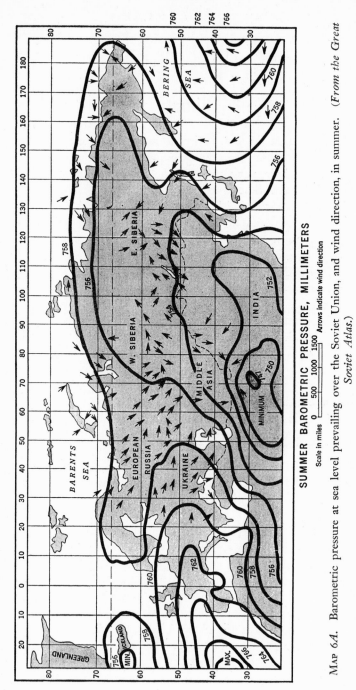

SUMMER BAROMETRIC PRESSURE, MILLIMETERS

Scale in miles 0   500   1000   1500   Arrows indicate wind direction

MAP 6A. Barometric pressure at sea level prevailing over the Soviet Union, and wind direction, in summer. (*From the Great Soviet Atlas.*)

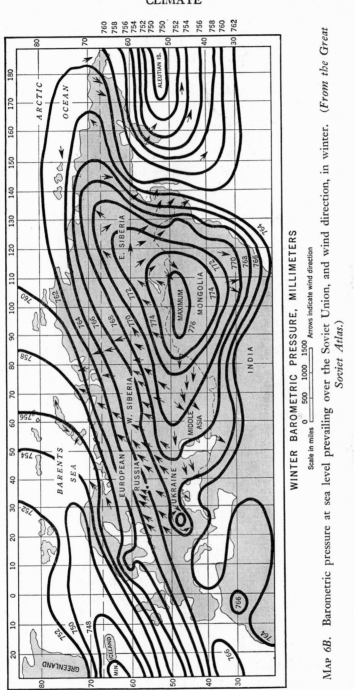

WINTER BAROMETRIC PRESSURE, MILLIMETERS
Scale in miles 0   500 1000 1500   Arrows indicate wind direction

MAP 6B. Barometric pressure at sea level prevailing over the Soviet Union, and wind direction, in winter. (From the Great Soviet Atlas.)

mendous influence not only on Siberia but also on the eastern part of Europe, as the high-pressure area extends to European Russia, approximately along the 50th parallel, known as the barometric axis of Eurasia. The cold air masses formed within the area move towards the areas of lower pressure, i.e., to Middle Asia, to Europe, and to North Caucasus. Only the south coast of Crimea (protected by the mountains on the north) and of the Transcaucasian region and the southern parts of Middle Asia (because of their low latitude) possess relatively mild winters.

On the other hand, in winter there is found in the North Atlantic a region of low pressure (Icelandic cyclone) where the barometric pressure is as low as 748 millimeters, or 29.17 inches. It remains near Iceland also in summer. Its influence is felt strongly in eastern Europe, extending as far northeast as the Barents Sea and as far southeast as the North Caucasus. The warm, moist air masses that it brings from the Atlantic Ocean clash here with the dry, cold air masses of the Siberian anticyclone; as a result, the winters in European Russia are not so steadily cold as in Siberia. Winter thaws and warm spells are not uncommon in European Russia. Beyond the Ural the effects of the Icelandic minimum (cyclone) are negligible.

Winter conditions of Eastern Siberia are dominated entirely by the Eurasian air pressure; the influence of the Pacific is not felt in winter even in the immediate vicinity of the coast, because the prevailing winds blow from the continent. In summer, because of the considerable heating of the land, a region of steady, low barometric pressure occurs over northwestern India and Afghanistan. It extends into Central Asia and the Transcaucasian region, causing the cold air masses of Siberia to move towards Central Asia.

On the Pacific coast of Siberia the distribution of the air masses undergoes an extensive change in summer. The area of high pressure is found over the Pacific, and the warm, moist air masses move towards the coast from the southeast. In the Far East the influence of this summer monsoon manifests itself in cloudy, foggy, and rainy weather; but it does not penetrate very deeply into the continent, and in Eastern Siberia the summers are, generally speaking, hot, clear, and dry.

The influence of the Atlantic on the temperature of the country is most pronounced in the western and northwestern part of the USSR. The closer to the Atlantic, the higher is the mean annual temperature. The January isotherms extend from the northwest to the southeast, so that the 14°F isotherm passes north of Leningrad in the northwest and through the delta of the Volga in the southeast. The lowest

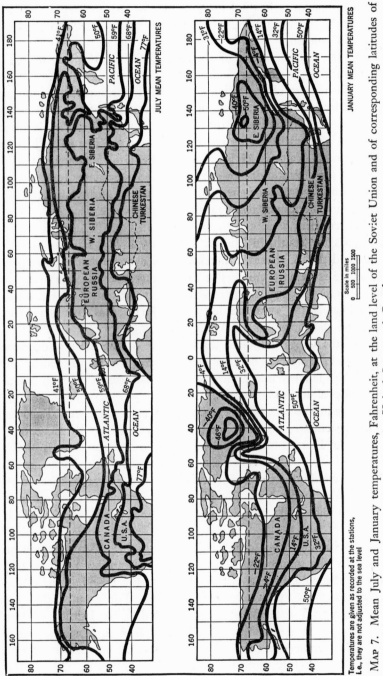

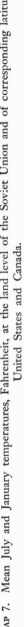

Temperatures are given as recorded at the stations, i.e., they are not adjusted to the sea level

MAP 7. Mean July and January temperatures, Fahrenheit, at the land level of the Soviet Union and of corresponding latitudes of United States and Canada.

January temperature in the European part of the country ($-8°F$) is found in the northeast between the low reaches of the Pechora and the Ural Mountains.

In the summer the effect of the Atlantic is not so great as in the winter, and the isotherms are more or less latitudinal.

The south coast of the Crimea and the Transcaucasian region are protected by high mountains from the penetration of the cold northern air masses; accordingly, the climate in these localities is much warmer in winter than in the rest of the country. The mean January temperature at Yalta is $25°F$. East of the Ural Mountains the influence of the Atlantic decreases rapidly, and the winter temperatures decrease until the pole of the cold is reached in northeastern Siberia. The absolute minimum temperature recorded here was $90.4°$ below zero, Fahrenheit.

Towards the south, in Middle Asia, only a few stations near the Iranian and the Afghanistan borders have average January temperatures above freezing. Winters in the northern part of Turkestan are rather severe: January temperatures near the Aral Sea (Kazalinsk) (approximately the same latitude as Crimea) are as low as in Murmansk (on the shores of the Arctic).

East of the Ural Mountains, the influence of the Atlantic decreases rapidly, and the winter isotherms are deflected towards the south. For instance, the January isotherm of $-4°F$, which passes through Novaia Zemlia, goes almost as far south as Omsk.

Summers in Western Siberia are as warm as in the eastern European part of the country. The mean July temperature at Tomsk is $66°F$. Although in Eastern Siberia the mean January temperature is $-22°F$ and even lower, the summer temperatures there are comparatively high, and conditions for agriculture are more favorable than at the same latitudes in the New World. In general, however, the climate of Eastern Siberia is more severe than one would expect for its latitudes.

The Pacific coast up to $58°$ latitude N and the Amur region are affected by the monsoons. The winter temperatures here are governed by the cold air masses brought from the inland. The winter temperatures are very low for those latitudes. For instance, the mean January temperature of Vladivostok, located at the latitude of Marseilles, France, or approximately at that of Boston, Massachusetts, is $10°F$. The summers on the Pacific coast, too, are comparatively cool. The Vladivostok July mean temperature is about $66°F$. The farther

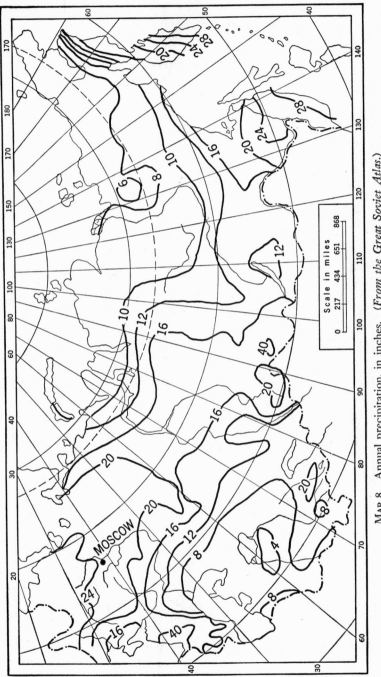

Map 8. Annual precipitation, in inches. (*From the Great Soviet Atlas.*)

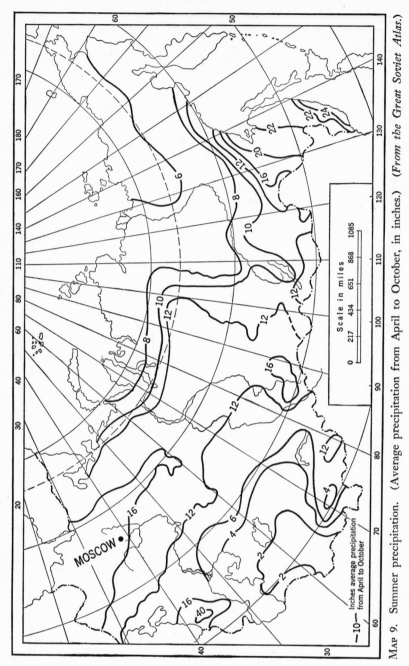

MAP 9. Summer precipitation. (Average precipitation from April to October, in inches.) (*From the Great Soviet Atlas.*)

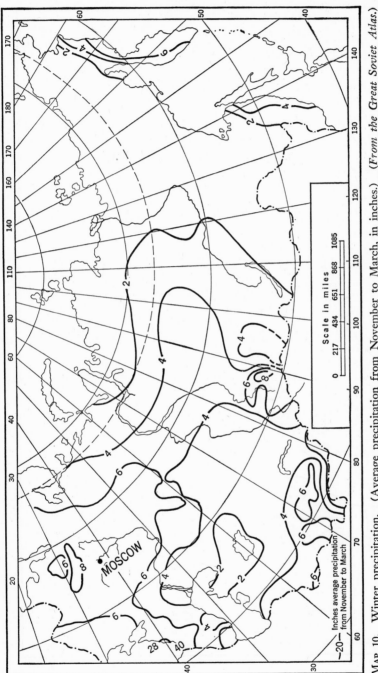

MAP 10.   Winter precipitation.   (Average precipitation from November to March, in inches.)   (*From the Great Soviet Atlas.*)

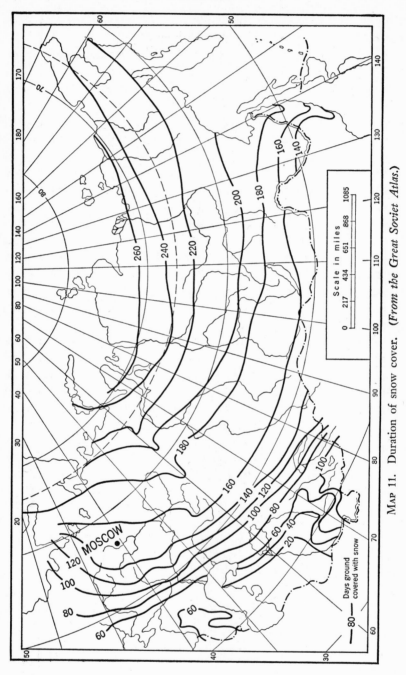

MAP 11. Duration of snow cover. (*From the Great Soviet Atlas.*)

from the coast, the higher the temperature in summer. At Blagoveshchensk the mean July temperature is about 72°F.

The distribution of precipitation throughout the year follows closely
the distribution of the cold and warm air masses over the Eurasian
continent. The most abundant precipitation occurs on the Black Sea
coast of the Transcaucasian region; at Batumi it is up to 100 inches a
year and it is distributed rather uniformly. In European Russia the
precipitation decreases from west to east and especially to the southeast. Moscow has 24 inches a year; farther east it drops to 16 to 20
inches, but in the Ural Mountains it increases again to 24 inches. Both
to the north and to the south the precipitation decreases. East of the
Ural it also decreases steadily, and the region of lowest precipitation is found in northeastern Siberia (below 8 inches and even as
low as 4 inches a year). The Transbaikal region has more rainfall
(12 to 16 inches), and the Yakut country has 8 to 12 inches. On the
Pacific coast, which is affected by the monsoons, the winters are dry
but the summers are foggy with rains and drizzles. Most rain falls in
August. The climatic features of specific regions will be discussed
in the appropriate sections of this book.

Several attempts have been made to subdivide the country (as such
or as a part of the world) into climatic regions. Köppen's classification, based essentially on the distribution of vegetation, appears to be
most generally accepted. In 1930 a climatic map of Soviet Russia was
published by A. V. Vosnessensky.* Vosnessensky somewhat modified
Köppen's classification; he described the prevailing climate of the
country as belonging to the cool boreal type characterized by snowfall in winter and by warm summers. Eighty-eight and five-tenths
per cent of the total area of the country has this type of boreal climate.
This area is further subdivided into three regions:

    (*a*) With sufficient rainfall   65% of the total area
    (*b*) With insufficient rainfall   20% of the total area
    (*c*) With very meager rainfall   about 4% of the total area
         (deserts)

Typical polar climate is found only in 6 per cent of the area of the
whole country. Moderately warm southern climates are found in 5
per cent of the total area of the Soviet Union.

* *Trans. Bureau of Agrometeorology,* Vol. 21, pp. 3–130. In Russian, with an
English summary and a map.

Permanently Frozen Ground

By the term permanently frozen ground * is meant that part of the earth's crust which, being located at a certain depth, always possesses temperatures below the freezing point and always contains water in the solid phase, i.e., in the form of ice. Permanently frozen ground has two surfaces: the upper, which varies in depth throughout the year; and the lower, which is at a constant depth. Below the lower surface the temperature is again above freezing point.

The area occupied by permanently frozen ground within the boundaries of the Soviet Union is about 4 million square miles, or about 47 per cent of the whole USSR. The southern boundary of this area begins from the strait connecting the White Sea and the Barents Sea. It passes about 25 miles north of the town of Mezen, crosses the Ural towards Berezov, and crosses the Yenisei above Turukhansk. Turning south, it then follows the east bank of the Yenisei and crosses the Mongolian border. It reappears again in the Soviet Union somewhat west of Blagoveshchensk on the Amur and reaches the Pacific coast near De Castri Bay in Tatar Strait (see Map 12). Most of the Kamchatka Peninsula, the island of Sakhalin, and most of the area between the Amur and the Ussuri (i.e., the Maritime Province) are free of permanently frozen ground.

The term permanently frozen ground does not mean that the surface of the soil is permanently frozen all over the area of 4 million square miles; surface temperatures that are always below the freezing point occur only in occasional parts of the tundra region.

Usually the upper layer of the soil, the so-called active layer, thaws to a varying depth every summer, permitting the growth of herbaceous vegetation, shrubs, and even trees. Agriculture is possible in the areas having permanently frozen subsoil. Often during spring plowing in the permafrost regions, the turned-over slabs of soil are glistening with ice crystals. At the time of harvest, in August, the active layer may recede in depth as much as 6 to 10 feet. Permafrost is not considered a hindrance to northern agriculture; on the contrary, it may even be beneficial to the raising of crops, as it conserves moisture in the soil in the regions where precipitation is not very abundant.

The whole area where permafrost is found may be divided into three large regions:

---

* In the United States the term permanently frozen ground has become abbreviated to permafrost.

1. The northern region, descending from the shores of the Arctic almost to the 60th parallel and extending from the Ob estuary to the Chukotski Peninsula. Here the temperatures at a depth of 35 to 50 feet are always $-5\,°C$ ($23\,°F$). This region may be truly called a region of permanently frozen ground.

2. The intermediate region, which touches the Arctic coast in the European part of the country and the shores of the Bering Sea and the Okhotsk Sea in Siberia. In this region the prevailing temperatures at a depth of 35 to 50 feet vary from $-5\,°C$ ($23\,°F$) to $-1.5\,°C$ ($29.3\,°F$). Occurrence of permafrost is not continuous here; patches of unfrozen ground are found within the region also. Conditions of this kind are common to the area of the upper Lena River.

3. The southern region, which touches the Arctic in European Russia at the Kanin Peninsula and extends to the southern part of the Okhotsk Sea and the shores of Tatar Strait near the Amur estuary. There is even more discontinuity of permafrost in this region than in the intermediate region; the northern section contains patches without permafrost, and in the southern section the permafrost occurs only in patches. The temperatures at a depth of 35 to 50 feet below the surface are predominantly above $-1.5\,°C$ ($29.3\,°F$).

The thickness of the permafrost varies from 3 to 6 feet to many hundreds of feet. Near Nordvik (at the estuary of the Khatanga in northeastern Siberia) the layer of permanently frozen ground is about 2000 feet thick. The farther south, the thinner the layer of permanently frozen ground. At Yakutsk the thickness amounts to about 450 feet. In the Transbaikal region (Skovorodino, in the upper Amur country) the layer is about 160 feet thick; at the lower reaches of the Amur, about 3 to 6 feet thick; south of the Soviet border at Ulan-Bator in Mongolia, about 80 feet thick.

In some places in the north fossil ice is found, i.e., ice formed during the glacial period and buried under debris. Occasionally fossil ice serves the local population as a source of water supply.

In permanently frozen ground there are occasionally found well-preserved remains of now-extinct animals, such as mammoths. Opinions differ as to the origin of permanently frozen ground, but some maintain that since it contains these remains of extinct animals it must have originated during the glacial period. Others, however, believe that it was formed relatively recently. To support its opinion the latter group points out that the relatively recent mining dumps in the Kolyma gold fields developed a layer of permanently frozen ground. Apparently both opinions are correct: some permanently frozen

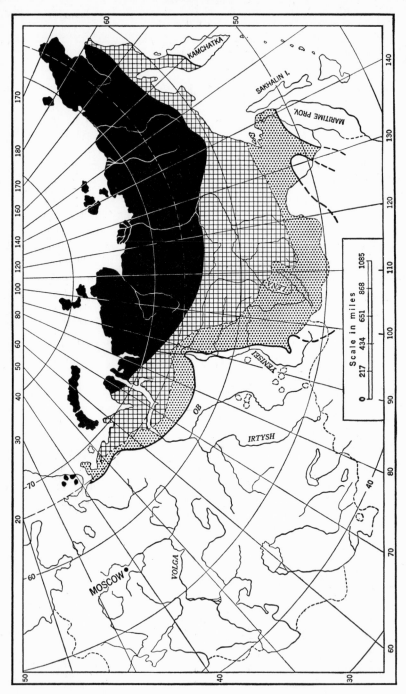

MAP 12. Permanently Frozen Ground.

Black: Region of continuous distribution of frozen ground. Temperature at the depth of 30 to 50 feet below the surface is lower than −5°C.

Cross-hatched: Region of permanently frozen ground with patches of not frozen ground. Temperature at the depth of 30 to 50 feet below the surface is predominantly between −5° and −1.5°C.

Dotted: In the northern part of this region there are patches of not permanently frozen ground in the generally frozen ground; in the southern part of this region are found only occasional patches of permanently frozen ground. Temperature at the depth of 30 to 50 feet below the surface is predominantly above 1.5°C.

Black dots: Permanently frozen ground in peat hillocks of Kola Peninsula.

Circles along the Upper Ob and Yenisei and in the Pamir represent patches of permanently frozen ground.

ground has been preserved since the ice age, and some of it is of recent origin.

Because of the general warming of the northern regions, the southern boundary of permafrost has somewhat receded. In 1837 this boundary passed by the town of Mezen; in 1933 it was 25 miles north of the town.

Permafrost causes a great deal of trouble in building roads and houses, digging wells, drilling, excavating, or laying out water systems. An apparently solid mountain cut during a railroad or highway construction may turn, with the advent of spring, into a flowing mass of mud. Building a substantial structure usually is quite a problem. Frost heaving (caused by the expansion of water in winter and its contraction in the spring) in the active layer of the soil causes the ejection of telephone poles from the ground, cracks in brick walls, and twists in log houses.* In some parts of Siberia permanently frozen ground serves a good purpose as a natural cold storage for fish, fowl, and game.

* Water, unlike any other substance, has its highest density (i.e., it occupies the smallest volume) at 4°C. It expands when it becomes either colder or warmer. For a description of permafrost see George Cressey, "Frozen Ground of Siberia," *J. Geol.*, 1939, Vol. 47, pp. 472–488.

Chapter 4

Rivers and Lakes

The rivers of the northern part of European Russia and most of Siberia drain into the Arctic Ocean; those flowing into the Baltic and Black seas and into the Azov Sea are a part of the Atlantic Ocean drainage. Some rivers of northeastern Siberia and those of the Far Eastern Region flow to the seas of the Pacific. The Volga River system and all the rivers of Middle Asia except the Kara Irtysh belong to the inner basin and do not find their way to any ocean. The Volga flows into the land-locked Caspian Sea, and the two largest rivers of Middle Asia, the Amu Darya and Syr Darya, drain into the Aral Sea.

The Soviet Union possesses some of the largest rivers in the world. The Lena River is 2644 miles long; the Ob, 2508 miles; the Yenisei, 2360 miles; the Amur, 2700 miles; and the largest European river, the Volga, is 2287 miles long.*

Sixty per cent of the total area of European Russia is drained by the rivers flowing into the Arctic and the Atlantic oceans. Forty per cent of the area belongs to the great inner basin of the Caspian Sea. As the elevations within European Russia are rather low, the sources of the rivers are not very high above sea level. For instance, the source of the Volga in the Valdai Hills is only about 800 feet above sea level, or about 885 feet above the level of the Caspian Sea.

The rivers of European Russia are slow-flowing. They are fed predominantly by melting snow. Spring floods are common, especially in the rivers flowing south. In winter the rivers of European Russia are covered with ice.

As the watersheds are low, the sources of rivers flowing in opposite directions are in many instances very close to each other. Many a small lake and swamp is the source of two rivers, one of which flows into the Baltic Sea and the other into the Caspian. Formerly the upper reaches of the rivers were connected by portages. At pres-

---

* Different sources give different figures. The figures given here are from N. N. Baransky, *Physical Geography of the USSR*, Moscow, 7th ed., 1943, 100 pp. (In Russian.)

ent an extensive system of canals connects the rivers draining into the Arctic Ocean and into the Baltic, Black, and Caspian seas.

The most important eastern European rivers radiate from the central part of the country towards the periphery, a phenomenon that has had considerable importance in the origin and growth of the Moscow Principality. The main watershed between the Baltic Sea and the Arctic on one hand and the Black Sea and the Caspian Sea on the other is located closer to the Arctic than to the Black Sea. Accordingly, the rivers of European Russia flowing south are longer than those flowing north. The rivers of the north, however, flow through the regions where summers are cool and evaporation is low and through extensive forested areas where snow melt is greatly retarded. For that reason they have a better-regulated flow, they are not so likely to flood in the springtime as the southern rivers, and in summer they maintain their full volume of flow.

The rivers of the Kola Peninsula and of Karelia are of a different nature. They rush down their courses, which are cut in granite ledges, and are full of rapids and waterfalls. Some of them, such as the Niva, never freeze.

The rivers of the south, although having their sources in the lakes and swamps of the northern part of Russia, soon leave the forested regions and enter the southern prairies or Caspian semideserts. There are very few tributaries to these rivers in the southern part of the country. For example, no rivers drain into the Volga below Stalingrad. Some rivers flowing towards the Caspian Sea never reach it, becoming lost in the sands.

Of all the rivers of European Russia, and indeed of the whole Soviet Union, the Volga is the most important. It flows from the Valdai Hills, at an elevation of 800 feet, to the Caspian Sea, which is 85 feet below sea level. Its two largest tributaries, the Kama, flowing from the Ural, and the Oka, flowing from the central Russian upland, are found in the forest region of the country. Moscow, the capital of the Soviet Union, is located on the River Moskva, a small tributary of the Oka. Before emptying into the Caspian Sea, the Volga breaks into numerous branches, forming a delta that occupies an area of about 2300 square miles.

Other important rivers flowing south are the Dnieper (1400 miles long), flowing into the Black Sea, and the Don, which discharges its waters into the Azov Sea. After World War II the Soviet Union extended its borders to the east bank of the low reaches of the important central European waterway, the Danube.

Several large rivers flow into the Arctic, namely the Pechora, the Mezen, and the Northern Dvina; and a short but very important river, the Neva, flows into the Baltic Sea. The former capital of Russia, St. Petersburg, now Leningrad, is located at the mouth of the Neva.

The lakes of European Russia may be divided into two types: fresh-water lakes of the formerly glaciated northwest, and salt-water lakes of the southeast. Numerous relatively small lakes of the northwest are located in the region of the terminal moraine, along the border of the Valdai Hills. The largest lakes in this region, however, are of a fault type: Lake Ladoga has an area of about 7000 square miles and is 730 feet deep, and Lake Onega, which occupies an area of 3760 square miles, is 400 feet deep.

The salt lakes of the Caspian lowlands are mostly sinks or depressions filled with rainwater that gradually brought leached salts from the surrounding country. The largest of them, however—Elton and Baskunchack—are apparently of a fault origin.

On the shores of the Black Sea, the Azov Sea, and the Caspian Sea so-called limans are found. Limans are the estuaries into which the large rivers of the eastern European plain discharge. They were formed during the Quaternary period (New Euxine time), when considerable areas of the Black Sea coast sank, flooding the low reaches of the rivers.

Western Siberia is drained by the Ob-Irtysh system. In length, this system is surpassed only by the Mississippi-Missouri system, the Nile, and the Amazon. The Irtysh is longer than the Ob but carries less water at their confluence. The Ob is formed by the merging of two rivers, the Katun and the Biia. Both have their sources in the glaciers and snowfields of the Altai Mountains. The Irtysh has its source south of the border. The lowlands of Western Siberia have a very gentle slope towards the Arctic, and the flow of the rivers is, therefore, extremely slow. The upper reaches of the rivers, being located in warmer areas, are freed from ice much earlier in the spring than the northern and lower parts of the river systems. Thus the freshet waters, rushing north across the Western Siberian lowlands, are blocked by the ice, and as a result the surrounding areas are flooded. Western Siberia is notorious for its immense swamps.

The rivers that originate in the Altai Mountains and that are fed by the melting glaciers have a fuller and more uniform flow of water in summer than the eastern European rivers. The Ob and the Yenisei discharge their waters into the Kara Sea. The volume of relatively warm water borne by these rivers during the summer months is truly

enormous and has a considerable effect on the thermal balance of the
Kara Sea.

There are many small lakes in the lowlands of Western Siberia.
Some of them are fresh; others, farther south, have brackish water;
and still others are salty. Whereas in European Russia most of the
lakes are located in the glaciated area, in western Siberia the lakes are
found chiefly in the southern part, which has never been glaciated.

There are very few large lakes in the Altai Mountains. Teletskoie
Lake and Marka Kul Lake will be described in Chapter 21.

The Yenisei River does not play an important part in the drainage
of Western Siberia. It has no large tributaries from the west. It is
located approximately on the border between Western and Eastern
Siberia, but the area drained is predominantly in Eastern Siberia. The
Yenisei begins in the Tuva country, a mountainous region south of
the Siberian periphery chain of Sayan and north of the Tannu Ola
Mountains. Some of the sources of the Yenisei are located in Mongolia. The Ulu Kem and Kemchik join to form the Yenisei River.
The Ulu Kem, in turn, is formed by the Kha (or Kua) Kem and
the Bei Kem, both flowing from the densely forested, abundant in
water, northeastern part of Tuva. Russian settlers often call the Ulu
Kem, together with the Bei Kem, the Big Yenisei, whereas the Kha
Kem is called the Little Yenisei. The Yenisei breaks through the west-
ern Sayan Mountains in a narrow, rapid stream and flows towards the
Arctic. In its course across Siberia this majestic fast-flowing stream
takes from the east three of its largest tributaries: the Angara, the
Stony (or Podkamennaia) Tunguska, and the Lower Tunguska. The
Angara emerges from Lake Baikal as a wide full-bodied stream that,
for a few miles, does not freeze in winter. At its confluence with the
Yenisei the Angara, known here as the Upper Tunguska, carries more
water and has traversed more territory than the Yenisei. The rapidly
flowing Angara freezes at Irkutsk only in January and sometimes
floods the surrounding country. After leaving Irkutsk Province and
passing through a series of treacherous rapids, it assumes the name of
Upper Tunguska. The Stony Tunguska is also noted for its rapids.
The Lower Tunguska is 2550 miles long.   ·

The Lena is the second longest river in the Soviet Union, its total
length being 2644 miles. Its source is a few miles from Lake Baikal.
In its course across Siberia it receives several tributaries, of which the
Vilui, Aldan, and Vitim are the largest. Below the mouth of the
Aldan the Lena is over 6½ miles wide. Between the Yenisei and Lena

are several large rivers—the Khatanga, Anabar, and Olenek—and between the Lena and Bering Strait are the Yana, Indigirka, and Kolyma. The Anadyr flows into the Bering Sea.

Lake Baikal, the largest fresh-water lake in the Old World, is located within the borders of Eastern Siberia. It will be described in Chapter 23.

The longest river of the Soviet Union is the Amur. It is formed by the Shilka and the Argun. The Shilka, in turn, is formed by the Onon and the Ingoda. The Amur flows eastward for some distance, being joined by several large tributaries: the Zeia and the Bureia from the north, and the Sungari from the south, which is totally in the territory of Manchuria. After its confluence with the Ussuri, which flows from the south, the Amur turns northeast and for some distance parallels the Pacific coast. It empties its water and silt into the Tatar Strait, just opposite Sakhalin Island. The total length of the Amur, including the Shilka and the Onon, is 2700 miles.

The inland basin of Middle Asia occupies an area of about 773,000 square miles. The two largest rivers of this basin—the Amu Darya, with the Panj, 1558 miles long (called Oxus by the English geographers); and the Syr Darya (the ancient Jaxartes, 1773 miles long)— flow from the snowfields of the Middle Asian mountains to the Aral Sea. In the lower reaches these rivers freeze during winter. The Amu Darya is formed by the Vakhan Darya, which originates at an elevation of 15,000 feet from a glacier in the Hindu Kush Mountains, and the Pamir River, which flows from Lake Sara Kul (Lake Victoria) in the Russian Pamir highland. At 9000 feet elevation the Vakhan Darya and the Pamir join to form the River Panj. After the Panj receives a tributary, the Vaksh, it assumes the name of Amu Darya. The people call it simply Darya (the River). The Amu Darya has two periods of high water: one in the spring when snow in the relatively low mountains begins to melt, and one in the summer (June–July) when most of the water is supplied by the glaciers. In crossing the desert, the Amu Darya carries a great deal of silt, which is deposited in its delta. The banks, composed of soft, loose material, are easily eroded by the river, which changes its channel frequently.

The Syr Darya is longer than the Amu Darya but it carries less water. It originates from the glaciers of the Tien Shan Mountains and assumes its name after the confluence of the Naryn and the Kara Darya. After leaving the mountains it flows through the Ferghana valley, crosses the desert, and empties into the Aral Sea.

TABLE 2. COMPARATIVE LENGTHS OF THE LARGEST RIVERS OF THE SOVIET UNION
AND THE AREAS OF THEIR DRAINAGE

(After Baransky) [1]

		Length in Miles	Drainage Area in Thousands of Square Miles
Baltic Sea basin	Western Dvina	631	32.4
	Neman	532	37.7
	Neva	44	97.2
White Sea basin	Northern Dvina (with Sukhona)	802	158.6
	Vychegda	684	46.4
Barents Sea basin	Pechora	1108	126.2
Black Sea basin	Dnieper	1414	193.2
	Dniester	881	27.8
Azov Sea basin	Kuban	582	19.2
	Don	1218	162.8
Caspian Sea basin	Volga	2287	146.7
	Kama	1261	202.2
	Oka	916	94.6
	Ural	1572	85.0
	Kura	940	72.6
Aral Sea basin	Amu Darya (with Panj)	1558	196.6
	Syr Darya (with Naryn)	1773	84.6
Arctic Ocean basin	Ob (with Katun)	2508	937.0
	Irtysh	1840	413.5
	Tobol	1040	127.0
	Ishim	1120	52.9
	Yenisei	2360	1046.0
	Angara	1150	194.6
	Lower Tunguska	1580	182.5
	Olenek	1450	95.2
	Lena	2644	931.5
	Aldan	1390	272.5
	Vilui	1510	189.5
	Kolyma	1332	248.6
Pacific Ocean basin	Amur (with Shilka and Onon)	2700	711.8
	Zeia	750	90.9
	Ussuri (with Ulu-he)	532	72.4

Area drained by all other rivers is approximately 1.3 million square miles.

[1] N. N. Baransky, *Physical Geography of the USSR*, 7th ed., Moscow, 1943, p. 65. (In Russian.)

TABLE 3. DRAINAGE AREAS OF THE SOVIET UNION
(After Baransky)

Drainage Basins	Area in Millions of Square Miles
Arctic Ocean	4.4
Barents and White seas	0.5
Baltic Sea	0.1
Black Sea	0.4
Caspian Sea	1.5
Inland drainage other than the Caspian Sea	0.8
Pacific Ocean	0.9
Total	8.6

The Aral Sea is a very large but rather shallow lake. It covers approximately 26,166 square miles, and its maximum depth is 250 feet. It is of more recent origin than the Caspian Sea, and its waters are less saline. The eastern and southern shores are low; the western and northwestern shores, where the Ust Urt Plateau comes close, are high and abrupt.

Another important river of the inland basin, although smaller than the two Daryas, is the Chu River, which begins in the Tien Shan Mountains, passes near Lake Issyk Kul, occasionally discharging into the lake a part of its water, then passes through the Buam(ski) gorge, and finally reaches the lowlands. Here a great deal of its water is taken for irrigation and lost in evaporation. It grows smaller and smaller and at last ends in a small desert lake—Saumal Kul. Another river of this type—the Murghab—flows from the Paropamisus Mountains. Some of its waters are used in Afghanistan oases, and a great deal more is utilized after it crosses the Soviet border. It ends at the oasis of Merv (now Mary). The waters of the Zeravshan, which flows from the huge Zeravshan glacier, are used entirely for irrigation. The Ili River flows from Chinese Turkestan to Lake Balkhash, forming a long, narrow delta covered with reed thickets.

Lake Balkhash occupies an area of 8400 square miles. It is very shallow—from 35 to 65 feet in depth. Its southern shores are sandy and low; the western and northern shores are steep and rocky. Water in the western part of the lake where the River Ili empties into it is fresh, whereas the water in the eastern end of the lake is brackish. Apparently this lake is of relatively recent origin.

The rivers of the Caucasus are of an alpine type. Their sources are in high altitudes in the glaciers and snowfields. Their largest volume of water flows in summer. In the North Caucasus there are two notable rivers: the Kuban, which flows into the Azov Sea; and the Terek, which flow into the Caspian Sea. Both are swift, turbulent streams in their upper parts. Their low reaches are swampy and subject to destructive floods.

Part 2

The People

Chapter 5

Historical Geography

At the end of the glacial age man appeared in the territory now occupied by the Soviet Union. Mousterian implements and remains of Neanderthal man have been found in the southern part of European Russia and also recently (1938) in Uzbekistan. There exists ample evidence that upper paleolithic and especially neolithic man inhabited European Russia and the southern parts of Asiatic Russia. Upper paleolithic and neolithic places of habitation have been found also on the upper Lena, the Angara, and the upper Yenisei rivers and in the Lake Baikal region. Towards the beginning of historical times the country was already populated by scattered inhabitants. As early as 600 B.C. the northern part of European Russia as far southwest as the Baltic republics was populated by different Finno-Ugrian tribes of the Ural-Altaic group of peoples that migrated westward from Siberia.

The southwestern part of eastern Europe was occupied by some settled tribes and the southeastern part by roaming nomads. The Greeks, who at that time founded several trading colonies on the northern shores of the Black Sea, called these natives, both settled and roaming, Scythians. During these early historical times considerable migrations of peoples took place in Siberia. Samoyeds were pushed from the southern part of the country towards the Arctic, and the paleoasiatic descendants of the neolithic population were pushed also, chiefly northeast. Some of them apparently moved to the North American continent.

At the beginning of the third century, the Goths, a Scandinavian people, invaded the western Ukraine; towards the beginning of the fourth century, their eastern subdivision, the Ostrogoths, subjugated a territory as far east as the Azov Sea. The Ostrogoths were expelled from the Ukraine by the Huns; they did not leave much of an imprint on the local population, which probably was Vendic, i.e., Slavic.*

* For a more detailed discussion of the early population of the country, see Ales Hrdlička, "The Peoples of the Soviet Union," *Smithsonian Institution War Background Studies*, No. 3, Publication 3690, Washington, D. C., 1942.

After having suffered the effects of the Hun invasion, the southern part of European Russia fell under the rule of the Khazars (between 600 and 950 A.D.), the invaders who came from beyond the Caucasian Mountains. This invasion was followed by a series of minor invasions by Asiatic hordes.

At the close of the fifth century the name Slavs came to designate certain tribes that inhabited western Russia, East Prussia, and the area south to the Balkans. Their earlier history is uncertain, although according to some sources their division into the western and eastern Slavs took place as early as the fourth century A.D.

In the ninth century the tribes of eastern Slavs living along the Dnieper and west and north from this river, being disturbed by the intrusion of some armed bands of Varangians, or Scandinavians, hired another Varangian band under the leadership of Rurik to protect them. Rurik united several Slavic tribes and became their ruler. The thus united Slavic nation became known as Rus, i.e., the nation of the fair-haired people. In 988 the country accepted Christianity. The further history of the new nation of Russia was one of expansion and consolidation and of fighting off various enemies: Swedes, German knights, and Asiatic hordes.

Gradually the activity of the new Russian state became concentrated in the geographically important Moscow Principality, and in 1147 the city of Moscow appeared on the map.

Early in the thirteenth century Russia suffered the worst Asiatic invasion. Carried out by the Tatars,* this invasion continued for about 300 years. The southern part of the country was devastated, and part of the population was exterminated and part driven westward to Galicia and Poland.

Muscovite princes pursued their course of consolidation of the numerous Russian principalities under their leadership, and towards the end of the fifteenth century they were able to liberate the country from the weakened rule of the Tatars. For a long time different groups of Tatars maintained independent states within Russia along the Volga and in Crimea. The Crimean Khanate was conquered by Russia in 1783. During the Tatar rule, gradually the Russian people became separated into three large groups: the Great Russians, who became the empire builders, the Ukrainians, and the Belorussians; the last two peoples under the influence of Poland and Lithuania developed certain languages and customs different from those of the Rus-

* Often referred to as the Mongol invasion. The Tatar hordes were a part of the Mongolian Empire.

sian people. The expansion of the Moscow Principality continued, and towards the end of the sixteenth century Siberia was annexed to the czardom of Russia.

For some time the Ukraine existed as an independent state. It became a part of Russia in 1654. In the reign of Peter the Great (1682–1725) Russia was proclaimed an empire. Estonia and Latvia were annexed. Parts of Poland were acquired at the end of the eighteenth and at the beginning of the nineteenth centuries; Finland was won from Sweden in 1809, and Bessarabia was annexed in 1812.

The conquest of the Caucasian region began in the eighteenth century. The Caspian shores as far down as Baku were occupied in 1722–1723. The southern shores of the Caspian Sea belonging to Persia also were occupied during this period but were later returned to Persia.

The conquest of the Caucasus was rather a bloody affair and was completed only in 1859 when wild mountain valleys of eastern Daghestan fell to the Russians. Georgia, which is located on the southern slopes of the main Caucasian chain, was annexed by the Russian Empire during a period extending from 1801 to 1829, partly by force, partly by peaceful means. Georgia has existed historically for more than 2000 years, and the Georgian capital, Tbilisi, was founded in the first century of the Christian era. Armenia, parts of which were wrested from Turkey early in the nineteenth century, also has had a centuries-long and very turbulent history. Two Turkish provinces, Kars and Ardahan, acquired in 1878, were returned to Turkey in 1921.

The revolution of 1917 signified the end of imperial Russia and resulted in a considerable loss of territory (Finland, Bessarabia, the Baltic states, and the Russian part of Poland). The Union of Soviet Socialist Republics was established in 1922. During World War II the southwestern part of the country from Leningrad to a point near Moscow, to Voronezh, to Stalingrad, to the foothills of the Caucasus was occupied by the Germans and was utterly destroyed in their retreat. After the war, most of the territory lost during the revolution of 1917 was restored to the Soviet Union, except Finland, parts of Poland, and the provinces of Kars and Ardahan. Moreover, some territorial gains were made in the Far East (the Kuril Islands and the southern part of Sakhalin Island), in Eastern Siberia (the Uriankhai Territory, renamed Tuva Autonomous Region—Oblast), and on the extreme western borders of the country (the province of Ruthenia or Carpathian Ukraine and the Königsberg region of East Prussia).

Occupation of Siberia by the Russians was a rather spectacular en-terprise. Apparently, contact between Russian traders and the Ural-Altaic tribes (especially the Finno-Ugrian) of Siberia already existed in the eleventh century, perhaps earlier. Early knowledge of Siberia by the Russians was rather grotesque. In the sixteenth century some merchants named Stroganoff, of Perm, obtained large trade conces-sions in the Ural region and in a rich fur country farther east. They employed bands of Volga freebooters, known as Cossacks, or, more correctly, Kazaks,* to protect their interests. One of these bands under the leadership of Yermak invaded Western Siberia and took the Tatar fortress of Sibir, located on the Irtysh near Tobolsk, and thus in 1581–1582 started the conquest of a vast territory. The subsequent occupation of Siberia (in Russian, Sibir) was done mostly by fur traders, accompanied by armed detachments and officials and followed by missionaries. Somebody once said that the conquest of Siberia was one continuous hunt for sable. When the Russians were well into Eastern Siberia, instead of turning south towards warm-water ports, they turned north and reached the Pacific (in 1650) in its most in-hospitable locality, at Anadyr, on the Chukotski Peninsula. Thus, the whole of Siberia was crossed by the Russians in only 68 years. Some tribes, such as the Ostiaks and Samoyeds, were conquered without difficulty; those who resisted, as, for instance, the Buriats and Kam-chadals, were subjugated by the force of arms.

A government expedition under Bering was sent in 1725–1730 to find out whether Siberia was connected with America. In 1784 Rus-sians landed in Alaska and extended their fur-trading and fur-hunting pursuits as far south as San Francisco Bay in California. Fort Ross was founded north of San Francisco in 1812. Alaska was sold to the United States in 1867.

When the Russians reached the Amur in the middle of the seven-teenth century, they came in touch with the peoples who were sub-jects of the Chinese Empire and met resistance from regular troops armed with guns and cannons. In a series of treaties, the last one signed in 1858, the Amur was decided upon as a boundary between Russia and China. Later Russia acquired the area between the Sea of Japan and the Ussuri River (i.e., the Maritime Province).

At the beginning of the present century, Russia began to expand farther south in Manchuria. A war with Japan (1905), however, curbed further aspirations of Russia in Manchuria and resulted in the

* See footnote on p. 65.

loss of some territory (the southern half of Sakhalin), which was regained after World War II. Russia's position in Manchuria has improved since the war. In contrast to the occupation of Siberia, the conquest of parts of Central Asia had all the marks of a military operation.

Middle Asia has possessed an ancient civilization: Alexander of Macedonia once conquered it; Tamerlane had his capital at Samarkand. Settled Indo-European peoples and Turkic nomads were found there in Alexander's time. When the Russians learned of Middle Asia in the sixteenth century, there existed three princely Moslem states: the Khanates of Khiva and of Kokand and the Emirate of Bukhara. The last of the three was a world-renowned center of Moslem education, possessing libraries and religious schools. Parts of the region were under the nominal rule of Persia; the rest of the country was an unclaimed territory. When Russia penetrated into Siberia, the southern Siberian steppes, the home of the Kazakhs, remained unconquered; no definite boundary existed between Russian Siberia and the Moslem south. Hordes of native Kazakhs caused a great deal of trouble to the Russian lines of communication, and the Kazakh people * had a great Moslem world (including Turkey) backing them.

At the beginning of the eighteenth century, Peter the Great realized that the conquest of the Middle Asiatic princely states was necessary in order to tame the Kazakhs. Besides, there were plans of trade with Chinese Turkestan and India. Several military expeditions were sent to Middle Asia: some from Siberia up the Irtysh, others across the Caspian Sea; one army sent against Khiva perished in the desert. In the eighteenth century Russians began to press harder against the south, to the great concern of Great Britain. Towards the middle of the nineteenth century the pincers reaching into the Kazakh country were closed and most of the Kazakhs surrendered.

In 1860, however, after Kokand, with help of the Kazakhs, attacked the Russians, a large expeditionary force was sent against the princely states. In 1865 Tashkent fell; in 1868 the Bukhara army was defeated and Samarkand was taken. Khiva surrendered in 1873. The Khanate of Kokand was abolished, but Khiva and Bukhara retained their rulers and became semi-independent states, apparently in imitation of the princely states of India.

Then the Russians turned their attention to the Turkmen territory, along the Afghan border. Ashkhabad was taken in 1881, but the war

* See footnote on p. 65.

continued until 1885.   The acquisition of the Pamirs in 1895 alarmed
Great Britain considerably, and in order to prevent direct contact between India's northwestern territory and the Russian Pamirs a narrow
(about 10 miles in places) Afghanistan panhandle was created.   Several years were spent in the establishment of the border line; finally
it was established and the farther advance of the Russians to the south
was blocked.   After World War II when Great Britain relinquished
her right to protect the border of the northwestern territories, the
Afghanistan panhandle apparently lost its importance.*   Russians occupied parts of Chinese Turkestan on several occasions.   During the
Moslem Revolt, 1871 to 1881, Kulja was occupied.   After the 1931
Moslem trouble in Sinkiang, the Soviet Union occupied parts of this
territory (near Urumchi) in 1934 but withdrew in 1942 after nego-
tiations with China.

With the conquest of Middle Asia and acquisitions in western Europe, the country (to quote one Russian geography book) † reached
the limits of its possible geographic expansion.

* See footnote, p. 5.

† M. I. Pavlov and V. P. Goroschenko, *Geografia SSSR*, Moscow, 1946, p. 7.
(In Russian.)

Chapter 6

Peoples

The Soviet Union inherited from the Russian Empire a vast geographic expanse populated by many different peoples. Some had united with Russia in the course of historical events; others had been subjugated by the force of arms; still others had migrated to the old Russia voluntarily. In their centrifugal expansion from the Moscow region, the Russians had infiltrated and assimilated many small tribes; larger groups of peoples preserved their national and territorial identity to a greater or lesser degree.

In 1950 there lived within the borders of the Soviet Union 180 nationalities, more or less, depending on how far one wants to go in splitting or lumping different ethnic groups. Some of the non-Russian peoples of the Soviet Union number in the millions; others consist of only a few survivors of almost extinct tribes.

Just before World War II, the total population of the Soviet Union amounted to 193 million people. The war losses in population were great, about 10 million; but at the same time the increase in the population was great. According to Hrdlička,* the yearly increase in the population of the Soviet Union as a whole is 1.4 per cent, and of the Russians alone 1.5 per cent. Thus the 1950 population of the country was probably about 210 million. Of this number, the Russians comprised about 110 million; the Ukrainians over 36 million, and the Belorussians over 10 million; these three peoples made up the Slavic core of the Soviet Union, amounting to over 156 million persons, about three-quarters of the total.

The Russian nucleus is located in the central part of eastern Europe, around Moscow. The population in this region is entirely Russian. No minority groups having territorial identity are found here.

The Russians, in their expansion from the center to the periphery of eastern Europe, cut broad corridors in the midst of the non-Russian population. One of these corridors reached the Baltic Sea at Leningrad; another extended towards the Arctic. To Asia the Russian

---

* Ales Hrdlička, "The Peoples of the Soviet Union," *Smithsonian Institution War Background Studies*, No. 3, Publication 3690, Washington, D. C., 1942.

population poured in two broad streams: one up the River Chusovaia towards Sverdlovsk (formerly Ekaterinburg), and another between the Urals and their southern continuation, the Mugodjars. A broad stretch of land extending from the Russian center to the River Don near the Caucasus is also populated by the Russians.

Beyond the Urals, the Russians settled in the fertile prairies of Western Siberia and northern Kazakhstan and penetrated to the southern part of Siberia, near Lake Baikal, along the rivers Amur and Ussuri, and to the coast of the Pacific. Scattered Russian settlements are found all over Siberia, especially along the rivers. A great many people have been exiled to Siberia since the seventeenth century for either criminal, political, or religious reasons. All these exiles have contributed to the development of the area. The Russians mixed freely with the natives of Siberia, so that the descendants of many of the early Russian settlers acquired Paleo-Asiatic, Tungus, or Mongol features.

The Ukrainians live in the south and southwest European section of the Soviet Union. Many Ukrainians moved as far into the Asiatic part of the country as the Pacific coast.

The Belorussians occupy the western part of the country, bordering Poland. In the extreme southwest live over 1 million Moldavians, who are related to the Romanians. They have a considerable admixture of blood of many neighboring peoples. North of the Belorussians dwell about 2 million Lithuanians, whose ethnic identity is uncertain. They are a Baltic people whose survivors are still found in East Prussia. Still farther north live the Latvians, or Letts, who are related to the Lithuanians, and the Estonians, who originally belonged to the Finno-Ugrian group; these nationalities have been mixed with others, such as the Swedish. The Finns live around Leningrad. The Karelians, also a Finnish people, inhabit an area between Finland and lakes Ladoga and Onega. On the Kola Peninsula live scattered Lapps, a population extending to the Scandinavian Peninsula. Under the Soviet Union the Russian Lapps received the new name of Saami.*

Along the shores of the Arctic eastward from the Kanin Peninsula and in Western Siberia as far inland as below the 60th parallel live

---

* Since the establishment of the Soviet Union, the names of many minorities have been changed, especially those which had a derogatory meaning. The new names are usually those by which the people called themselves. This rule is not always observed, however. For instance, the Yakuts, who call themselves Saqalar, are still known by their old name, and the Germans are still called by the old Slavic name Niemtsy, meaning persons unable to speak.

about 20,000 Samoyeds (now known as Nentse) and related tribes. The Samoyeds originally inhabited the southern part of Siberia but were pushed north by southern invaders.

South of the Samoyed country of eastern Europe live several Finno-Ugrian peoples: the Zyrians, or Komi (142,000), whose neighbors on the east are 9000 Voguls (Manse) living west of the Urals and between these mountains and the River Ob. Still farther east, along the Ob, are found some 20,000 Ostiaks or Khante. The Voguls and Ostiaks are related to the Magyars of Hungary. East of Moscow, near the Volga, live Finno-Ugrian peoples: the Mordva (1.4 million); the Cheremiss (or Mari, about 500,000), who are the most strongly Mongolized of all Finns; and 1.4 million Chuvash, a mixed people of blond Finns and dark Mongolians. They speak Turkic. Near the Urals may be found another Finno-Ugrian people: the Udmurts (formerly known as the Votiaks and totaling 605,000 persons). In the region east of the confluence of the Volga and the Kama live the majority of the 3 million Soviet Tatars. Here they reside in a territory set aside as the Tatar Republic. Besides in this locality, a considerable number (125,000) of the Tatars live in Crimea.

The Crimean Autonomous Soviet Socialist Republic was abolished after World War II, and geography textbooks published since then * do not mention the Crimean Tatars as one of the peoples inhabiting the Crimean Peninsula. Tatars are also scattered all over the Soviet Union, especially in the southeastern part of European Russia and in Western Siberia.

In the Southern Ural live 843,000 Bashkirs, an Ugro-Mongolian Turkic-speaking people.

In the Lower Volga Area, between Saratov and Stalingrad, was located an old and prosperous colony of Germans who settled there during the reign of Catherine II. The Soviet government elevated this colony into an autonomous republic. During World War II, however, the republic was abolished and the Germans are no longer listed among the peoples occupying that region.

The total number of Germans in the Soviet Union before the war amounted to 1,800,000, scattered all over the country, in both cities and agricultural communities in the Ukraine, Crimea, and North Caucasus.

* For instance, according to N. N. Baransky, *Economic Geography of the USSR*, 6th ed., Moscow, 1945, p. 171 (in Russian), the majority of the population of Crimea consists of Russians and Ukrainians, with an admixture of Greeks, Bulgars, Armenians, and Jews. Tatars are not mentioned.

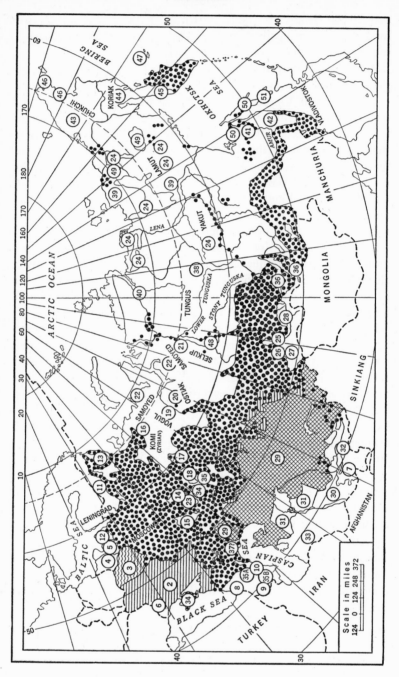

Map 13. Ethnic Map of Soviet Union.

A. Indo-Europeans.
  1. Russians (dotted area).
  2. Ukrainians (horizontal line area).
  3. Belorussians (wavy line area).
  4. Lithuanians.
  5. Latvians.
  6. Moldavians.
  7. Tajiks.

B. Peoples of Caucasus (other than Azerbaijanis).
  8. Georgians and related tribes.
  9. Armenians.
  10. Daghestan tribes.

C. Finno-Ugrians and Samoyeds.
  11. Karelians.
  12. Estonians.
  13. Lapps.
  14. Mari.
  15. Mordva.
  16. Komi Zyrians.
  17. Komi Permiaks.
  18. Udmurts.
  19. Voguls.
  20. Ostiaks.
  21. Selkups.
  22. Samoyeds.
  23. Chuvash.

D. Turko-Tatars.
  24. Yakuts.
  25. Khakass.
  26. Shortsi.
  27. Oirots.
  28. Tuva (Uriankhai).
  29. Kazakhs (cross-hatched area).
  30. Uzbeks.
  31. Kara-Kalpaks.
  32. Kirghiz.
  33. Turkmen.
  34. Tatars.
  35. Bashkirs.
  35A. Azerbaijanis (Iranian Turks).
  35B. Nogai.

E. Mongols.
  36. Buriats.
  37. Kalmyks.

F. Tungus.
  38. Tungus proper.
  39. Lamuts.
  40. Dolgans.
  41. Nanais.
  42. Ude.

G. Paleo-Asiats.
  43. Chukchi.
  44. Koriaks.
  45. Kamchadals.
  46. Eskimos.
  47. Aleuts.
  48. Kets.
  49. Yukaghirs.
  50. Giliaks.
  51. Ainus.

Still farther south in the dry steppes between the Don and the Volga was located the Kalmyk Autonomous Soviet Socialist Republic, populated by some 135,000 Mongolian people, the Kalmyks, whose original home was in northwestern Mongolia. The Kalmyks migrated to the Lower Volga Area in the middle of the seventeenth century. In 1771 about 170,000 of them attempted to return to their native Mongolia; after a long and gory journey only 7000 reached their destination. Some remained in Russia. During World War II the Kalmyk Republic was invaded by Germans; after their retreat the republic was abolished, and the Kalmyks are no longer listed among the peoples of the region,* renamed Astrakhan Province.

In Eastern Siberia live 80,000 scattered Tungus (whose new name is Evenki). The Tungus group is divided into two branches: (*a*) the northern, to which belong the Tungus proper, Lamuts, and other northern tribes, and (*b*) the southern or Manchurian, whose members are less numerous and live mostly along the Amur. This latter branch includes the Manchus, Solons, Dahurs, Goldi (Nanais), and other small tribes.

Of the Paleo-Asiatic peoples of Siberia, resembling ethnically the American Indians, the most numerous are the Chukchi (13,000), renamed Luoravetlans; they occupy the very northeastern part of Siberia. A mere sprinkling of Eskimo (Uit) inhabit a few places on the coast of the Bering Sea; in 1926 some were moved to Wrangel Island. South of the Chukchi live 8000 Koryaks, or Nymylans, and on the Kamchatka are found the survivors (less than 1000) of the once numerous, warlike Kamchadals (Itelmen). Many Kamchadals perished during the conquest of Kamchatka; most of the others intermarried with Russians. Some 600 Aleuts live on the Commander Islands; their new name is the Unanghan. The Yukaghirs, renamed the Oduls, live on the Arctic coast between the Indigirka and the Kolyma and also along the upper reaches of the latter river. The Kets (formerly misnamed the Yenisei Ostiaks) occupy the area around the middle reaches of the River Yenisei. The Giliaks (Nivkhs), numbering about 5000, inhabit the low Amur region and Sakhalin Island. The Ainus live in the newly acquired territory of southern Sakhalin and the southern Kuril Islands. More of them are found on the northern island of Japan (Hokkaido). The Ainu men are notable for their ample beards.

* N. N. Baransky, *Economic Geography of the USSR*, 6th ed., Moscow, 1945, p. 163. (In Russian.)

Around Lake Baikal live a numerous (500,000) Mongolian people—the Buriats. There has been a great deal of intermarriage between the Russians and the Buriats, and individuals with mixed Slavic and Mongolian features are very common there.

The Turko-Tatar people residing within the borders of the Soviet Union total about 18 million. The Tatars, the Chuvash, and the Bashkirs have already been mentioned in the description of the racial minorities of European Russia. Beyond the Caucasian Mountains along the Caspian coast live 2.5 million Iranian Turks, now known as Azerbaijanis. Small, scattered Turkic-speaking tribes are found elsewhere in the Caucasian region. Across the Caspian Sea along the Iran and Afghanistan borders live 812,000 Turkmen.

The westernmost Turkish people of the Soviet Union are the Orthodox Christian Gagaus; 56,000 of them dwell in the Moldavian Republic. They speak Turkic.

Along the lower Amu Darya and around the southern part of the Aral Sea live 186,000 Kara-Kalpaks.

East of the Amu Darya and towards the Afghan border lies the region of 4 million Uzbeks. The former name, Sart, which applied to any settled people of Central Asia, mainly to the Uzbeks, is not used any more. The Uzbeks are a conglomeration of many Turkic tribes with an admixture of Iranian and Mongolian elements. The Kirghiz, formerly called Kara (or Black) Kirghiz, numbering 884,000, occupy the mountains of southern Soviet Middle Asia. Many of them also roam in the mountain pastures of the nearby parts of Sinkiang and Kashmir. Between the Uzbeks and the Kirghiz live about 1 million much Turkicized, but basically Indo-European (Iranian), Tajiks —an ancient agricultural people. Two million Tajiks live across the border in Afghanistan.

Three million Kazakhs,* formerly known as Kirghiz, are scattered over the enormous dry pastures of the northern part of Soviet Middle Asia, penetrating in the north into the region of Western Siberia colonized by the Russians and the Ukrainians. To the south the Kazakh

* Not to be confused with the Kazaks, whose English rendering is Cossacks, originally Russian freebooters, later frontier guards and colonizers of borderland, and now living in agricultural communities and supplying men for the cavalry units of the army. Prosperous Cossack settlements are found along the Don, in the Southern Urals in Siberia, and in the Far East. In Russian, both names are spelled and pronounced almost identically: Kazakhs—the people; Kazaks—cavalrymen. The Cossacks' villages are known as stanitsas.

area extends to the international border, and some of these people live in Chinese Turkestan.

Besides these major groups many other peoples inhabit Soviet Middle Asia: Dungans (Chinese Moslems) (20,000), Arabs (22,000), Uigurs (most of whom live in Chinese Turkestan), Central Asiatic Jews, a few Baluchi, and numerous small Iranian tribes along the border of Afghanistan.

Farther east, in the Altai region live Turkic-speaking Oirots (48,-000), formerly listed under the general name of Altai people. Their region touches the border of northwestern Mongolia. Farther north reside several small Turkish tribes, such as the Shortsi. Along the west bank of the Yenisei, not far from Minusinsk, live 52,000 Khakass, formerly known as Abakan Tatars.

The upper reaches of the Yenisei are populated by several clans of Turkic-speaking, much Mongolized, Uriankhai Soyots, now known as the Tuva.

In the Sayan Mountains and the adjacent stretches of the Siberian taiga live the survivors of several Turkic-speaking peoples: the Karagas, now known as the Tofalar, the almost completely Russianized Kamasins (500 people), and a few hundred woods Soyots (Tuba).

To understand the ethnic complexity of the peoples living in the Sayan-upper Yenisei-eastern Altai Territory, a few words about their past are necessary. This region, and especially the basin of the upper Yenisei, was a scene of many ancient civilizations, great movements of peoples, leaving behind them remnants of roads, irrigation structures, burial grounds, and Runic inscriptions. At the beginning of the Christian era the original inhabitants of the upper Yenisei were dolichocephalic Yeniseians. The Altai Territory was at that time already populated by the Turkish people. In the fourth century A.D., the Ding-Ling people of the Yellow River were pushed (once more) north and mixed with Altai Turks to form the Uigur nation. The Uigurs mixed with the Yeniseians and gave origin to the Ugro-Samoyed tribes. Under pressure from the south, most of these tribes were pushed north, but some small Samoyed tribes escaped to the mountains of the Sayan-Baikal region and probably to the eastern Altai. These tribes gradually became Turkicized, but they still retain many Samoyed words in their language.

The Kamasins until the middle of the last century still spoke Samoyed. Relatively recently the region underwent a considerable Mongolization, especially evident in the Tuva country. Therefore, when we speak of the Turkic peoples of the southern Siberia, we should

keep in mind that they are merely Turkic-speaking peoples and that
their ethnic background is rather complicated.*

In the middle reaches of the Lena and its tributary the Vilui live
300,000 Turkic-speaking Yakuts. Their settlements extend as far
north as the shores of the Arctic. The Yakuts are separated from the
Turkic tribes of the Altai-Sayan region by the Buriats and surrounded
by the Tungus. The ethnic origin of the Yakuts is uncertain; previously they inhabited the Baikal-Sayan region, where they became
considerably Mongolized. Under the pressure of southern invaders
they migrated north to their present habitation in the thirteenth and
fourteenth centuries and mixed to some extent with Tungus, perhaps
with Paleo-Asiatics, and later with Russians. It is possible that the
Yakuts originally were not a Turkic people but acquired their Turkic
language from their former neighbors in southern Siberia.

The location of the Caucasus in the path of ancient migrations and
invasions both from the Near East and from Central Asia resulted in
its present conglomeration of numerous peoples. The majority of the
population, however, belongs today to three native groups: Azerbaijanis (who are Turkic people); Gruzins, whose Anglicized name
is Georgians; and Armenians. Russians comprise 40 per cent of the
present population of the Caucasus.

The Georgians, who call themselves Kartveli and their country
Sakartvelo, are an ancient Japhetic † people, related to many smaller
tribes of Transcaucasia. Their country once was known as Iberia.
They number 2.5 million. On the high plateau bordering Turkey
live 2 million Japhetic-Indo-European people, the Armenians.

There are many other smaller groups in the Caucasian region. The
mountains of Daghestan alone are inhabited by more than thirty different peoples; in almost every valley is found a different tribe speak-

---

* B. N. Vishnevski ["Anthropology in the USSR in the Course of 17 Years
(1917–1934)," *Am. J. Phys. Anthrop.*, Vol. 21, No. 1, p. 17, 1936], however, says
that results of recent investigations (1926) of the Tuva indicate no relation between this people and the Samoyeds but a similarity to the Buriats, the Kalmyks,
and the Khalkha Mongols.

† The term Japhetic was used in earlier English literature to designate certain
groups of Caucasians and some other peoples of Europe and Asia whose languages
are not Indo-European. Lately this term has fallen into misuse. In the Soviet
Union, however, Marr and his school have attached great importance to the
terms Japhetic peoples and Japhetic languages. The name Japhetic is given by
Marr to the peoples whose languages are neither Indo-European nor Semitic nor
Hamitic. Later Marr included in his Japhetic group many dead and living languages and suggested that Japhetic traces are found in all languages.

ing its own language. In some instances a whole "people" is limited
to one village. All Daghestan inhabitants, such as the Avars, Lezghians, Andians, Lak, are listed as Japhetic peoples. Among Iranian
peoples of the Caucasus are Ossets, Talyshins, Tates, and others.

No longer listed among the peoples of the Caucasus are 407,000 Chechen, 92,000 Ingush, and 55,000 Karachais. Their autonomous regions
(Chechen-Ingush and Karachai) were abolished after the German occupation forces were expelled from North Caucasus.

Besides the peoples who are identified with a certain territory, there
are several minority groups in the Soviet Union who have no territorial identity. Among them are: 700,000 Poles, of whom most live
near the Polish border but a great many are scattered all over the
country; about 30,000 Czechs, who are scattered throughout the Soviet
Union; 3,000,000 Jews, living mostly in western Ukraine, Belorussia,
and Moldavia but also scattered all over the country. In the Amur
region near Khabarovsk a Jewish Autonomous Region was established
in 1934. Its some 20,000 people came chiefly from the western part
of the Soviet Union and perhaps from adjacent parts of Poland and
Romania. The name Jew, in its Russian rendering, is considered in
the Soviet Union as derogatory; the name Hebrew is always used instead. A small group of Jews (not over 9000), known as Karaites,
live in Crimea, where they speak Tatar, and in the western part of
the country, where they speak Polish.* Near the Black Sea live about
300,000 Greeks and some Bulgarians. Kurds (a Japhetic people) are
found in the Caucasian region. Chinese inhabit many parts of the
country but chiefly the Far East. Some 45,000 gypsies roam everywhere; most of them are found in the Moldavian Republic, where they
came in the fifteenth century. Near Sukhumi, on the Black Sea shores
of Transcaucasia, there are still found descendants of the Negro slaves
brought by Abkhasian merchants from Africa. Their number is small,
and apparently as a race they have more or less dissolved into the
native population.

To sum up, the Russian population of the Soviet Union amounts to
more than one-half of the total. The three Slavic peoples, the Russians, Ukrainians, and Belorussians, make up about three-quarters of
the total. The admixture of Finno-Ugrian elements is considerable.
The Turkish peoples comprise the largest non-Slavic population of the
Soviet Union, concentrating mostly along the southern border of the

---

* There are also some Jews who have lived for a long time in the Caucasus
and in Middle Asia. In their habits and in their picturesque robes they resemble
the Jews of the Near Eastern Moslem countries.

country but also spreading to the Arctic in Siberia (the Yakuts) and to the north in the Ural-Volga region.

The settlements of all the peoples living along the southern borders of the country extend across the international line, so that there are Soviet Tajiks and Afghan Tajiks, Soviet Turkmen and Iran Turkmen, Soviet Armenians and Turkish Armenians, and Soviet Kazakhs and Sinkiang Kazakhs.

All three branches of the eastern Slavs, Veliko-Russians, Ukrainians, and Belorussians, descend, as other Slavs, from the neolithic inhabitants of the region between Moldavia and the upper Vistula, and are related to the predecessors of some of the Germanic tribes and also to the Alpine European population.* The prehistoric Slavs of Bohemia were almost entirely dolichoid. The Veliko-Russians in their expansion mixed with the Baltic people in the west, with the Scandinavians in the north, and with various Finno-Ugrian tribes in the east. The comparatively dolichoid population of Riazan, Penza, and Tambov provinces, somewhat darker than the average run of the population, is designated as the Riazan type. A brachycephalic people with light eyes and light hair and of a medium stature is found in the regions of Valdai, Vladimir-Suzdal, and Kostroma. It has been designated as the Valdai type.

A distinctly blond, dolichoid people exists in the eastern part of Belorussia, around the city of Mogilev; in the western part of Belorussia; and north near Lake Ilmen. The Belorussian population in general is, however, brachycephalic, of medium stature, with light hair and eyes. This type is somewhat similar to the Valdai type. On the other hand, the Belorussians are physically very similar to the Lithuanians also. The Ukrainians absorbed the physical traits of many peoples: the Ostrogoths, Scythians, Greek colonists, Iranian invaders, and Asiatic invaders. In the Ukraine, along the large rivers and on the watersheds between them, there occurs a rather dark, tall, brachycephalic type of people. As a whole, the Ukrainians are more brachycephalic than the Russians. Vishnevski † suggests that the Riazan type belongs to an ancient population of Russia, having a pronounced admixture of the Finno-Ugrian element characteristic of the Mordva people. The Valdai type seems to be related to the blond brachycephalic-Baltic tribes of northern Europe. It is more recent than the

* Ales Hrdlička, "The Peoples of the Soviet Union," *Smithsonian Institution War Background Studies*, No. 3, Publication 3690, Washington, D. C., 1942.

† B. N. Vishnevski, "Anthropology in the USSR in the Course of 17 Years (1917–1934)," *Am. J. Phys. Anthrop.*, Vol. 21, No. 1, p. 17, 1936.

Riazan type. The Mogilev type is close to the Nordic type of western Europe; probably it migrated up the Dvina River into the Mogilev region. The dark, tall, brachycephalic population of the Ukraine is apparently related to the Alpine stock of western Europe.

Among the peoples of Estonia and the northern part of Latvia the original Mongoloid Finno-Ugrian traits can be noticed only occasionally, whereas Nordic and Slavic features are quite common.

Among the peoples of Middle Asia a dolichocephalic type is found among the Turkmen, who show a similarity to the Hamites of North Africa and the Sikhs of India. "A relatively high statured brachycephalic type is found among Tadjiks and some Uzbeks. The relation of this type to the European Alpine type is not clear. The Armenoid type is found among native Jews, Tadjiks and rarely among Uzbeks." * Generally speaking, the Tajiks are an old brachycephalic Iranian stock, somewhat admixed with the Turkmen, but different from the Iranians and the Afghans. The most Mongoloid of the Central Asiatic people are the Kirghiz.

All three larger Caucasian groups, the Georgians, Armenians, and Azerbaijanis, are highly brachycephalic. The Armenians are related to the "old Tadjik population of Iran and also to the pre-Turkish people of anterior Asia." †

Apparently the autochthonous population of Siberia was dolichocephalic, of blond hair and light eyes, but because of numerous invasions from the south it acquired very complicated anthropological characters, to discuss which would be beyond the scope of this work.

The distribution of blood types in the Soviet Union follows certain interesting patterns.‡ Blood type A predominates in western Europe. The change from type A to type B is rather abrupt along the Soviet western boundary, but the blood type of the European autochthonous people appeared to be predominantly of the O type; this type had evidently been predominant also among the blue-eyed autochthons of Siberia. The neolithic dolichocephalic population of the Baikal region possessed a high proportion of type O blood, moderate amounts of type B blood, and a very small amount of type A. The present

* *Ibid.;* but see Hrdlička, who says that the Turkmen are predominantly brachycephalic.

† Ales Hrdlička, "The Peoples of the Soviet Union," *Smithsonian Institution War Background Studies*, No. 3, Publication 3690, Washington, D. C., 1942.

‡ P. B. Candela, "The Introduction of Blood Group B into Europe," *Human Biology*, Vol. 14, pp. 413–443, 1942.

population of Tungus north of Lake Baikal is also characterized by a high percentage of type O blood.

Among the Buriats, type B predominates, especially east of Lake Baikal. "No Asiatic population is as consistently high in B as are the Buriats." * The other Mongolian people, the Kalmyks, also possess a high proportion of blood type B. Type B is chiefly Mongolian; it appeared in Europe rather recently, between the fifth and the fifteenth centuries of the Christian era. Its predominance is seen in southern Siberia, in Central Asia, and also in the Ukraine, which was subject to the infiltration of more Asiatic type B blood and for a longer period of time than was Russia proper.

Peoples living in the Caucasian region were lacking in type B blood before the period of invasions from Asia. The Georgians have a surprisingly high proportion of type O blood, which may be comparable to the proportion of this type in the Basque people of the Pyrenees. The Ossets, who exhibit Nordic characteristics, are relatively low in type B.

All the non-Russian population of the Soviet Union, i.e., the Iranian, Finn, and Turko-Tatar, possess very high amounts of type B blood. The Tajiks are relatively high in type A and low in type B. Of the Finns, the Karelians have less type B than the tribes situated farther east; the Komi Zyrians also are relatively low in type B. The Votiaks have predominantly type B, and the Cheremiss apparently possess more B type than any Finns living in European Russia.

The distribution of the blood types is shown on Map 14.

The average density of population of the Soviet Union is approximately twenty-five people per square mile, but the distribution is far from being uniform. In some densely populated regions more than 250 people live per square mile, whereas in the other parts of the country it drops to one person per square mile. The northern island of Novaia Zemlia, as well as most of the other islands of the Arctic, the northern part of the Taimyr Peninsula, and some parts of the deserts between the Caspian Sea and the Aral Sea, is devoid of population. The most populated portion of the Soviet Union is the southwestern area, roughly within the line that extends from Leningrad to Kirov, across the Ural, to Tiumen; turns south to Chkalov and to Stalingrad; and then goes southwest and west including the North Caucasus, the Ukraine, Belorussia, and the Baltic regions. Within this area the density of population as a rule is never lower than sixty-five people

* *Ibid.*, p. 423.

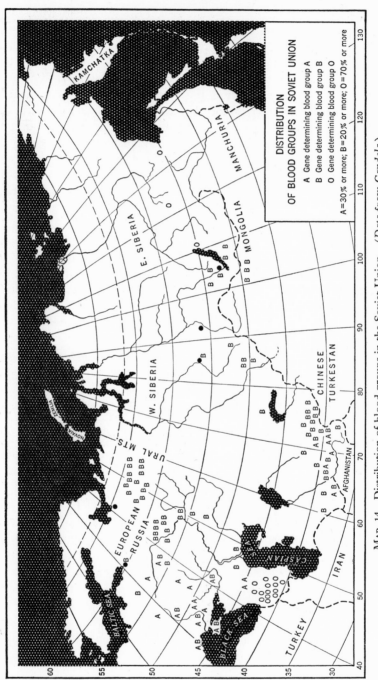

MAP. 14. Distribution of blood groups in the Soviet Union. (*Data from Candela.*)

per square mile; in places it reaches 155 people and more. North and east of this area the density of population decreases. In the oases of Middle Asia the population is concentrated to the density of 250–500 people per square mile. In the northeastern part of European Russia and in Siberia people live mostly along the rivers, whereas the forest areas between the rivers are practically uninhabited. Part of Siberia along the Trans-Siberian Railroad and south of it, especially the Altai region, also is densely populated. Surprisingly many Russians live in the Tuva Autonomous Region.

Very interesting, although incomplete, information is available in regard to the age groups of the population of Soviet Union.

Below 7 years	18.6 per cent
From 15 to 39 years	41.0 per cent
Over 60 years	6.0 per cent

The two missing age classes—from 7 to 14 and from 40 to 60—thus amount to 34.4 per cent. The above figures show a strikingly small percentage of people above 60. The percentage of young people is rather high.

Chapter 7

Languages

The approximately eighty main languages spoken within the borders of the Soviet Union may be divided rather arbitrarily into the following groups: *

1. Indo-European.
2. Japhetic.
3. Semitic.
4. Ural-Altaic.
5. Paleo-Asiatic.
6. Other languages, such as Chinese and Korean.

To the Indo-European group belong (1) the Balto-Slavic languages, which may be further subdivided into Slavonic (Russian, Ukrainian, Belorussian, Polish, and others) and Baltic (Lithuanian, Lettish), and (2) the Indo-Iranian languages, which include Kurdish, Ossetic, Afghan, Persian (Iranian), and Gypsy (Indic, closely related to the Sanskrit).

Armenian is considered by Marr as a transition from the Indo-European to the Japhetic group. Japhetic languages (see footnote p. 67) are spoken by several peoples inhabiting the Caucasian region, such as the Georgians, Adighe, Adjarians, and the numerous peoples of Daghestan. These languages have no affinity to any other groups of languages and generally are classified as Caucasian languages.

The Semitic languages spoken in the Soviet Union include Arabic and Hebrew. Arabic is used by the Arabs in Middle Asia. Written Arabic is the church and literary language of all the peoples of the Moslem religion. The Hebrew alphabet is used by the Jewish people, although their different groups also use the languages of the peoples of the regions in which they live. Yiddish occasionally is spoken in the western part of European Russia and in the Jewish Autonomous

* This division is not universally accepted. The concept of Japhetic languages, designating languages of many Caucasian peoples, has been developed chiefly in Russia by Marr.

74

Region; most of the Jewish population of Russia, however, speaks exclusively Russian.

The Ural-Altaic group of languages may be divided into:

(1) Samoyed.
(2) Tungusic or Manchu, spoken by several peoples of Siberia.
(3) Mongolic, spoken by the Buriats, Kalmyks, and Mongols.
(4) Turko-Tatar.
(5) Finno-Ugric.

The Turko-Tatar is divided into:

(a) East Turki, spoken by the Uzbeks, Kara-Kalpaks, Turkmen, and Uigurs.*
(b) West (or Osmanli) Turki used in the USSR by the Azerbaijanis and by the Chuvash of the Volga region.
(c) Kipchak, the language of the Kazan Tatars, Kazakhs, Nogai, and Kirghiz.
(d) Siberian Tatar, used by the Bashkirs and by the Turkic peoples of south Siberia.
(e) Yakut, used exclusively by the Yakuts.

The Finno-Ugric languages include:

(a) Ugric branch (Ostiak and Vogul. This branch also includes the Magyar language of Hungary.).
(b) Finnic branch is more diversified. Permian Finnic languages are those of the Udmurts and Komi. Volga Finnic languages are those of the Mari and Mordva, and west Finnic languages are Estonian, Finnish, Lapp, and Livonian.†

Moldavians are the only territorial inhabitants of the Soviet Union who speak a language belonging to the western subdivision of Indo-European languages (i.e., French, Spanish, etc.). Even so, it contains about 30 per cent of Slavic roots. It is very similar to the Romanian language, which was formed by mixing the Latin of Roman colonists and soldiers with the language of native Dacians. Later, languages of many nearby peoples contributed to the shaping of Romanian. The Moldavian written language employs the Cyrillic alphabet.

* People living mostly in Chinese Turkestan.
† An almost extinct people. In 1950 there were only about 1000 Livonians (Livs) living in Latvia.

The main medium of communication among different peoples of the Soviet Union is the Russian language. Although each nationality uses its own language in its own region, Russian is taught in all the schools of all the republics. Russian is the state language of the Soviet Union. It belongs to the eastern division of Indo-European languages and, within the division, to the eastern group of the Slavonic branch of the Balto-Slavic family. Ukrainian and Belorussian are the other two members of the group. Russian and Lithuanian are considered the two most obsolete languages of Europe. Ukrainian and Belorussian have developed under the strong influence of the Polish language (which belongs to the western group of the Slavonic branch). The difference between the Russian and the Ukrainian or the Belorussian languages is so great that a Russian cannot read Belorussian or Ukrainian books very fluently, although Ukrainian songs are often sung by the Russians. The old spoken language of pre-Mongol times was understood well by all three eastern Slavic peoples.

In A.D. 988, when Christianity penetrated to the Kievan Rus, the written language came to Russia from Bulgaria in the form of the church Slavic. When two Bulgarian monks, Cyril and Methodius, devised the old Slavic alphabet, they combined the letters of the Latin and of the Greek alphabet, but there were sounds in the Slavic language that could not be represented with Greek or Latin letters. To fill the gap new characters were invented: Ж, Ц, Ч, Ш, Щ, Ы, Ю, and Я (and some others), representing the sounds *zh*, *ts*, *ch*, *sh*, *shch*, *I* (as in "it"), *iu*, and *ia*.* The result was the so-called Cyrillic alphabet, consisting of 35 letters and reduced by the Soviets to 33 letters. In this alphabet, letter *v* is the third from the beginning, and *z* is in the middle of the alphabet. The main difficulty in learning Russian is the grammar, involving six declensional cases, three genders, and rather complicated conjugations, although there is only one future tense and there is no difference between the present perfect and the imperfect: "has been" and "was" are expressed by the same word "bil." There are no articles in Russian; instead of the article "a" a person speaking Russian says "one" and instead of "the" he often uses the pronouns "this" or "that." Omitting auxiliary verbs adds to the confusion for the beginner. For instance, an almost telegraphic sentence "Brat tut

* There are several ways of representing Cyrillic characters by the Latin letters, and at present every writer chooses his own way of transliterating Russian words. The Library of Congress uses a transliteration somewhat different from that used in scientific publications. For the latter method see C. A. Hoare, "Transliteration of Russian Names," *Science*, Vol. 99, p. 321, 1944.

brat tam" means "[One] brother [is] here [and another] brother [is] there." Not all words or sentences are as simple as that.

Idioms are difficult in any language, and so they are in Russian. Instead of "blind street" Russians say "deaf street"; an "eye" of a needle is called an "ear." For understanding geographic terminology it should be noted that the Russians do not orient themselves as easily as the Americans; they do not say a south or north fork of a river or an east or west branch of a river; to them it is either the left or the right. That is why an eastern (left) tributary of the Dnieper was named the River Desna (meaning right); it was discovered by Slavs going *up* the Dnieper.

The Armenian alphabet is of an ancient origin, and it does not resemble either the Latin or the Cyrillic alphabet. Georgian script also is dissimilar to any other written languages of the Soviet Union. Turkic-speaking peoples, as well as Paleo-Asiatic peoples, who had not possessed written language were given such after the Revolution. The new written languages were designed by Soviet scientists according to the modern ideas of linguistics: the Latin alphabet was used in all these languages, and the international phonetic rules were employed for representing different sounds. Recently, however, the Latin alphabet of many of these scientifically designed languages was changed to the Cyrillic, which may be considered, according to Bates,* as a definite step backward.

In the course of time the Cyrillic alphabet became associated with the Orthodox religion, with the East, with Panslavism, and with Russia, whereas, from a Russian point of view, the Latin alphabet is identified with the Catholic religion, with westernization, with a step towards estrangement from Russia of a minority group. Apparently because of these considerations, the Cyrillic alphabet is regarded as more desirable than the Latin alphabet in the Soviet Union.

* E. S. Bates, *Soviet Asia—Progress and Problems*, Jonathan Cape, London, 1942, p. 158. Cf. L. S. Berg, *Bessarabia*, footnote p. 123.

Chapter 8

Religions

In a study of Russian geography, a brief account of Soviet Union religions is desirable. Certain geographic regions have a predominance of one religion; for instance, Middle Asia is largely a Moslem region. The Estonians are more western in their habits than the Karelians not only because of their geographic position but also because they are Protestants. Even such an apparently unrelated phenomenon as the distribution of hogs in the Soviet Union is in some degree a matter of geography of religions. The Moslem peoples do not eat pork, and accordingly hogs are not raised in those parts of the country where the population is composed, say, of Tatars or Uzbeks.

The Russians, as well as the Ukrainians and the Belorussians, in their overwhelming majority belong to the Orthodox Church. A few do not belong to any religion. Some are members of sects separated from the mother church, and a few accept the teachings of some Western denominations.

Christianity came to Russia in the year 988 from Byzantium with all the splendor of the Greek Church and spread rather thinly over the pagan substratum of the Slavic tribes. The Eastern Orthodoxy separated from the Western Roman Catholic Church early in the eleventh century, and the Council of Nicaea of 787 is the last ecumenical council that it recognizes. The Orthodox Church does not believe in the procession of the Holy Ghost from the Son, as well as from the Father, it omitted the *filioque* clause from the Nicene Creed, and it also does not recognize the supremacy of the Pope.* However, it is not the small dogmatic variances that make the Russian Orthodox Church so different from the Roman Catholic and other Western churches † but the developments of the whole concept of religion in the two different civilizations. The East had no Renaissance and no

* *A Handbook of Siberia and Arctic Russia,* compiled by the Geographical Section of the Naval Intelligence Division, Naval Staff, Admiralty, c. 1918, Vol. 1, *General.*

† For instance, there are very few dogmatic differences between the Anglican Episcopal Church and the Orthodox Church.

philosophers of the Renaissance period. Dissensions with the Catholic Church in the West resulted in reformation, the further development of which has been associated with the progress of the most cultured countries of the Western world. Dissension in Russia manifested itself in the Great Schism of the end of the seventeenth century. But even the large religious bodies of dissenters, such as the Dukhobors and the Molokans, groups that developed in the middle of the seventeenth century under the influence of Protestantism, have retained all the characteristics of sects and have contributed very little to the advancement of Christianity. Numerous other groups split away from the Orthodox Church mostly because of ritualistic disagreements; some of them developed into rather grotesque small sects, such as the Khlysty (Flagellants) and the Pryguny (Jumpers).

The Christian religion never penetrated very deeply into the masses of Russian people. Much more importance was attached to the ritual than to the essence of Christianity. The Church of pre-Revolution Russia was a part of the state, and the Emperor of all-Russia was also the head of the Church. This so-called Caesaro-Papism was terminated with the Revolution of 1917. For many years thereafter the Orthodox religion, as well as other religions both Christian and non-Christian, were ruthlessly prosecuted. During World War II, however, the rights of the Orthodox Church, as well as of other churches, were restored. The Orthodox Church at present is separated from the state. The Orthodox Church of the Ukraine maintained its autocephalous status for some time after the 1917 revolution but at present does not possess it. Moldavians are also Orthodox Christians.

The ancient Armenian Church differs from the Greek Orthodox Church inasmuch as it adheres, together with the Coptic and the Abyssinian churches, to the Monophysitic belief, recognizing only one, divine nature in Christ. It is independent of the Russian Orthodox Church and is ruled by its own Patriarch, the Catholicos. Another ancient church, which is also autocephalous, is that of Georgia. There are no dogmatic differences between the Georgian and the Russian Orthodox churches.

All Turkic-speaking people, except the Orthodox Gagaus of Moldavia and the nominally Christian Yakuts and some pagan Altai tribes, are of the Moslem faith. The Moslem religion is professed not only by the Turkic-speaking peoples but also by some Iranian inhabitants of the Caucasus, such as the Ossets, and by some Japhetic tribes, such as the Circassians. The Tajiks of Middle Asia belong to the Ismaelite sect of the Moslem faith. The head of this sect is the well-known

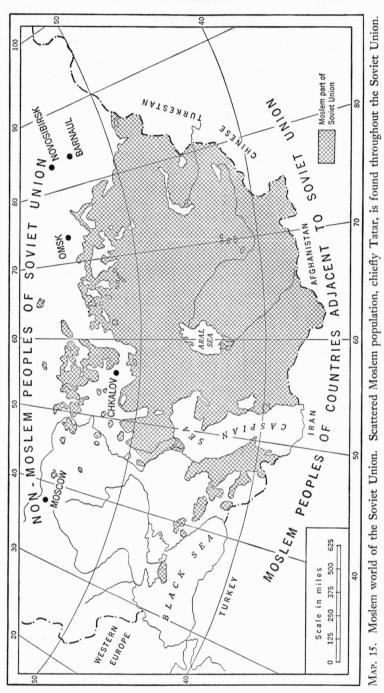

MAP. 15. Moslem world of the Soviet Union. Scattered Moslem population, chiefly Tatar, is found throughout the Soviet Union.

Aga Khan, whose official residence is in Bombay. It appears that the Tajiks of the Soviet Union do not support the Aga Khan financially. The center of the Moslem religion is in Uzbekistan. President Mufti of the Moslem Administration of Middle Asia and Kazakhstan, elected in 1943, was a Uzbek with a Russianized name.*

The Protestant Churches within the Soviet Union are chiefly represented by the Lutheran Church, whose membership lies largely in Latvians, Estonians, and scattered Germans. Many Germans living in the Soviet Union are Mennonites. Lithuanians are mainly Catholic, although in the eastern part of the country some are of the Orthodox faith. The Presbyterian Church existed in Lithuania for a long time when that country was a large and independent kingdom. The Polish populace in the Soviet Union belongs to the Roman Catholic Church. In the minds of the Russian people a Pole and a Catholic are almost synonymous, and the Catholic religion is often called by the Russians "the Polish faith." In the parts of Ukraine that were previously under Poland there are found some people who belong to the Uniate Church, established in 1596, which uses Byzantine Orthodox rites but recognizes the Pope and the theological doctrines of the Vatican. It is highly probable that this church no longer exists within the border of the Soviet Union.

Most Finnish peoples living in the northern part of European Russia are Orthodox Christians. The Finns proper are Protestants; the Karelian Finns profess the Orthodox religion. Baptists appeared in Russia before the Revolution of 1917, and they have made considerable gains numerically. The 1937 census data listed 1 million Baptists in the Soviet Union, but more recent information regarding their number is very controversial. Both Baptists and Evangelicals, apparently, may be considered well established in the Soviet Union. There are also some Adventists in Russia.

The Kalmyks—the few that still exist—and the Buriats of the Transbaikal region belong to the Lamaistic branch of Buddhism. The Buriats west of Lake Baikal adhered to Shamanism. Many of them, nominally at least, are Christian. The Paleo-Asiatic and most of the Tungus tribes in Siberia also adhere to one type or another of primitive paganism, which often has a curious admixture of the Christian religion. Many Finno-Ugrian minorities of northeastern Europe are Orthodox Christians. Voguls, Ostiaks, and Samoyeds also are nominally Christian, although vestiges of primitive religions still exist among them.

* Paul B. Anderson, *People, Church and State in Modern Russia*, The Macmillan Company, New York, 1944, p. 213.

Part 3

Geographic Regions

Chapter 9

Tundra Region

Within the borders of the Soviet Union there are extensive regions of rolling plains, in eastern Europe; of lowlands, in Western Siberia and Middle Asia; and of low-lying plateaux, in Eastern Siberia. In the European part of the country these stretches of land of a general lowland character extend from the shores of the Arctic to the Black Sea and in the Asiatic part to the southern border mountains. There are no latitudinal mountain chains within the lowlands of the country, and the change of climate from the Arctic region to the southern prairies and deserts is thus very gradual. This gradual change of climate has resulted in the development of broad latitudinal soil-and-vegetation belts. It is the climate and not the relief that has been responsible for forming the natural zones of the lowlands of the Soviet Union. Russian botanists, ecologists, and geographers, as well as foresters and agronomists, for a long time have recognized these broad soil-and-vegetation belts extending across the continent of Eurasia. The belts are: (1) northern barren or tundra, (2) forest, (3) woodland, (4) prairie or steppe, (5) semidesert or dry steppe, and (6) desert. Dokuchaev, as early as 1898, attempted to extend the idea of natural zonation to the whole world. He formulated his concept of natural geographic zones as regions where there exists "an orderly correlation between the matter, the forces and the phenomena; between the animated and non-animated world; between the mineral, the vegetative and the animal worlds on one hand and man, his activities and even his intellectual life, on the other." *

Berg † has contributed a great deal to the elucidation of the concept of geographic landscapes, or geographic aspects as he prefers to

* V. V. Dokuchaev, *On the Concept of Natural Zones,* St. Petersburg, 1899; quoted by L. S. Berg, *Geographic Zones of the USSR,* 3rd ed., Moscow, 1947.

† Dr. L. S. Berg, member of the Russian (All-Union) Academy of Sciences and president of the Russian Geographic Society, was born in 1876. He started his scientific career as a limnologist and ichthyologist and later became one of the leading geographers of Russia. Berg's chief contribution is in bringing order into Russian physical geography, in bringing together the results of numerous

call them.* The geographic aspects are combined into larger units that most conveniently may be called geographic regions. Berg has influenced the whole development of the study of the physical geography of Russia, and his subdivision of the Soviet Union into geographic regions has been followed, with some modifications, by all Russian geographers. Berg divides the geographic regions of the Soviet Union into two large groups: the lowland regions and the mountain regions. To the first group belong the broad latitudinal belts of tundra, forest, prairie, semidesert, and desert. The latter group includes the rest of the country.

In his several publications Berg presented brilliantly the concept of broad, natural, latitudinal zones, different one from another, each possessing its own more or less uniform climate, soil, and vegetation. However, when an attempt was made to classify mountain regions, certain difficulties were encountered, partly because some remote mountain regions have not yet been sufficiently explored and partly because of the heterogeneous nature of any mountainous area. The Caucasus, for instance, is essentially a mountain region, but it also includes two areas of forested lowlands and some rather extensive deserts. Berg included the forested lowlands of the Caucasus in his group of lowlands as a region of subtropical forests. The desert areas are, however, discussed as a part of the Caucasus mountain region. In fact, almost any mountain region of the country contains more or less extensive lowland or plain areas. These comprise an integral part of the region, and it seems unwise to treat them separately. Accordingly, Berg's classification is slightly modified, and in this book the geographic regions of the Soviet Union will be described as follows:

1. Tundra, or northern barrens.
2. Taiga or conifer forests.
3. Mixed forests of European Russia.
4. Woodland.
5. Prairies.
6. Semideserts.
7. Deserts.
8. Mountains of Middle Asia.
9. The Caucasus.
10. Carpathian Mountains.

previous investigations, and in dividing the country into geographic regions. Berg's influence has been felt in all recent books on physical geography of Russia.

* The German term *Landschaft*, in its translation into English, became landscape—not a very fortunate term—and lately the word landscape has apparently been abandoned by many American geographers.

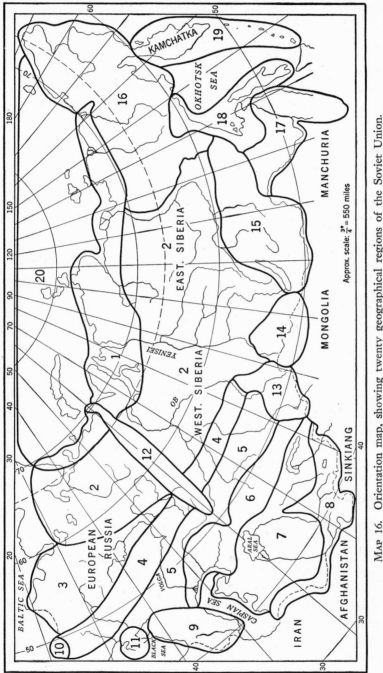

Map 16. Orientation map, showing twenty geographical regions of the Soviet Union.

11. Crimea.
12. Ural Mountains.
13. Altai system and Kuznetsk Basin.
14. Sayan Mountains and Tuva Region.
15. Transbaikal region.
16. Northeastern Siberia.
17. Far Eastern Region (basin of the middle Amur and of the Ussuri).
18. Okhotsk coast and island of Sakhalin.
19. Peninsula of Kamchatka and Kuril Islands.
20. Islands of the Arctic.

Tundra is a Finnish word that originally meant bare mountain tops and later was extended to include any barren areas. Even peaty bogs in southern Siberia are sometimes called tundras * by the local people. In geography the tundra region is understood to be the stretch of northern barrens of Europe and Asia (as well as of North America) characterized by the absence of trees, possessing long and severe winters and short and cold summers, and with long summer days. The mean temperature of the warmest month is not higher than 50°F but not lower than 32°F. Cloudiness is prevalent and the winds are strong. The precipitation is very low.

The tundra region occupies the portion of the Kola Peninsula northwest of the line extending from the Varanger Fiord to the lowest reaches of the Ponoi River. (Map 3, I.) On the European mainland its southern boundary, roughly, follows the Arctic Circle. In Western Siberia the southern boundary of the tundra region extends approximately from the point where the Arctic Circle crosses the Ob estuary to the delta of the Lena (somewhat south of it), and then it follows the 70th parallel to the estuary of the Kolyma. The most extensive areas occupied by tundra are found in Siberia, north of the line extending from the Ob estuary to the Khatanga estuary.

Climate

The climate of the tundra region is characterized by a mean temperature, during the warmest month, of 32° to 50°F.

The entire true tundra region is located north of the 50°F July isotherm; the summer temperatures there are thus very low; moreover, the summers are very short although summer days are very long. The sun does not set below the horizon for about three summer months; thus photosynthesis may continue for 24 hours a day, provided that

---

* Tundry is the plural form of tundra, which is often used in Russian geographic literature.

all other conditions (such as temperature) are favorable. On the other hand, during the three winter months the sun does not appear at all above the horizon. The winters are cold, but not so cold as farther inland.

Precipitation in the region is very light—almost as light as in deserts —but evaporation is insignificant; there is considerable cloudiness, and the relative humidity of air is high. The precipitation occurs mostly in summer in the form of drizzles. All these conditions, augmented by poor drainage of permanently frozen soils, are very favorable for the formation of extensive swamps similar to the muskegs of the North American Arctic Regions. It is not the severe winters but the cool, short summers that prevent the growth of trees in the tundra.

The climate of the coastal Kola Peninsula is relatively mild; the precipitation is rather heavy, amounting to 16 inches a year. There is no permanently frozen ground. Farther east, however, the climate becomes more continental and the precipitation decreases. In the tundras of Western Siberia, winter temperatures are lower; mean January temperature in the western part of the typical tundra is about $-6°$ and in the eastern part about $-17°F$. Occasionally the temperature drops to $-60°F$. In the southern part of the tundra region of Western Siberia winters are more severe than in the northern part, the absolute minimum being $-80°F$.

Winter blizzards in the Western Siberian tundra are more violent than in the European tundra; southern winds blow at a rate of 25 to 30 feet per second continuously for many days. Snow cover in the tundra of Western Siberia is not very deep, varying from 8 to 12 inches, and because of strong winds it does not cover the ground uniformly, rather piling up in drifts, leaving extensive areas of bare ground. In summer, frosts occur occasionally and snowfall is not infrequent. In some years, however, the frostless period may extend for 60 to 75 days. During July and August the mean daily temperature may sometimes be as high as $50°F$, and occasionally the thermometer registers $70°F$. In the southern part of the Western Siberian tundra region, where the tundra begins to merge into the forest, summers are much warmer than in the north. In Western Siberia, mean July temperatures are $54°$ to $56°F$, and the vegetative period is about 100 days in the western part and 75 days in the eastern part.

The climate of the Eastern Siberian tundra is even more severe; being located farther from the Atlantic, this part of the region is more continental than the Western Siberian tundra. Table 4 gives the mean

TABLE 4. TEMPERATURE AND PRECIPITATION AT RUSSKOE USTIE,
ELEVATION 20 FEET

Jan.	Feb.	Mar.	Apr.	May	June	July	Aug.	Sept.	Oct.	Nov.	Dec.	Year
Temperature, degrees Fahrenheit												Mean
−38	−36	−24	−4	20	40	48	42	33	10	−16	−29	3.7
Precipitation, inches												Total
0.16	0.24	0.24	0.12	0.48	0.9	1.1	1.1	0.6	0.3	0.4	0.3	5.94

temperature and precipitation for the Russkoe Ustie ("Mouth of the River") station, located in the low reaches of the Indigirka River.

The temperature range is very great. Whereas the mean January temperature at Dudinka, on the lower Yenisei, is −22°F and at Russkoe Ustie, at the delta of the Indigirka, is about −38°F, the mean July temperatures at these two localities are 55°F and 48°F, respectively. The temperature range, however, is 186°F at Dudinka and 180°F at Russkoe Ustie.

The length of the growing season at Dudinka is 78 days; at Russkoe Ustie, 63 days.

Precipitation in the Eastern Siberian tundras is very light. At Khatanga (on the Khatanga estuary) it is about 11.5 inches; at Russkoe Ustie, about 6 inches; and at the delta of the Lena, only 3.4 inches. Fifty per cent of this scanty precipitation occurs in July, and only 10 per cent in January; therefore, not much snow falls in the Eastern Siberian tundras. Cloudiness is negligible, especially in the eastern part; east of the Yenisei the wind velocity decreases considerably.

The recent general warming up of the Arctic Regions is noticeable in the tundra region. The ice cover on the River Dvina near Archangel remains now for 10 days less than at the end of the last century.

The southern boundary of the permanently frozen ground has retreated in places as much as 25 miles since the middle of the nineteenth century. Nevertheless, the tundra is gradually advancing southward, invading areas previously occupied by forests.*

* L. S. Berg, *Geographic Zones of the USSR*, 3rd ed., Moscow, 1947, p. 53. For more about the advance of the tundra, see *Climate and Life*, by the same author.

Topography

The tundra region is not a large, continuous, swampy lowland as often is supposed; for instance, on the Taimyr Peninsula a dry tundra actually predominates. The general topography, it is true, is flat, but, nevertheless, elevated places and even low mountain ridges may be found, and there are extensive areas of dry, rocky terrain.

The tundra region of the Kola Peninsula appears as a much dissected plain 500 feet to 700 feet above sea level, dropping abruptly at the Barents Sea coast, which is cut into many narrow, long, and rather deep fiord-like bays. Pre-Cambrian rocks—granite and gneiss—of the Kola tundra are covered with glacial deposits.

A rather prominent, low plateau-like range is located on the Kanin Peninsula. Its elevation is 500 feet to 600 feet, with occasional heights reaching perhaps 100 feet above the general level of the plateau. The Timanski Range in its northern part is located in the tundra region. It is composed of Paleozoic folds, and within the region its heights do not exceed 900 feet. Between the low Pai-Khoi range (northwestern continuation of the Ural) and the Barents Sea lies a great stretch of flat tundra * covered with glacial deposits and dotted with numerous small lakes.

On the northern island of Novaia Zemlia the tundra region is replaced with the nival, or ice, zone. The land here is covered permanently with a thick sheet of ice, and the rocky outcrops are in evidence only along the coast.

The Western Siberian tundras are very extensive, flat, once glaciated stretches of land. During the Quaternary period a sea occupied a considerable area of Western Siberia, especially along the rivers, as far south as the boundary of the Arctic Circle.

The rivers of the Western Siberian tundra (and as far west as the Pechora and to the east including the Yenisei and the Khatanga) flow into long and narrow estuaries, formed by sinking of the terrain and subsequent flooding of the low reaches of the rivers.

The Yamal Peninsula is about 600 miles long. The center of the southern part is over 300 feet high and is known by the Samoyed name Khoi (the Ridge). The northern parts of the peninsula are flat and low.

The area east of the Khatanga shores of the Arctic is known as the north Siberian lowland. It is connected with the western Siberian

* Its name is Bolshezemelskaia Tundra, meaning A Great Stretch of Land Occupied by Tundra.

lowland by the Piassina-Khatanga depression—a low, rolling (150 to 200 feet above sea level, and in some places over 500 feet) plain, partly of a moraine character, with many lakes located between low hills. Both the Central Siberian Plateau in the south and the Barranga Mountains in the north descend abruptly to the depression.

Farther east, between the Khatanga and the Lena, extends a synclinal depression of a Mesozoic sedimentary nature. In this part of the north Siberian lowland are found Mesozoic ranges of moderate altitudes, rising to 200–650 feet in the west and to 1300–2100 feet near the delta of the Lena. In these Mesozoic strata are located numerous salt domes. A boring 1312 feet in depth near Nordvik, on the lower Khatanga, revealed considerable deposits of salt. Oil also has been found in the area.

The delta of the River Lena extends from west to east for some 120 miles. The numerous islands of the delta are covered with thick layers of peat over heavy deposits of fossil ice. The lowland east of the Lena is composed of Quaternary deposits, with occasional elevated areas of granite and porphyritic rocks.

Soils and Vegetation

In the tundra region the subsoil is permanently frozen (except on the Kola Peninsula); drainage is poor, and although the precipitation is light, the ground is always supersaturated with water. Under these conditions the soils * of the tundra develop poorly, soil microorganisms are not very active, and decomposition of organic matter is slow. Oxidation processes are retarded; instead of ferric oxide, ferrous oxide is formed, giving a slate-blue color to the soil. Occasionally, leached podzol † soils are found in the tundra, but as a rule they are poorly developed.

The tundra region may be divided into the four following subregions: ‡

1. The arctic tundra lies in the northern part of the region, adjacent to the ocean. It occupies the northern portion of the Yamal Peninsula,§ a great deal of the Taimyr Peninsula, and the stretches of

---

* In this book the term soil means the surface layer of the earth crust which is altered by the climate, water, and organisms.

† Russian folk names of soil types, such as podzol (ash-like), chernozem (black soil), and solonets (salty soil) have been adopted by the Russian soil scientists and are used internationally in the soil literature.

‡ L. S. Berg, *Geographic Zones of the USSR*, 3rd ed., Moscow, 1947, p. 36.

§ Yamal in Samoyed means the Land's End.

land between the Yana and the Kolyma. The vegetation of the arctic tundra is very sparse. No shrubs, except in a few sheltered places along the rivers, are found here. Separate tufts of saxifrage,* cinquefoil, yellow arctic poppy, and a few species of grasses grow in the drier places. In wet places are solitary tufts of grasses and inconspicuous lichens † and mosses. Sphagnum moss and reindeer fodder lichens (such as *Cladonia*) are not found in the arctic tundra.

2. The typical or shrubby tundra is located south of the arctic tundra. Low shrubs are found here, not only along the rivers but also in the watershed areas. Sphagnum peat bogs begin to appear, but they do not develop to any great extent. The shrubby tundra is well developed on the Kanin Peninsula, on the Yamal Peninsula, and also in the northeastern part of the Kola Peninsula.

The vegetation of the shrubby tundra is more diversified than that of the arctic tundra. The low willow shrubs are intermixed here with shrubby birch (*Betula nana*, replaced east of the Yenisei by *B. exilis*); crystal tea (*Ledum palustre*, akin to Labrador tea) and bog bilberry (*Vaccinium uliginosum*) are found here in abundance. On the watershed areas these shrubs barely reach 1 foot in height, but along the rivers in sheltered places the birches and willows may grow to a height of 5 or 6 feet. Below the shrubs grow some sedges, grasses such as a fescue (*Festuca supina*), and ericaceous evergreens such as cowberry (*Vaccinium vitis-idaea*). Close to the ground cling lichens and mosses. In sandy places, lichens grow in profusion. Lichens are light-loving plants and prefer open spaces for their growth.

3. The southern tundra is characterized by the presence of trees along the rivers. Occasional trees are found even on the watersheds. Sphagnum peat bogs cover extensive areas. This subregion is found in many parts of European Russia. On the Kanin Peninsula, south of the shrubby moss-lichen tundra, is commonly found a type of tundra where the terrain is covered with peat mounds 5 to 10 feet in height. These mounds are formed by *Sphagnum*, *Dicranum*, and *Polytrichum* mosses and by lichens, and covered with bilberry, cowberry, scrubby birch, willow, and many other plants, the most prominent of them being cloudberry (*Rubus chamaemorus*).

---

* All plant names used in this book are in accordance as far as possible with the *Standardized Plant Names*, 2nd ed., prepared for the American Joint Committee on Horticultural Nomenclature by Harlan P. Kelsey and William A. Dayton, J. Horace McFarland Company, Harrisburg, Pa., 1942.

† Lichens are symbiotic organisms consisting of fungi and algae.

On steep southern slopes one encounters meadows strewn with bright flowering plants:

Polemonium	(*Polemonium caeruleum*)
Veronica	(*Veronica longifolia*)
Yarrow	(*Achillea millefolium*)
Chive	(*Allium schoenoprasum*)
Fescue	(*Festuca ovina*)
Bluegrass	(*Poa pratensis* *)
Geranium	(*Geranium silvaticum*, a dominant species)
Veratrum	(*Veratrum lobelianum*)
Fireweed	(*Epilobium angustifolium*)
Globeflower	(*Trollius europeus*)
Viviparous bistort	(*Polygonum viviparum*)
Myrtle whortleberry	(*Vaccinium myrtillus*)
Goldenrod	(*Solidago virgaurea*)

All these plants are also found much farther south in the forest region and cannot be considered typical tundra plants. This list is given to show that a relatively luxurious herbaceous vegetation may develop under certain conditions in the tundra region. Similar herbaceous meadows are found in the Western Siberian tundras. Mosses and lichens are absent there, and a fairly low-growing, continuous cover of angiosperms (buttercups, valeriana, and other already mentioned species) resembles that of the alpine meadows of the mountain regions.

Widely distributed east of the Lena are the hummock tundras covered with tufts of sheathed cottonsedge (*Eriophorum vaginatum*). A lichen type of tundra develops on sandy soil; in the west the *Cladonia* type predominates; east of the Yenisei, where the climate is more severe, it is replaced by the *Alectoria* lichen; in the extreme northeast, however, *Cladonia* again tends to dominate. On the clay soil there are found considerable areas of spotted tundra; here patches of bare soil 10 to 20 inches in diameter are surrounded with a border of dwarf willows and birches and other tundra vegetation.

Generally speaking, the composition of tundra vegetation is very striking indeed. There is an almost complete absence of annuals. The short growing season is not very favorable for the germination, growth, blooming, and seed production of annual plants; even some perennials of the arctic tundra have lost their habit of reproduction by seed and resort exclusively to vegetative propagation. The typical tundra plants are woody perennials, often evergreen (such as various

---

* This species is known in America as Kentucky bluegrass.

species of *Vaccinium*). Some tundra plants bear large showy flowers in profusion.

Of lichens the most common and the most important are different species of *Cladonia*. Reindeer moss (*Cladonia rangiferina*) is the chief fodder lichen of the reindeer.

Some plants of the tundra region are found farther south also. Some plants occurring in the Siberian tundra are absent in the forested plains but reappear in the southern Siberian mountains.

It is of interest to note that the preglacial vegetation of the Eastern Siberian tundra had a great deal in common with the present flora of the Pacific coast of North America. Fossil cones of western white pine (*Pinus monticola*) and Brewer spruce (*Picea breweriana*) were found in the tundra region between the Lena and the Yana rivers.*

In the southern part of the tundra region the vegetation is gradually replaced by forest. The northern fringe of the forest advances into the tundra along the river valleys, where the drainage is better, where the ground thaws in the summer to a greater depth, and where there is more protection from the wind than in the rest of the tundra region. The trees in the fringe belt are suppressed, crooked, and short. On the Kola Peninsula the transition forests between the tundra and the forest regions consist of scattered trees of a Lapp birch (*Betula kusmischeffi*) 10 to 15 feet high. On the European mainland east of the White Sea the northern forest outposts are composed of Siberian spruce (*Picea obovata*). Along the sheltered river valleys the fringe forests are the densest and of the best quality. On dry, sandy soil the ground cover is the light-loving reindeer moss. Where the soil contains more moisture the ground cover consists of green mosses, such as *Hyphnum*, and in swampy localities the soil is covered with *Polytrichum* and *Sphagnum* mosses, with an admixture of dwarf birch and *Ledum*.

In Western Siberia the fringe forests are composed of scattered, malformed Siberian larch (*Larix sibirica*), the ground being covered with reindeer moss and occasional dwarf birch and alder (*Alnus fruticosa*). These fringe forests serve as winter pasture for the reindeer. Extensive patches of sphagnum tundra are found in these transition forests.

Eastern Siberia has an extremely continental climate; although winters are very cold, summers are relatively warm and conducive to the growth of trees. Here the fringe of park-like forests penetrates far-

* V. N. Sukachev, "New Data on Pre-glacial Flora of the North of Siberia," *Bull. Geol. Museum Acad. Sci.*, Vol. 4, pp. 55–62, 1910. (In Russian.)

ther north than anywhere else in the world. Along the rivers the Dahurian larch (*Larix dahurica*) advances as far as 72°25′ latitude N. The vegetation in these transition forests consists of an upperstory of scattered larch—about 10 to 20 trees per acre—with an understory of alder, willow, and birch scrub. A mixture of tundra and forest herbaceous plants covers the ground. Mosses and lichens are abundant.

Attempts to grow vegetables in the tundra region could hardly be called agriculture, but it should be kept in mind that some vegetables do grow there. On the Murman Coast potatoes, radishes, onions, and turnips are planted. Experiments conducted at Salekhard (on the Ob) have shown that potatoes, turnips, beets, and radishes matured well towards the middle of September. Carrots and cabbage, however, failed.

Animal Life

The tundra is almost devoid of animal life during the long, cold winters. The shores of the Arctic are visited by the polar bear (*Thalarctos maritimus*). This animal, which does not hibernate, is really an inhabitant of the Arctic Ocean, its islands, and its ice floes. The polar bear maintains the white color of its fur throughout the year.

The arctic fox (*Alopex lagopus*), which is one of the most important fur-bearing animals in the Soviet Union, roams the tundra, and occasionally it penetrates the adjacent forest region. It is somewhat smaller than a common fox; its coat is brownish in summer and snow-white in winter. The blue fox is a rare and valuable variety of the arctic fox; its bluish color persists throughout the year.

During the winter two species of ptarmigan (*Lagopus lagopus* and *L. mutus*) are also found in the forested part of the tundra, where they migrate from the north. Some of the birds, however, remain in the tundra throughout the year. Ptarmigans are killed in considerable numbers, particularly *Lagopus lagopus*, which is by far the more important hunting bird of the two species.

The arctic or snowy owl (*Nyctea nyctea*) is another winter habitant of the tundra region. It is a ground bird; even when it flies south for the winter, as far as Central Asia, it prefers open flatlands and never perches on trees. In the tundra the snowy owl nests on the tops of low hillocks. In the north it is not a nocturnal bird.

With the advent of summer the wild reindeer migrate north to the tundra from the adjacent forests. The migration is not only a search for summer pastures but also an escape from the gnats, mosquitoes, and gadflies that make life intolerable for the animals in the taiga. In the tundra the summers are cooler and the winds stronger than in the forest, and the reindeer do not suffer as much there. In the European tundras the wild reindeer is considerably depleted, but in Siberia it is still found in large numbers, some herds consisting of 1500–2000 head. The reindeer population of the eastern European tundras has been decreasing not because of a direct extermination of the animal by man but rather because the wild reindeer has been crowded out from its grazing grounds by the domesticated reindeer.

In the spring, lemmings (*Lemmus obensis, L. lemmus,* and *L. torquatus*) appear in the tundra after spending the winter underground. Lemmings as well as other tundra animals, such as arctic fox, do not hibernate. This small rodent (about 6 inches long) remains active throughout the winter under the snow cover. It is enormously prolific, and exists in large numbers despite the presence of many predators, such as arctic foxes and hawks. Occasionally lemmings migrate in great multitudes across the rivers toward the Arctic shores. A peculiar urge for migration often forces them to plunge into the ocean and perish. Reindeer devour lemmings (as well as birds' eggs) with avidity, thus satisfying their need for proteins. *Cladonia,* the staple food of reindeer, is very poor in digestible proteins, and lemmings provide a welcome supplementary diet for this animal.

The wolf may be considered a common summer inhabitant of the tundra. The tundra wolf is a very big animal of a rather light color. Its chief food is reindeer; towards the end of the summer wolves follow the reindeer south, to the forest.

Occasional summer visitors to the tundra are the common fox, the weasel (*Mustela nivalis*), the ferret (*Putorius*), the ermine, and the snowshoe rabbit (*Lepus timidus*).

Bats do not occur in the tundra region.

In summer the lakes, ponds, rivers, and shores of the ocean in the Arctic Regions are invaded by waterfowl: geese, ducks, and swans. The rocky shores of the Arctic and the nearby islands are crowded by sea birds: puffins or sea parrots (*Fratercula*), razorbills (*Alca*), guillemots (*Uria*), sea gulls, and eider (*Somateria*). The bird population of the tundra is characterized by a small number of species and an enormous number of individuals.

Man has affected the animal life of the tundra only to a very small degree. In spite of the wholesale slaughtering of geese at the end of summer, when the birds are molting and are unable to fly and when a group of hunters armed with clubs may kill several thousand of them in one day, the number of geese has not appreciably decreased.

The tundra region is not very rich in insect life, which consists mainly of two or three species of bumblebees and some beetles (*Feroma arctica, F. borealis*); mosquitoes are numerous in the southern part of the region. There are no snakes. The only reptile, a viviparous lizard (*Lacerta vivipara*), is found in European Russia near the White Sea. The amphibians are represented by two frogs: *Rana terrestris* on the Kanin Peninsula and the *R. temporaria* on the Kola Peninsula. Generally, however, amphibians and reptiles are not found in the tundra.

Reindeer is the most important domestic animal of the tundra region. It can be called a domesticated animal only with some reservations as man does not provide food for it. When the day's work is done, the reindeer is turned loose on the tundra, where it finds its food. Occasionally, domestic reindeer mingle, and probably cross, with wild reindeer.

The people who inhabit the tundra region use reindeer as draft animals and do not ride them as do the forest inhabitants, such as the Tungus.

Reindeer meat, often raw, is used for food by the natives. The light elastic hide provides an indispensable material for clothing and foot gear especially suitable for the cold climate of the tundra. Reindeer milk is rarely consumed by the natives of the tundra—with the exception of the Lapps—but the Tungus and Soyot peoples of the forest drink it.

West of the Yenisei, watchdogs are used for herding reindeer, whereas, east of that river, dogs are not used for that purpose. Sled dogs are similar to, but not identical with, the watchdogs. They are used more in the northeastern part of Siberia than in other parts of the tundra region. Ten to fourteen dogs is the usual number to hitch to a sled, and they are capable of pulling a load that weighs up to 1 ton, making from 2.5 to 4 miles per hour. On a light sled a traveler may cover 40 to 45 miles a day, making about 6 miles per hour. The staple food for the dogs is fish.

In the forested tundra on the islands of the Ob estuary at 67° latitude N, where fair pastures are found, the Russian settlers raise horses, cattle, and even sheep, pigs, chickens, and geese. Cattle and sheep are raised also on the Murman coast.

People

The human inhabitants of the tundra region are not very numerous. On the Kola Peninsula live reindeer-tending Lapps or Saami and, in some places along the coast, old Russian settlers, so-called Pomors, i.e., the seashore folks. The Pomors are engaged in fishing and in hunting sea animals.

Most of the mainland tundra of European Russia and of Western Siberia, including the southern part of the Taimyr Peninsula, is sparingly populated by some 20,000 Samoyeds (Nentse) and related tribes. Farther east, towards the delta of the Lena, live some Yakuts. Still farther east are found the scattered places of habitation of the Russian settlers and of the Lamuts (Evenes). The Lamuts are a branch of the Tungus tribe; they live in settlements by the coast of the Arctic and along the rivers. The Lamut sled dog is considered the best throughout northeast Siberia. In the very northeastern part of the tundra region live Paleo-Asiatic Yukaghirs and Chukchi.

The reindeer-keeping peoples of the tundra move from one place to another, following their herds. In the summer they move closer to the coast; in the winter they retreat to the forests, where they find more fuel and more protection from the wind.

Chapter 10

Forest Region
Conifer Forests

The forest region of the Soviet Union occupies about one-half the total area of the country. In the north the forests merge into the tundra region; in the south they either are replaced by woodland (in Europe and Western Siberia) or merge into the mountain forests of the northeastern Altai region and the mountains of Eastern Siberia. The southern boundary of the forest region in Europe extends roughly from the Carpathian Mountains northeast to the 50th parallel and then to Kiev, thence northeast again to Gorki (Nizhni-Novgorod) and east to the confluence of the Kama and the Volga. The boundary line then descends south along the west slope of the Ural Mountains to Chkalov (formerly Orenburg) and, after crossing the Ural, follows north along the east slope of the mountains for some distance, and then turns northeast, roughly to Cheliabinsk and Sverdlovsk. Farther east the southern boundary of the forest zone extends latitudinally to Tomsk and then turns southeast, merging into the forests of the Altai Mountains. Still farther east the forests extend all the way to the borders of Mongolia and Manchuria. There are, however, some patches of woodland and prairie-like open areas near Irkutsk, in the Transbaikal region, in the upper Yenisei and the Tuva basins.

The forest region of the country consists of two separate parts: (1) the coniferous forest, or taiga, and (2) the mixed forests of the European part of the USSR.

Originally, in the language of the natives of southern Siberia, taiga apparently meant forested mountain ridges. In Mongol taiga means forest. Russian settlers in Siberia still call any primeval, uninhabited conifer forest the taiga. In ecological and geographical literature the name taiga is used to designate conifer forests of both eastern Europe and Siberia. (Map 3, II.)

Climate

Extending from the northwestern borders of the country to the mountains of northeastern Siberia, the taiga region, in its western part, is influenced by the Atlantic Ocean; its eastern part, however, is fully under the influence of the continental atmospheric conditions prevailing in Eastern Siberia. In the taiga region of eastern Europe and Western Siberia the summer isotherms are more or less of a latitudinal character, whereas the winter isotherms have a diagonal direction, extending from northwest to southeast. This is because in summer the temperatures depend on the heating of the continent and in winter they are subject to the influence of the Atlantic Ocean. Table 5

TABLE 5. TEMPERATURE AND PRECIPITATION AT MOLOTOV (PERM), LOCATED IN NORTHEASTERN EUROPE AT 58° LATITUDE N AT 535 FEET ABOVE SEA LEVEL [1]

Jan.	Feb.	Mar.	Apr.	May	June	July	Aug.	Sept.	Oct.	Nov.	Dec.	Year
				Temperature (approx.), degrees Fahrenheit								Mean
2	9	20	35	50	59	64	59	48	34	19	8	34
				Precipitation, inches								Total
1.5	1.3	1.0	1.0	2.0	2.8	3.1	2.8	2.2	2.0	2.1	1.7	23.5

[1] After L. S. Berg, *Geographic Zones of the USSR*, 3rd ed., Moscow, 1947.

gives temperature and precipitation data for a station of northeastern Europe located at 58° latitude N at 535 feet above sea level.

In the portion of the taiga west of the Yenisei River, the climate is less continental than east of the river; winters are milder, precipitation (including snowfall in winter) is more abundant, and cloudiness is greater. In the taiga of Eastern Siberia there exists in winter a region of heavy air masses—the so-called Siberian anticyclone. In winter the high pressure penetrates as far west as European Russia, creating a barometric axis * that separates the climate of the forest region from the climate of the prairies. In Eastern Siberia the presence of heavy cold masses of air in winter manifests itself by an almost complete absence of wind. The winters are still, sunny, and very cold.

At Yakutsk, winter temperatures drop to –60°F to –75°F and even lower, and near Verkhoyansk the lowest temperature (94°F below zero) has been recorded. During January, temperatures at Yakutsk

* Cf. p. 30.

are never higher than 16°F. But summers in the Eastern Siberian taiga are very warm. Precipitation is low, ranging from 6 to 14 inches a year. Most of the rain falls in July and August. Near Olekminsk summers are so dry that irrigation of fields and vegetable gardens is necessary.

At Yakutsk the absolute maximum temperature recorded in July was 100°F. Temperatures of about 80°F to 85°F are not unusual. During the day the temperature may be as high as 95°F, and after sunset it may drop to 40°F. Nowhere else in the world, at the same latitudes, have such high summer temperatures been observed.

The short but warm summers, and long daylight hours permit growing grain crops and vegetables in the vicinity of Yakutsk and even farther north. Summer wheat, rye, barley, and oats are cultivated here, and tomatoes, cucumbers, peas, and other vegetables are also raised.

Permanently frozen ground is encountered throughout the taiga region. It is most widespread in Eastern Siberia, where temperatures are lowest and the snow cover is thin. It does not interfere with growth either of natural vegetation (including trees) or of cultivated crops. Table 6 shows the annual course of temperatures and precipitation at Yakutsk.

TABLE 6. TEMPERATURE AND PRECIPITATION AT YAKUTSK, NORTHEAST SIBERIA, LATITUDE 62° N, 356 FEET ABOVE SEA LEVEL [1]

Jan.	Feb.	Mar.	Apr.	May	June	July	Aug.	Sept.	Oct.	Nov.	Dec.	Year
				Temperature, degrees Fahrenheit								Mean
−46	−34	−8	+16	42	60	66	58	42	16	−20	−40	12
				Precipitation, inches								Total
0.3	0.3	0.1	0.3	0.6	1.2	1.4	1.8	0.9	0.5	0.4	0.2	8.0

[1] After L. S. Berg, *Geographic Zones of the USSR*, 3rd ed., Moscow, 1947.

Topography

The topography of the taiga region is generally either gently undulating or flat. In the extreme northwestern part of the region, on the Kola Peninsula and in Karelia, the crystalline pre-Cambrian rocks of granite and gneiss are exposed in places at the surface. The Khibin Mountains, composed of intrusive rocks, are a rather prominent topographic feature of the Kola Peninsula. They are of a plateau-like character, elevated more than 4000 feet above the plains. Considerable deposits of apatite (calcium phosphate-fluoride) have been discovered in the Khibin Mountains. This mineral is being mined for the production of phosphate fertilizers.

Between the Kola Peninsula and the Ural Mountains is found only one more or less prominent range, called the Timanski Range. It is located between Cheshskaia Guba (a bay of the Barents Sea) and the upper reaches of the Pechora. Its southern part, belonging to the taiga region, extends 1000 feet high.

The Ural Mountains separate the taiga of eastern Europe from the taiga of Western Siberia. Beyond the Ural the northern part of the taiga region is 300 to 650 feet in elevation and is composed of Quaternary gravelly sand and clay deposits containing many boulders. The land appears as a rolling plain with moraine hills and ridges elevated about 100 feet above the plain. River valleys are cut into the plain to a depth of about 200 feet. In the western part of the region are found numerous swamps and lakes. The elevated watershed divides, west of the Ob, towards the Urals, reach 1000 feet above sea level.

In the eastern part of the Western Siberian taiga the land is somewhat hilly and is cut with broad river valleys that drain swampy watershed areas 230 to 250 feet above the valleys. The southern part of the Western Siberian taiga is flat, slightly rolling country, somewhat over 300 feet above sea level, composed of glacial deposits and crossed by large rivers. As a whole, the Western Siberian lowland is composed of horizontal Tertiary and Quaternary deposits. In some places in the north are found small patches of upper Jurassic and Cretaceous rocks. The glaciation extended as far south as the confluence of the Ob and the Irtysh. The Western Siberian taiga is poor in mineral deposits.

The Eastern Siberian taiga occupies almost the whole Central Siberian Plateau. The plateau extends west to the Yenisei, in the north it descends abruptly to the lowlands of northern Siberia, in the east it reaches the basin of the Aldan, and in the south it touches the mountains of the Transbaikal region and the foothills of the Sayans. The highest points on the plateau are found in the sources of the Kureika River; they are about 5000 feet above sea level. The elevations are also considerable, approximating 3500 feet, in the upper reaches of

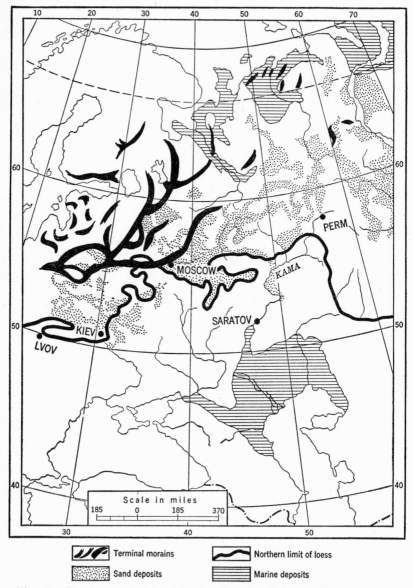

MAP 17. Quaternary glacial and marine deposits of the east European plain.

the Khatanga, the Vilui, and the Olenek rivers. However, along the Lower Tunguska elevations do not exceed 2000 to 2300 feet. The tectonic structure of the plateau is somewhat similar to that of eastern Europe. The crystalline shields, such as the Anabar Shield, are exposed in places, and, again, in other places they are submerged under almost horizontal Paleozoic and Mesozoic strata. As a whole, the plateau appears as a flat, slightly elevated plain.

There are some mountains within the borders of the plateau. These are caused by differential erosion and have the form of flat-topped table mountains. The rivers cut deep and broad valleys in the plateau. From the bottom of a river valley the territory appears to be rather mountainous. But as soon as the rim of the valley is reached the plateau presents itself as a monotonous, slightly undulating plain covered with dense forest. Because of the relatively dry climate and elevated terrain the Eastern Siberian taiga region is not so swampy as the taiga of Western Siberia.

Although the Western Siberian taiga is poor in mineral resources, areas of potentially great mineral wealth are found in the Eastern Siberian taiga; such are: the Tunguska coal basin; the Anabar area, with its gold deposits; the newly explored Angara-Ilim iron range located on both sides of the Angara where the river forms a series of rapids and where the construction of powerful hydroelectric stations is planned. The iron deposits of the Angara-Ilim area are supposed to amount to 200 million tons. South of this iron region is located the Irkutsk coal basin, stretching as a 45- to 50-mile-wide belt along the Trans-Siberian Railroad, from Nizhneudinsk to the southern end of Lake Baikal.

Because of the low elevations,* the rivers of the eastern European and Western Siberian taiga are slow-flowing, meandering, and continually changing their channels. In the spring freshet floods are common. As precipitation in the region as a whole is relatively high and evaporation low, the rivers maintain their full flow throughout the summer. The Ob and its upper tributaries have their sources in the snowfields and glaciers of the Altai Mountains, which provide adequate water for the summer flow.

Rivers of the Eastern Siberian taiga are swift streams of considerable volume, maintaining a uniform flow throughout the warm season. Cutting through hard pre-Cambrian rocks, they often form rapids, thus providing a potential source of hydroelectric power.

* The elevation of Novosibirsk, located on the River Ob at a distance of about 1900 miles from its mouth, is only 310 feet above sea level.

Soils and Vegetation

In the taiga region, as well as in the other forest regions of the temperate climate, a characteristic soil-forming process takes place which results in the so-called podzol soil.* Under the dense forest canopy not much organic matter, or humus, is found. A layer close to the surface containing humus is known as horizon A. The relatively abundant precipitation causes leaching of certain minerals from horizon A, such as calcium and potassium, as well as iron oxide, leaving behind a whitish ash-like layer of silicates just beneath horizon A. This leached podzol layer is known as horizon B. The minerals, which are leached from horizon B, especially iron oxide, which is reddish in color, accumulate in a deeper layer called horizon C, which acquires a reddish-brown color. Podzol soils are not so fertile as the black prairie soils; nevertheless, agriculture in the forest zone is entirely feasible.

In addition to podzol soil, swamp-type soils are found similar to those encountered in the tundra region. Because of saturation of the ground with stagnant water and consequent poor aeration, iron is found, not in a ferric (Fe^{+++}), but rather in a ferrous (Fe^{++}), state, imparting to the soil, not a reddish, but a bluish, color, similar to that of modeling clay. As oxygen is lacking in these soils, only certain plants can grow in the swamps; trees generally suffer a great deal under these conditions. Black soils akin to the prairie soils of the south occur in Eastern Siberia in the open areas in the midst of the taiga region.

The soil along the rivers is of an alluvial nature. Spring freshets flood the river bottomlands and deposit fertile silt. These soils are rich in organic matter.

In European Russia the northern part of the taiga region is occupied by swampy open forests of spruce. On the Kola Peninsula there is a considerable admixture of birch (*Betula pubescens*) and common pine.† These two species extend farther north here than any other trees. Farther east the northern taiga outposts of forest are composed of spruce and birch. South of the open fringe forests is a broad

* Podzol means, in Russian, ash-like. This term is used internationally by soil scientists.

† *Pinus sylvestris*, known in America as Scotch pine, is the most widely distributed forest tree of Eurasia. It grows from Spain to the Pacific Coast of Siberia and from the Kola Peninsula to the Balkan countries. In Russia it is known as common pine. It is a very valuable timber tree.

belt of the taiga. The main species there are European spruce (*Picea excelsa*) in the western part and Siberian spruce (*Picea obovata*) in the northeastern part. Common pine (*Pinus sylvestris*) occupies considerable areas, especially on the sandy soils.

Karelia contains some extensive pure pine forests, chiefly on sandy soil. Common pine is an intrazonal tree, and pine forests occur in patches far south of the taiga region. Pine also grows in swamps. In the northeastern part of the European taiga Siberian species begin to appear, and in addition to Siberian spruce we find here Siberian or cembra pine (*Pinus cembra*) * and Siberian larch (*Larix sibirica*). The growth of forest trees is better along the rivers because of better drainage. Here intensive logging operations are conducted. Logs are floated to the northern seaports, where they are sawed into export lumber. Part of the timber goes south down the Volga.

Extensive sphagnum moss swamps are found among the forested areas. The taiga forests on the swampy divides between the rivers are of an inferior quality and remain as yet untouched by man.

Towards the south the European taiga is less swampy and, although spruce still predominates, there is an admixture of broadleaf trees—linden (*Tilia cordata*) and maple—in the western part, whereas in the east Siberian fir makes its appearance in the spruce forests.

When a conifer forest is burned or logged, a temporary covering of light-loving birch and aspen becomes established. Soon, under the canopy of these species, shade-enduring conifers—mostly spruce—begin to appear. When the spruce reaches above the crowns of the birch and aspen, the latter trees die out and the area regains its conifer stand.

In the river valleys where spring floods deposit great quantities of silt every year, luxuriant meadows develop, which are used by the inhabitants as hayfields or pastures. Cattle raising in the taiga region of eastern Europe is limited to the open river valleys. Settlement of the region along the rivers has been due partly to the abundance of livestock feed in the valleys.

* In Russia *Pinus cembra* is called Kedr, from the Greek kedros, i.e., cedar, probably to commemorate the cedar of Lebanon. True cedars do not grow naturally within the borders of the Soviet Union. A rather common reference to cedar forests of Siberia, found in many books, is misleading. In America, too, many different conifers, such as *Thuya, Chamaecyparis*, and *Juniperus virginiana*, are called cedars. Cembra pine is a beautiful and very useful white pine. Its soft wood is used for pattern making; its nuts are gathered for food and for extracting a much prized edible oil. It is immune to the dreaded blister rust, which attacks some of the white pines of North America.

Although in the northern part of the taiga region of Western Siberia open scrubby spruce forests are quite common, Siberian larch (*Larix sibirica*) begins to play an important part here.* The soils in this area are either swampy or podzolized. The ground is covered with lichens, which provide food for reindeer. Sphagnum moss swamps are very common. Farther south the Western Siberian taiga consists mostly of cembra pine, with an admixture of fir and spruce and some birch and aspen. In the western part spruce is as important as cembra pine. In the river valleys pure cembra pine stands are found.

Sphagnum peat bogs are common on the low watershed divides. Often the bogs develop in dry places as a result of a very complicated process in which invasion of a forest by sphagnum moss plays an important part. Sphagnum moss, being very hygroscopic, retains considerable amounts of water and gradually kills off the forest trees, converting previously dry land into swamps. These bogs obtain their moisture and nutrition entirely from the atmosphere, the sphagnum moss being very sensitive to ground water and soil nutrients. Accordingly, better growth takes place in the central part of the bog than at the periphery, where there is contact with mineral soil. As a result, the peat bogs are higher at the center than at the edges. In addition to sphagnum moss, other vegetation found in these bogs usually includes bog bilberry (*Vaccinium uliginosum*), cloudberry (*Rubus chamaemorus*), black crowberry (*Empetrum nigrum*), cowberry (*Vaccinium vitis-idaea*), cotton sedge (*Eriophorum vaginatum*), crystal tea (*Ledum palustre*), and scattered suppressed pines and birch.

In the southern part of the Western Siberian taiga and to the southern limits of the taiga region the forests are denser and have a much better growth. They are known as the Urman forests and consist of the usual taiga species: cembra pine, spruce, and fir; larch, however, is less conspicuous here than elsewhere in the region. Birch and aspen are also present, and the typical taiga shrubby understory consists of mountain ash (*Sorbus aucuparia*), elderberry (*Sambucus racemosa*), and occasionally linden (*Tilia cordata*) and other species. Extensive swamps occupy the watershed divide between the Ob and the Irtysh. Magnificent forests of common pine are found on the sandy soils.

* Siberian larch (*Larix sibirica*) grows under optimal conditions in Western Siberia to a height of 150 feet, to a diameter of about 6 feet, and to an age of 350 years. Its wood is very durable and is used for railroad ties and telephone poles. It is very heavy and cannot be floated. Delivering logs to the mills by the way of the rivers is a difficult problem.

East of the Yenisei the taiga changes its character. Here the climate is more continental; the geology is different from that of Western Siberia; the terrain is better drained; swamps and peat bogs occur throughout the region, but they are less numerous and not so extensive as in Western Siberia. Because of the drier climate, prairie-like areas may be found here and there in the taiga, especially in the Yakut country.

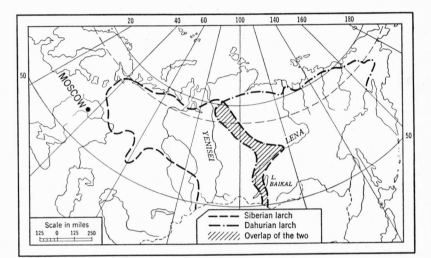

MAP 18. Distribution of Siberian and Dahurian larches in the Soviet Union. Siberian larch is a component of the taiga region of European Russia and of Western Siberia. Dahurian larch is a forest tree of Eastern Siberian plateaux and mountains. In an area extending from the lower Yenisei to Lake Baikal, the two larches overlap, hybridize, and form gradations from pure Siberian larch to the pure Dahurian larch.

Fir and spruce assume a subordinate place in the composition of the forests; common pine occupies large areas. Siberian larch is gradually replaced by Dahurian larch (*Larix dahurica*), a species resembling American *Larix laricina*. Where the range of Siberian larch overlaps that of Dahurian larch, these two species cross. Dahurian larch is a light-loving, cold-enduring tree growing on any kind of soil. It grows well where permanently frozen ground is found not more than 2 feet below the surface. Its wood is very durable, heavy, and difficult to handle.

In Eastern Siberia, above the Arctic Circle, the taiga is of a rather scrubby character. The forest is somewhat open, with an abundant ground cover of reindeer moss (lichen). Together with the Dahurian larch, an admixture of spruce and common pine is found. Cembra pine is absent. In the river valleys on alluvial soils are typical taiga meadows. Forest fires are not frequent here; when they occur, the burned-over areas reseed with Dahurian larch.

Where the terrain is more elevated, as on the flat tops of table mountains, the forests are replaced by alpine tundras of moss, dryad (*Dryas octopetala*), or *Alectoria* lichens.

The taiga of Eastern Siberia south of the Arctic Circle and down to the 60th parallel may be divided into two parts designated as western and eastern. The former embraces the basins of the Lower Tunguska and the Stony Tunguska. The taiga forests of this region are composed of Siberian larch, common pine, fir, spruce, and cembra pine. Pure fir stands are found in places. Sphagnum peat bogs are more common here than in the rest of the Eastern Siberian taiga. Above 1500 feet, in the Lower Tunguska basin, forests disappear and are replaced by alder thickets. Some forest stands are of good quality and of merchantable size. These are being logged and floated down to the lumber town of Igarka (population 20,000–30,000), located in the low reaches of the Yenisei.

The eastern part of the area south of the Arctic Circle is located in the middle flow of the Lena and its two largest tributaries, the Aldan and Vilui. This is Dahurian larch country, with occasional forests of common pine located, as usual, on sandy soil. The herbaceous ground cover of these rather open forests consists of columbine (*Aquilegia sibirica?*), a small red-berried *Rubus* (*saxatilis*), alpine clematis (*Atragene sibirica*), and many other dicotyledons. Of the monocotyledons, the orchids of the genus *Cypripedium* are noteworthy.

In the Lena-Vilui lowlands extensive prairie-like areas are found with such grass species as needlegrass (*Stipa capillata*) and fescue (*Festuca lenensis*). The subsoil here is rich in carbonates. The upper horizons contain 12 to 15 per cent humus; i.e., the conditions resemble those of the steppes of the Ukraine with one difference: at a depth of 40 to 60 inches below the surface here, permanently frozen ground is found.

In places black alkali soils are found similar to those in the semi-deserts of Middle Asia, supporting such unusual (for the taiga region) vegetation as sagebrush (*Artemisia jacutica*) and glasswort (*Salicornia herbacea*). Because of hot summers and long daylight hours, the vegetation develops very rapidly in this region; barley requires 70 days from sowing to harvesting. South of the 60th parallel and all the way to the southern mountains or the patches of woodland, common pine predominates in the west and Dahurian larch in the east, chiefly on sandy soils where permafrost is absent. The low watershed divides are, however, covered with the usual cool, dark, gloomy taiga of fir, spruce, and cembra pine. Excellent pine forests grow along the Angara.

The river valley meadows, being enriched every spring by the silt-carrying floods, support a luxurious herbaceous growth consisting of bluegrass (*Poa pratensis*); redtop (*Agrostis alba*); white false hellebore (*Veratrum album*); true lilies; daylilies (*Hemerocallis*); and many flowering dicotyledons, such as white chrysanthemums (*Chrysanthemum sibiricum*), bright orange Siberian globeflower (*Trollius asiaticus*), blue forget-me-not, and delphinium. Hayfields in this region at the time of mowing appear a continuous multicolored sea of flowers.

In the Lena region, open larch forests are most common. The ground is covered with many shrubs, such as rose, spiraea, honeysuckle, and alder. In the abundant herbaceous ground cover one may notice yellow hawksbeard (*Crepis sibirica*), dark-violet *Iris ruthenica*, and many grass species. On the open slopes the herbaceous vegetation is very similar to that of the prairie region.

Animal Life

The taiga region is divided by the Yenisei River into two distinct faunistic subregions. The animals that occur east of the river are: muskdeer, stone grouse (*Tetrao uragalloides*), northern pika (*Ochotona hyperborea*), and eastern moose (*Alces americanus pfizenmayeri*). The carrion crow (*Corvus corone*) of the Eastern Siberian taiga is replaced west of the Yenisei with the gray crow (*Corvus corone charpii*).

However, south of the city of Krasnoyarsk, i.e., above the locality where the Trans-Siberian Railroad crosses the Yenisei, this river loses its significance as a faunistic boundary between the Western Siberian and the Eastern Siberian taiga.

The dense, gloomy taiga forests are surprisingly devoid of animals. The dead stillness of the Siberian taiga has been described by many explorers. The wild life is concentrated in areas where the forest stands are intermingled with open patches. Here the wild animals find more food. The animals of the taiga, unlike the majority of the tundra animals, remain in their habitat throughout the year. A possible exception is the not-too-numerous bats, which migrate south for the winter.

The northern conifer forests are populated by bear, timber wolf, fox, lynx, smaller carnivores, hare, squirrel, moose, wapiti, reindeer, and various birds. The brown bear (*Ursus arctos*) is found throughout the region. The Siberian bear is larger than the European bear. The timber wolf (*Canis lupus*) of the European forest, on the other hand, is larger than the Siberian wolf. The abundance of food in Siberia makes wolves in that part of the country less aggressive than in European Russia, although in Siberia also they cause a great deal of damage to cattle and reindeer.

Several subspecies of red fox (*Vulpes*) are found in the taiga region. The red fox is still quite common in European Russia. The red fox of Siberia has a richer red color. The Siberian silver fox (melanistic individuals of the common red fox) has valuable black fur in which the guard hairs are banded with silver.

An occasional visitor from the Amur region to the Eastern Siberian taiga is the tiger. It may even penetrate as far north as Yakutsk.

The lynx (*Lynx lynx*) and wolverine (*Gulo gulo*) are more abundant in Siberia than in European Russia. The wolverine is usually active throughout the winter and is almost entirely nocturnal in habit.

Badger (*Meles meles*) is found all over the conifer forest region: in Europe as far north as the 69th parallel, and in Siberia to the upper reaches of the Lena (53rd parallel).

There are several subspecies of the snowshoe rabbit (*Lepus timidus*). In Siberia they are called ushkans.

Of the smaller carnivorous animals (family Mustelidae), mention should be made of the pine marten (*Martes martes*); black fitch (*Putorius putorius*), in Europe only; marsh otter (*Lutreola lutreola*); ermine; and weasel. The Siberian yellow mink, or kolonok (the kolinsky of fur trade) (*Mustela sibirica*); alpine weasel (*Mustela alpina*); and the most valuable member of the family, sable (*Martes zibellina*), are found only in Siberia. The distribution of sable is not continuous. It occurs in patches between the Ural and the River Ob. Small colonies of sable are found further east along the 60th parallel, connecting the western sable area with the main sable region of Eastern Siberia. In Eastern Siberia sable is found in areas between the 70th parallel and the borders of southern Siberia, including the Altai Mountains. It also exists in Kamchatka, on Sakhalin Island, along the Amur River, and in the Maritime Province, but not in the upper corner of Eastern Siberia, i.e., east of the 130th meridian, and north of the 60th parallel. The best sables are found in the Vitim and Olekma basins and in the headwaters of the Amgun and the Zeia. White sable of Barguzin is very rare. In pre-Russian days in Siberia the sable was a common animal of the Siberian forest region, but, because a sable pelt was considered a unit of the yassak (tribute) imposed by the Russian invaders on the natives, the complete extermination of this animal was in sight at the end of the nineteenth century. In 1913 the Russian government inaugurated rigid conservation laws. At the present time there are several sable sanctuaries in Siberia.

Fur squirrel (*Sciurus vulgaris*) is the most abundant and commercially the most valuable fur-bearing animal in the Soviet Union, especially in Siberia. Several races of squirrel are distinguished in the trade, such as the "low ridge squirrel" of Western Siberia and the "high ridge squirrel" of Eastern Siberia. In Siberia the winter hunting season is known as the squirrel-hunting season, since the squirrel is the chief object of hunting. The rest of the animals—lynx, bear, wolverine, and others—are hunted only when there is an opportunity. An interesting biological phenomenon is the mass migration of squirrels from one locality to another. Most of these migrations are caused by lack of food, but some still await explanation. Widely distributed in the region are the flying squirrel (*Pteromys volans*) and the chipmunk.

The otter (*Lutra lutra*) is found throughout the region and up to the Arctic Circle. This fur-bearing animal has been considerably reduced in numbers.

The beaver (*Castor fiber*) is found sporadically in the conifer belt between the Ural and the River Ob. It is becoming very rare. Recently, however, measures have been taken to protect the beaver, and since then it has begun to increase.

Of the hoofed mammals the moose * (*Alces alces*) is probably the most widely distributed. It has been considerably depleted in the European part of the country, but in Siberia it is still hunted commercially. The moose has no predatory enemies, and its complete extermination in certain European parts of the Soviet Union is due solely to human activity. Moose is especially abundant in the northeastern part of Siberia. The moose found east of the Yenisei is closely related to the American moose.

The stag, or red deer (*Cervus elaphus*), has been exterminated in European Russia, although it is still found in Crimea and in the Caucasus. It is not found in Asia.

* In European English the Old World *Alces* is called elk.

An inhabitant of the southern part of Siberia, west of Lake Baikal, is the wapiti (*Cervus canadensis asiaticus*). It is called maral by the Russians. It is hunted for its antlers which, when in the velvet, are sold to the Chinese for medicinal purposes.

The roebuck (*Capreolus pygargus*) of the Siberian taiga is a much larger animal than the European roebuck.

The muskdeer or kabargah (*Moschus moschiferus*) is found in Eastern Siberia. It is the size of a newly born calf, and the upper canine teeth of the male protrude and are turned backwards. The male is hunted for its musk, a fluid that is found in a gland under the skin of the abdomen. The dried gland is sold chiefly to the Chinese for perfumery purposes. Man has left but little imprint on the fauna of the taiga. Although reindeer has decreased in numbers throughout the region and some animals, such as roebuck, are not so numerous in the southern parts of the taiga, nevertheless, the most important commercial animals of the taiga—squirrel, fox, hare, ermine—do not show any signs of decrease.

The occurrence of some southern prairie-like areas in the taiga of Eastern Siberia is very striking. The ground squirrel (*Citellus parrii jacutensis*) lives in such areas in the middle Lena region.

Of the smaller birds—there are about 300 species in Siberia and more in the European part of the country—the following are found in the taiga: finch, linnet, bunting, grosbeak (*Coccothraustes*), crossbill, (*Loxia*), bluethroat or nightingale (*Luscinia*), ruby-throat (*L. calliope*), thrush (*Turdus*), tit or chickadee (*Parus*), goldcrest (*Regulus*), accentor, warbler, lark, crow, shrike, flycatcher, waxwing (*Bombicilla*), swallow, woodpecker, owl, golden eagle, falcon, hawk, and many others. As a rule, the small birds prefer forest fringes where woody groves mingle with the meadows. Jays (*Perisoreus infaustus* and *Garrulus glandarius*) are found all over the northern parts of Europe and Asia. The jay and the nutcracker (*Nucifraga caryocatactes*) eat a great deal of the cembra pine wingless seed and help to disseminate this important tree. The game birds that should be mentioned include the large European grouse or capercaillie (*Tetrao urogallus* and *T. urogalloides*), the black grouse (*Lyrurus tetrix*), a small grouse (*Tetrastes bonasia*), woodcock, snipe, curlew, ducks, and geese.

Among the reptiles of the taiga region mention should be made of a poisonous viper (*Vipera berus*) and several non-poisonous snakes (*Tropidonotus, Erix, etc.*). Snakes are more numerous in the southern part of Siberia near the Altai Mountains. The widely distributed viviparous lizard (*Lacerta vivipara*) is found throughout the taiga.

The amphibians include several species of frogs (*Rana esculenta,* *R. temporaria*) and two species of toads (*Bufo variabilis* and *B. viridis*). Mosquitoes, black flies, gnats, and horse flies (*Tabanus*) are so numerous in the Siberian taiga that they interfere with human activities and cause a great deal of trouble to the domestic and wild animals also. These blood-sucking insects probably can be considered one of the most important obstacles in the colonization of certain parts of Siberia.

Agriculture in the region is of a purely local character. In the European taiga the most common crops are, in order of their importance: rye, oats, and barley. In some places wheat is also grown. In the southern part of the Western Siberian taiga and in southeastern Siberia are sown rye, oats, and wheat. In the Yakut country the staple crop is barley; rye, wheat, and potatoes are also grown.

Flax is raised in the southern part of the European taiga, although it can be successfully grown as far north as 65°30' latitude N.

Of the vegetables the most important are turnips, rutabagas, and cabbages. Carrots and table beets are grown in the southern part of the European taiga and also in Western Siberia.

Fruit growing is not practiced in the taiga, except for some cherry and apple trees that are grown for domestic use in warmer places in the European taiga. To satisfy the need for vitamin C the population of the taiga, as well as of the tundra, depends entirely on the wild berries of different species of *Vaccinium* and *Rubus.* In Siberia small fruits of wild apple (*Malus baccata*) and chokecherry (*Prunus padus*) are put up in large quantities for winter use.

Cattle is raised as far north as 69° to 70° latitude N. The so-called Veliko-Russian black or red breed of cattle is found in the European taiga region. These animals are descended from the European wild cattle (*Bos taurus primigenius*), originally a typical prairie animal. Carcasses of Veliko-Russian cattle are small, weighing from 110 to 285 pounds. This breed can stand a great deal of cold yet requires only a small amount of food.*

The Kholmogory dairy cattle of the Archangel Province are better than the Veliko-Russian breed. Apparently they originated as a result of crossing some imported Holland stock with the local cattle, although opinions differ on this subject.

Siberian dairy cattle are very primitive, akin to the *Bos taurus.* They are red in color and resistant to the severe cold of Siberia. In winter their hair is shaggy and long.

* L. S. Berg, *Geographic Zones of the USSR,* 3rd ed., Moscow, 1947.

The cattle of the Yakut region (of the Lena basin) are apparently related to the banteng (*Bos sondaicus*). They serve both as beef and as milch stock and apparently were brought by the Yakuts from their former home in the south. If the cold-endurance of Siberian cattle is great, the ability of the Yakut cattle to withstand cold is simply unbelievable.

In summer cattle suffer a great deal from mosquitoes and gnats.

Oxen are used by the Yakuts as draft animals.

The horses of the European taiga region are of a Finnish type. In Western Siberia they are of Mongolian origin. There are several breeds: some are excellent draft animals. Yakut horses are of a southern origin and rather light in color. They serve as harness or saddle animals. The Yakuts, whose ancestors were southern nomads, use horse meat and mare's milk for food. Generally speaking, Yakut horses spend the entire year in the field, providing their own fodder even in the middle of winter. Fermented mare's milk or kumiss is a favorite drink of all Turkic-speaking nomads of Asiatic Russia.

Reindeer husbandry is practiced by many native peoples both in the European taiga and in Siberia. In Eastern Siberia Tungus tend reindeer throughout the region, riding on the animal * rather than using it in harness as the peoples of the tundra do. Reindeer milking is practiced, but on a limited scale. Watchdogs are not employed in reindeer herding.

The native taiga dogs are of the same type as the Samoyed dog but larger. Some breeds are used for hunting, and others are used for drawing sleds.

The domestic honeybee was introduced into Siberia by the Russian settlers.

Recently some progress has been made in the domestication of the moose, partly for meat production, but chiefly for service as a pack and draft animal suitable for the taiga conditions. The moose can be domesticated rather easily and reproduces in captivity very readily; the female brings forth two calves, which reach maturity (reproductive stage) in 16 months.†

People

The Eastern European taiga is sparingly inhabited by several Finnish peoples—Zyrians (Komi), Udmurts, Permiaks—and also by the

_____

* The saddle is placed on the shoulders of the animal rather than on the back in "horseback fashion."

† Bobrinsky et al., *Animal Geography*, 1946, p. 371.

Russians. The inhabitants live along the rivers, and the intervening areas are void of human inhabitation. Some Voguls (Manse) live west of the Ural, but the majority of this people, some 8000 of them, live between the Ural and the Ob. Some 20,000 Ostiaks (Khante) live farther east. The Selkup people, a Samoyed tribe, formerly known as the Ostiak-Samoyeds, inhabit the area on both sides of the River Taz, as do a small tribe of Paleo-Asiatic Kets, formerly known as the Yenisei Ostiaks, although they are not related to the Ostiaks. The taiga east of the Yenisei is the home of the Tungus, who live in the region of the three eastern tributaries of the Yenisei: the Lower, the Stony, and the Upper Tunguska rivers. The Turkic-speaking Yakuts live in the Lena-Vilui-Aldan area. The Yakuts raise horses and keep cattle, and grow some crops, whereas the Tungus are reindeer keepers and hunters.

Chapter 11

Forest Region
Mixed Forests of European Russia

South of the conifer forests of eastern Europe lies a belt of mixed conifers—spruce, fir, and pine—intermingled and sometimes replaced with broadleaf trees (Map 3, III). Broadleaf forests are well developed in western Europe, but within the borders of the Soviet Union, the farther east the fewer are the species of broadleaf trees. Beech (*Fagus sylvatica*) disappears first, being found only southwest of the Kishinev-Rovno line. Hornbeam (*Carpinus betulus*) extends farther east, to about the 45th meridian; ash (*Fraxinus excelsa*) disappears before it reaches the Volga. Maple (*Acer platanoides*) and oaks (*Quercus robur* and *Q. sessiflora*) reach the Ural Mountains; only linden, or basswood (*Tilia cordata*), is cold-resistant enough to cross the mountains into Siberia, where it occurs only sporadically. Thus broadleaf and mixed forests are not found east of the Ural Mountains except, of course, the ever-present birch and aspen.* These two cold-enduring species of the taiga sometimes form pure forests on the southern fringe of the Western Siberian forests in the burned-over areas. Nobody, however, refers to them as broadleaf forests.

In eastern Europe the mixed forests form a broad wedge at the western border of the country, with Leningrad in the north, the Polish border in the center, and Kishinev approximately in the south. This wedge gradually narrows along the 56th parallel towards the Ural Mountains.

Climate

The climate of the mixed forest region is milder than that of the taiga. It is fairly uniform throughout the region. Moscow is located approximately in the center of the region, and Berg describes as follows its climate as representative of the mixed forests: At the beginning of April a snow cover about 20 inches deep disappears from

* Technically, aspen and birch are broadleaf trees.

118

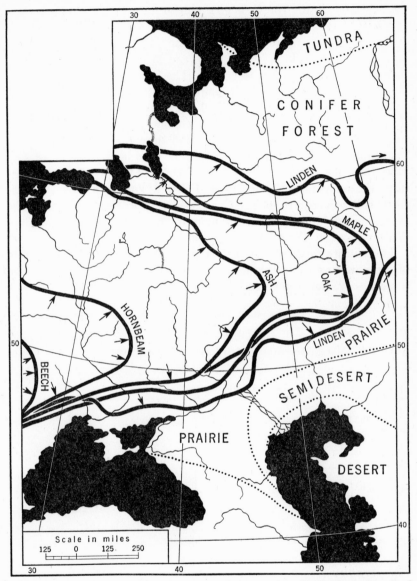

Map 19. Eastern penetration of western European broadleaf trees. Broadleaf forest trees essentially are warm-climate species. In their penetration into colder eastern Europe, beech stops at almost the borders of Russia. Hornbeam penetrates slightly farther east. Ash almost reaches the Volga. Oak and maple advance as far as the Ural Mountains. Only linden crosses the range, being found in patches in southern parts of Western Siberia. None are found in Eastern Siberia, with the exception of birch, aspen, and cottonwood.

the fields, but in the forests it may remain until May. At the end of April grass appears and plowing is started. Lilac bushes are in bloom at the end of May. The summer is warm. During hot days the temperature in the shade is 70° to 75°F, and in occasional hot spells the thermometer registers up to 95°F. The nights are cool, however, the temperatures sometimes dropping to 34°F.

Most of the precipitation falls in the second half of the summer. Rains are very frequent, occasionally coming in the form of thunderstorms. Winter at Moscow is long and snowy, snow remaining on the ground for 140 days. The first snow falls in the middle of October, and the Moskva River freezes about 1 month later. Sometimes the temperature drops to 40°F below zero, but again, in December, it may rise to 46°F. Occasionally frosts occur as late as the beginning of June. The mean monthly temperature and precipitation are given in Table 7.

The climate farther west, near the Baltic Sea, is milder than that of Moscow, and the precipitation is heavier. In some parts of Latvia it reaches 32 inches per year.

TABLE 7. TEMPERATURE AND PRECIPITATION NEAR MOSCOW [1]

Jan.	Feb.	Mar.	Apr.	May	June	July	Aug.	Sept.	Oct.	Nov.	Dec.	Year
Temperature, degrees Fahrenheit												Mean
12	16	23	26	54	61	66	60	50	38	28	18	25
Precipitation, inches												Total
1.0	0.9	1.1	1.3	1.7	2.6	2.8	2.9	2.1	1.9	1.5	1.2	21.0

[1] L. S. Berg, *Geographic Zones of the USSR*, 3rd ed., Moscow, 1947. The records were taken at the Agricultural College near Moscow.

Topography

The topography of the region is relatively simple. Near the southern shores of the Gulf of Finland are found some Silurian and Cambrian rocks forming a low plateau, the highest point of which does not exceed 600 feet above sea level; the average elevation is about 500 feet. Among other elevated areas that should be mentioned are the

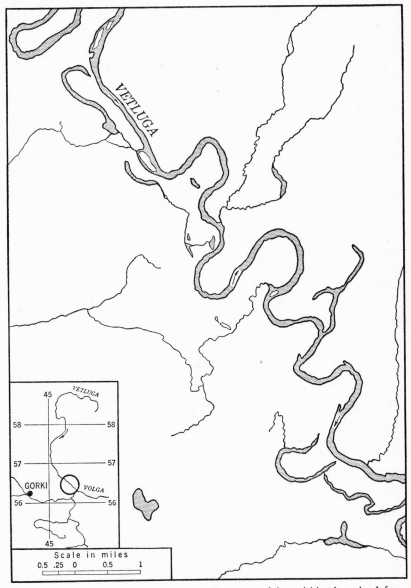

Map 20. Meandering stream of the east European plains within the mixed forest region. The River Vetluga not far from its confluence with the Volga. (*After Dobrynin.*)

Valdai Hills, an upland only about 1000 feet above sea level. The region has been glaciated, and terminal moraines and ice age deposits are found throughout the northern part.

An interesting geographic area known as Polesie is located in the mixed forest region. Polesie is an extensive, swampy, forested lowland lying roughly in the basin of the Pripiat. Swamps are found not only along the numerous meandering rivers and countless lakes but also on the low watershed divides. Occasionally dry, sandy areas covered with pine forests are found, and sometimes low hills. The whole aspect of the Polesie, its flora, and its fauna differ strikingly from the rest of the mixed forest region.

Soils and Vegetation

Soils of the mixed forest region are similar to those of the taiga; i.e., they are of the podzol type. But in the southern part of the region are found black soils of the prairie type. These soils are remains of the time when the climate was warmer and drier and when the region was occupied by the more southern, woodland type of vegetation. Later these soils were podzolized by the advancing forests. They are darker than the typical podzol soils.

The region may be divided into two large parts: (1) the southwestern part, composed of hornbeam (*Carpinus betulus*), oak, and spruce (in the extreme east, fir is admixed), and (2) the northeastern part, of the oak-spruce type. Hornbeam is absent in the second part. Summer oak (*Quercus robur*), known in North America as English oak, is the dominant tree of the region. It grows mixed with conifers —pine and spruce—and with broadleaf trees: ash, elms, maple. Near Poland and the Baltic Sea occur yew (*Taxus baccata*) and beech (*Fagus sylvatica*). Linden (*Tilia*) is a very common tree in the mixed forest. Strictly speaking, beech and hornbeam are western European trees. Birch and aspen also are found in the mixed forest. An undergrowth of shrubs (hazelnut, viburnum) is usually well developed.

The staple crops of the region are identical with those of the taiga, i.e., rye, oats, barley, flax, potatoes. Buckwheat is cultivated throughout the region but is not too important.

In the southern part of the region some millet and a great many lentils are grown. Hemp (*Cannabis sativa*) is raised both for the oil and for the fiber. It is never used as a drug source. Clover and alfalfa (the latter in the south) are sown for hay.

Fruit growing is practiced on a commercial scale; apples, cherries, plums, and berries are grown throughout the region. Pears are found principally in Belorussia. Of vegetables, the most important are carrots, cucumbers, and especially cabbage.

Animal Life

The mixed forests of the European part of the Soviet Union have fauna very similar to that of the conifer forests. This region, being more densely populated than the northern forest zone, is much depleted of wild life.

An endemic animal of this region until recently was the European bison (*Bos bonasus*), which lived under protection in the area adjoining Poland. It is now extinct, the last specimen having been killed in 1919.* The common brown bear and badger are found here occasionally. Squirrel is an inhabitant of this region but is not hunted on a large scale. In the marshes of the western part of the broadleaf forest region the beaver still lives. The moose, a rare inhabitant, dwells in open swampy patches. The wild boar (*Sus scrofa atilla*) is found only occasionally also. The roebuck (*Capreolus capreolus transsilvanicus*), wolf, and fox are quite common. Roebuck (deer) and stag (elk) prefer open broadleaf groves with shrubby undergrowth and tall grass in the openings. Forest marten is a typical predator of the mixed forest region. It is closely related to the sable, and the two animals occur together in the Ural region. Forest marten feeds chiefly on squirrel. It is an important commercial fur animal. Other small predators include stone marten (*Martes foina*), fitch (*Putorius putorius*), ermine (*Mustela erminea*), and weasel (*M. nivalis*). Still other animals occurring in the region that should be named are lynx (*L. lynx*), snowshoe rabbit (*Lepus timidus*), European hare (*Lepus europaens*), and rodents. In this region begin to appear rodent species not found in the taiga region. Among these are: dormouse (*Muscardinus avellanarius*), a garden dormouse or fruit rat (*Eliomys quercinus*), Asiatic dormouse (*Dryomys nitedula*), the black vole (*Clethrionomys glareolus*), hamsters (*Cricetus cricetus, C. migratorius*), and a mole-rat (*Spalax microphtalmus*).

The turtle, which is absent in the north, makes its appearance in the broadleaf forest region of the Ukraine. The viviparous lizard (*Lacerta vivipara*) occurs here sporadically but is absent farther south.

* L. S. Berg, *Geographic Zones of the USSR*, 3rd ed., Moscow, 1947, p. 260. See also Bobrinsky et al., *Animal Geography*, 1946, p. 385.

Another species of lizard (*Lacerta agilis*) is rather common. Vipers (*Vipera berus*) are found throughout the area.

The Veliko-Russian breed of cattle raised in the mixed forest region has a considerable admixture of the western European strains. Yaroslavl dairy cattle are found in the northern part of the region. In Belorussia, people keep the local breed of cattle.

The races of local horses of the region have not been studied well as yet.

Sheep raising is not of much importance. Swine raising involves both the local, rather primitive stock and imported Yorkshire stock. Swine raising is especially important in Belorussia.

The honeybee in its wild state is still found in Polesie and in Lithuania. Bee keeping, or honey hunting in the forests, has been practiced by Slavic tribes from time immemorial.

People

The western part of the mixed forest of eastern Europe was the original home of the eastern Slavs. At present the portions of the region adjacent to the Baltic Sea are inhabited by the Latvians, Estonians, and Lithuanians. Near Poland live Belorussians; south of this group live Moldavians and Ukrainians; farther east live Veliko-Russians. In the Oka region live Finnish people: Mari (Cheremiss), and old Bulgar (Finno-Mongol) people of Chuvash, who speak Turkic. Somewhat south is the home of another Finnish tribe, the Mordvas. At the confluence of the Volga and the Kama live Kazan Tatars, and southeast of this area is the home of a Finno-Ugrian Turkic-speaking people, the Bashkirs.

Chapter **12**

Woodland Region

Located between the forest and the prairie is a transition zone known in Russian literature as the forested steppe.* In the northern part most of the area is forested, small patches of grassland occurring only occasionally; in the southern part most of the area is covered with herbaceous vegetation, with occasional groves of forest trees. The name woodland may be used to designate this region, but one should keep in mind that it is not a savannah-like territory where single trees are scattered over an extensive grassland. In this region rather large forested areas are found. (Map 3, IV.)

The southern boundary of the woodland region extends from the northern part of the Moldavian Republic to Kremenchug and to Poltava. It reaches the Volga somewhat north of Saratov, follows the Volga up to the River Samara, and then extends up that river and finally to Sterlitamak. East of the Ural Mountains the boundary follows roughly the 54th parallel, and after crossing the Irtysh it turns southeast and reaches the Altai Mountains. Farther east the woodland type of vegetation is found only in separated patches along the southern border of the forest region.

Climate

Being a transition zone between the forest and the prairie, the woodland, in its northern part, has the climate of the forest region and in the south the climate of the prairies. Roughly, the 68°F July isotherm is located along the northern border of the woodland region, and on the southern border lies the so-called barometric axis of high pressure of Eurasia. North of the axis a characteristic climatic feature is the moist southwestern wind, which brings considerable amounts of precipitation. South of the axis the winds are from the north and east and are dry.

* The original Russian name, leso-stepie, is difficult to translate literally into English. The name conveys the idea of a region in which both forest and prairie elements are mixed.

125

Table 8 shows temperature and precipitation data for two stations of the woodland region: Kiev (elevation 600 feet) in the European section and Omsk (elevation 295 feet) in Western Siberia.

TABLE 8. MEAN MONTHLY TEMPERATURES AND PRECIPITATION
AT KIEV AND AT OMSK

Jan.	Feb.	Mar.	Apr.	May	June	July	Aug.	Sept.	Oct.	Nov.	Dec.	Year

Kiev
Temperature, degrees Fahrenheit   Mean

| 21.2 | 24.5 | 31.0 | 44.0 | 58.4 | 63.0 | 66.0 | 64.5 | 56.0 | 45.0 | 33.5 | 26.0 | 44.5 |

Precipitation, inches   Total

| 1.3 | 1.6 | 1.6 | 1.8 | 2.0 | 3.0 | 3.1 | 2.2 | 1.8 | 1.9 | 1.6 | 1.5 | 23.4 |

Omsk
Temperature, degrees Fahrenheit   Mean

| −3 | 0 | 10 | 32 | 52 | 63 | 68 | 62 | 51 | 34 | 16 | 3 | 32 |

Precipitation, inches   Total

| 0.5 | 0.3 | 0.3 | 0.4 | 1.1 | 2.2 | 2.0 | 1.8 | 1.1 | 0.9 | 0.7 | 0.8 | 12.1 |

The mildest climate within the region is found in the west, in the Moldavian Republic. Abundance of rain, early springs, and dry, warm falls are very conducive to an intensive agriculture.

In this region, forest groves and patches of prairie exist side by side under identical climatic conditions. If it were not for the interference of man, the forest would gradually occupy the whole region.

Topography

In the western part of the region the Volhynia-Podolia upland, composed of Cretaceous and Tertiary rocks with occasional outcrops of granite and gneiss, extends as far east as the middle reaches of the Dnieper. The elevation of the upland is seldom more than 1300 feet.

The central part of the woodland region is occupied by the glaciated Dnieper lowland, which farther east changes into a rather low, middle Russian upland not over 1000 feet in elevation. Towards the River Volga the terrain is more elevated, reaching its highest point (about 1200 feet, known as Zhiguli) near the city of Kuibyshev,* at the confluence of the Volga and the Samara. East of the Volga the terrain gradually rises toward the Ural Mountains. A part of the Ufa Plateau is located within the limits of the woodland region.

Beyond the Ural the country is monotonously flat and dotted with many small lakes, some fresh-water, some alkaline. An interesting feature of the Western Siberian woodland is the occurrence of low— 3 to 15 feet—broad hills extending parallel to one another for many miles. Kokchetav Hills, with heights reaching 3000 feet, are located in the southern part of the Western Siberian woodlands.

The Donetz Heights, well known for mineral deposits—coal, salt, etc. —are located south of the main woodland region in the prairies of eastern Ukraine. The general character of the Donetz Heights is that of a rolling plateau stretching from west northwest to east southeast for over 200 miles and extending about 100 miles in width. The highest points of the plateau reach 1200 feet. Originally the vegetation of the Donetz Heights was that of the woodland type; at present the whole area is under cultivation.

In places not covered by forests the loess soil (see below) is eroded easily, giving origin to ravines and gullies. Any mistreatment of the vegetation, such as the removal of forest trees or the overgrazing of the open areas, results in deep gullies that may be several miles long. The ravines, with almost vertical slopes and without any vegetation, are called the ovragi (plural). The gullies, with rather gentle slopes and with a covering of vegetation, are known as the balki.

Another characteristic feature of the region is the frequent occurrence of small circular depressions about 3 feet deep and 30 to 50 feet in circumference. These depressions are usually found on the watershed divide areas and sometimes are filled with water, forming a swamp or a small lake.

Soils and Vegetation

In the woodland region generally the subsoil consists of loess—an unstratified, porous deposit of a calcareous nature and of a yellow or

* Formerly Samara. Note that although the name of the city was changed the River Samara has retained its old name.

a buff color. About one-half of it is composed of fine particles from 0.05 to 0.01 millimeter in diameter. It is crumbly in structure and erodes easily. Very fertile soils develop on the loess deposits. Loess is not found north of the woodland. It is widely distributed in the temperate climates of Asia, Europe, and America.

In the northern part of the region the soil is still of a forest type— the gray forest soil. Farther south, however, it is replaced by the black prairie-type soil, the so-called chernozem.

The chernozem soil-forming process is entirely different from the podzol-forming process (cf. p. 106). The herbaceous prairie vegetation deposits a large amount of humus in the upper horizon of the soil. Under this layer of rich organic soil, which may extend to 25 inches in depth, an horizon saturated with calcium carbonate (lime) is found. The presence of calcium carbonate imparts a crumbly texture to the soil and thus improves its physical qualities. The light precipitation of the region occupied by the chernozem prevents leaching of minerals and the humus from the soil. Rich chernozem soils contain from 10 to 12 per cent of organic matter, and sometimes, in Western Siberia, even 15 per cent. Typical chernozem contains from 6 to 10 per cent of humus.

Occasionally in the woodland region are found alkali soils. However, most of the alkali soils are found farther south, especially in the semideserts and deserts of Middle Asia.

The dominant tree in the European woodland region is oak (*Quercus pedunculata*). In Western Siberia where oak does not grow, its place is taken by birch.

In the European part of the country (in Bessarabia) forests occur as far south as the 48th parallel, but in Western Siberia they generally do not extend farther than 53° latitude N. The typical forest groves of the central part of the eastern European woodland between the Dnieper and the Volga are composed of oak to which are admixed ash, elm, linden, aspen, and maples (*Acer platanoides, A. campestre,* and *A. tataricum*). *Acer tataricum* and hazelnut often form a shrubby undergrowth. West of the Dnieper, hornbeam appears as an undergrowth in the oak-ash forests, together with *Acer campestre.*

In western Ukraine (Podolia) and in the Moldavian Republic (Bessarabia) are found extensive beech forests. These forests have been badly cut over. Where they still exist they are composed of dominant beech with an admixture of individual trees of oak, ash, and maples (*A. platanoides* and *A. pseudoplatanus*). On the watershed divides of the European woodland, east of the Don, scattered patches of aspen occur. In Western Siberia similar patches are found but aspen there is replaced by birch. Birch (*Betula pubescens* and *B. verrucosa*) and aspen (*Populus tremula*) are the only deciduous trees found in the Western Siberian woodland.

Pine forests are not widely distributed in the woodland region. The common pine (*Pinus sylvestris*) grows either on sandy soils or on the chalk or lime cliffs.

Virgin prairie areas within the woodland region are very rare. The whole prairie portion of the region is under cultivation. In those few places where the virgin prairie has been preserved, the vegetation is composed mostly of dicotyledonous plants. Grasses comprise only about 20 per cent of all species present. Most of the plants are perennial; only 6 per cent of the vegetation is composed of annuals. The prairie of the woodland, with its luxurious growth and abundance of bright flowering plants, differs considerably from the true prairies located farther south inasmuch as in the latter areas grasses * predominate and flowering herbs occupy a subordinate position. Berg (after Alekhin) gives the following description of plant development in the virgin grassland of the central part of the European woodland region.†

Early in the spring, perhaps early in April, the purple *Anemone patens* begins to flower, to which are soon added the bright yellow *Adonis vernalis*, a hyacinth, two violas, *Gagea erubescens*, and, at the beginning of May, a primrose. During the month of May white *Anemone silvestris* comes into flower, accompanied by the lilac-colored *Iris aphylla* and a whitish vetch (*Orobus albus*). At the end of May or the beginning of June the grassland assumes the delicate blue color of forget-me-not (*Myosotis sylvatica*), attenuated by the darker blue *Veronica chamaedris* and lilac-colored *Veronica prostrata*. Early in June dark violet meadow sage (*Salvia pratensis*) begins to dominate. Later some variety is given to the dark violet tone by the bright yellow salsify (*Tragopogon pratensis*), white tansy (*Tanacetum vulgare*), white foamy dropwort (*Filipendula hexapetala*), and white clover (*Trifolium montanum*).

* The higher plants, or angiosperms, commonly known as flowering plants, are divided into two large groups: monocotyledons (to which grasses, with their inconspicuous flowers, belong) and dicotyledons, among which most of the plants with large brightly colored flowers are found. In the monocotyledon division there are also some brightly flowering plants, such as lily, iris, daylily (*Hemerocallis*) and others.

† L. S. Berg, *Geographic Zones of the USSR*, 3rd ed., Moscow, 1947.

Towards the end of June the sage gradually disappears and the white-flowering dropwort and clover begin to dominate. To these are added blue campanulas (*Campanula sibirica* and *C. persicifolia*). In July sainfoin (*Onobrychis sativa*) changes the white tone of the grassland to a subdued rose-lilac. Fewer and fewer new flowering plants appear during July; the last spectacular outburst is caused by the appearance of numerous blue *Delphinium rossicum* and dark red *Veratrum nigrum*. Towards the middle of August the grass species—meadow brome (*Bromus erectus*), velvet bentgrass (*Agrostis canina*), and others—become more conspicuous. Then the vegetation dries up and the grassland assumes the brownish yellow tone of autumn.

In some places in the woodland region open areas between the patches of forest were originally covered with thickets of such shrubs as ground cherry (*Prunus fruticosa*), blackthorn (*P. spinosa*), Russian broom (*Cytisus ruthenicus*), spiraea (*Spiraea crenifolia*), and Russian peashrub (*Caragana frutex*). Most of these brushfields, however, have been cleared for agricultural use.

On the chalk cliffs and hills where common pine occasionally grows are found many relict plants. Daphne (*Daphne cneorum*), a west European alpine shrub, is occasionally seen on the calcareous soils, and sometimes on the rich virgin chernozem. In springtime the hillsides in some districts of the woodland region are covered with a solid red carpet of extremely fragrant flowers of the daphne. This plant is found in many gardens in America.

At present almost the whole woodland region is under cultivation; patches of grassland are all plowed up, the forests have been removed, and the clearings are also turned to agricultural use. The staple crops of the European part of the region are rye, oats, and wheat, in the order of their importance. In the Western Siberian woodland, however, wheat predominates. Millet (*Panicum milleaceum*) is grown in Voronezh Province, near the Volga and in the Bashkir area. Buckwheat is also grown in large quantity. Corn is cultivated chiefly in Moldavia and in the western part of the Ukraine. Peas (*Pisum sativum*) are raised in the Ukraine. Lentils (*Lens esculenta*) are grown only occasionally. Emmer wheat (*Triticum dicoccum*), formerly grown on both sides of the Volga, is now almost entirely replaced by summer wheat. Hemp is cultivated as a source of both oil and fiber. Sunflower, an American plant introduced into Russia in the last century, grows very well on the rich black soil and is cultivated over very large areas for the oil. Sunflower seed oil is one of the main sources of fat for the population of the Soviet Union.

Of vegetables, the favorite in the Ukraine is the table beet. Farther east cabbage predominates. Sugar beet is considered a very suitable crop for the not-too-cold and at the same time not-too-dry woodland region. It is cultivated chiefly in the Ukraine and in the Kursk Province of Russia.

Tomatoes are gaining in popularity in the woodland region. Melons are grown in the southern area. Wine grapes are grown in Moldavia, although in its northern part the vines are occasionally killed by cold.

Of fruit trees in the Ukrainian woodland, cherry is the most common, followed by the apple, pear, and plum. Commercial apple growing extends as far east as the River Volga. In the Western Siberian woodland fruit growing is still in an experimental stage. With some precautions certain varieties of apples, and perhaps cherries, apparently can be grown in the southern part of the region.

Animal Life

Animals found in the woodland region are either forest animals or prairie animals. There are no distinctive woodland animals. Before the woodland became densely populated, bear, moose, and roebuck were common in the forests. The now extinct wild horse (*Equus gmelini*) was still numerous in the second half of the eighteenth century. Previously the saiga antelope (*Saiga tatarica*) was plentiful, but this animal is no longer found in the region. It became extinct there in the middle of the last century but is still numerous in the deserts of Middle Asia. Wild cattle (*Bos taurus primigenius*) became extinct at least 300 years ago.

Among the prairie animals found in the region are marmot (*Marmota bobac*) and ground squirrel (*Citellus citellus* in the western part, and *Citellus suslicus guttatus* in the eastern part). Jumping mouse (*Alactaga jaculus*) is a rare inhabitant east of the River Dnieper. Desman, a mole-like, aquatic, insectivorous animal (*Desmana moschata*), is trapped in the Don basin. The original beaver (*Castor fiber*) became extinct long ago. Those planted in 1886 in the River Voronezh have established themselves in the vicinity and spread to nearby places.

Roebuck (deer) feels at home in the woodland; when not disturbed by man it prefers to graze in the open areas. Apparently, before the intrusion of man, roebuck grazed in the tall grasses of the southern Russian prairies. In the Asiatic part of the woodland the elk (*Cervus*) is completely exterminated, although it was found here in appreciable numbers rather recently. Roebuck, however, has not only survived but has even become more numerous. In places in the Siberian woodland marmot is still numerous.

Man's interference with the wild life of this densely populated region has brought considerable changes. The bison has been completely annihilated; the beaver has been saved only by drastic conservation measures; the stag has been crowded out to the less populated parts of Polesie; the forest marten has considerably decreased in number. The change in composition of the fauna has been caused not necessarily by direct extermination of the animals (except of the bison) but rather by the changes that man has made in the environment: virgin forests were replaced with fields and pastures, and the birds and animals have been deprived of their habitat. The removal of forests has invited some animals and birds from the adjacent prairie; such prairie species as European hare (*Lepus europeus*) and the common partridge (*Perdix perdix*) occur now throughout the woodland region of European Russia, even penetrating into the adjacent parts of the taiga.

Considerable damage is done to the pine forests of the region by the *Dendrolimus pini* moth; both conifers and broadleaf trees fall prey to another destructive moth, *Ocneria monacha*.* In oak forests is found an interesting beetle, *Lucanus cervus*, commonly called the stag beetle.

Birds of the region, such as nightingale (*Luscinia luscinia*), turtle dove (*Streptopelia turtur*), and oriole (*Oriolus oriolus*), are of a western European origin. The great bustard (*Otis tarda*) is not uncommon on the prairie in the southern part of the region.

The woodland region of European Russia is famous for its two strains of domestic horses: a draft horse, called Bitiug, and a harness horse known as Orel racer, named after the city of Orel, where that breed was developed in the eighteenth century.

The hogs of the region are of primitive European stock. Because of the relatively mild climate and abundance of grain, poultry raising is rather widespread. The chickens are of local stock, rather poor egg producers, and not too good as meat. However, they are very sturdy stock. In the Orel Province a breed of especially fine-crowing roosters has been developed.†

* Closely related to gypsy moth.

† L. S. Berg, *Geographic Zones of the USSR*, 3rd ed., Moscow, 1947, p. 386. Recent information on animal husbandry may be found in Marvin Klemme's

In the southern part of the region turkey raising is practiced on a small scale.

People

The woodland region of eastern Europe is located between Russia and the Ukraine, so that its northern part is populated by Russians and its southern part by Ukrainians. In the vicinity of the Urals the woodland cuts through the Bashkir country. In western Siberia the woodland region is located along the northern border of Kazakhstan. The early settlers were Russians and the later ones Ukrainians; both were agricultural colonists. At present the Siberian woodland is undergoing a period of intensive industrialization and is experiencing a great influx of urban population.

book, *An American Grazier Goes Abroad*, The Desert News Press, Salt Lake City, Utah, 1940.

Chapter 13

Prairie Region

In American geographical literature by the term prairie is meant an area of tall grasses, whereas the Russian name steppe is applied to the short-grass region.* In Russian literature, as well as in common parlance, however, the word steppe, or rather stiep (plural stiepi), means both a tall-grass land where the soil is rich and the vegetation is luxurious,† and a short-grass land where the soil is poor and the vegetation is scant. In this book any extensive grassland areas, other than meadows, are called steppes, and the terms prairie and steppe are used interchangeably. A steppe is defined as a more or less flat area covered with herbaceous vegetation, developed on the chernozem type of soil, and containing trees only along the rivers.

The prairie region is located south of the woodland region, and in the European part of the country it extends to the shores of the Black Sea and the Azov Sea. In the North Caucasian region the steppes extend as far south as Krasnodar and Grozny, i.e., to the foothills of the Caucasian Mountains. From Grozny the boundary line turns north northwest until it reaches the Don, and then it turns to Stalingrad and passes somewhat south of Uralsk. East and south of this line the area adjacent to the Caspian Sea is in the semidesert and desert regions. (Map 3, V.)

In Asia the southern limit of the prairie region extends from Uralsk southeast towards Aktyubinsk and then along the 50th parallel to Semipalatinsk and the foothills of the Altai Mountains. Patches of steppe are found farther east in the upper reaches of the Yenisei and in the Transbaikal region. Steppe areas occur occasionally outside of the prairie region—in semidesert and in the mountains, generally where precipitation is too light to support forest growth, yet sufficient to maintain grass cover.

* See, for instance, Finch and Trewartha, *Elements of Geography*, McGraw-Hill Book Company, New York, 1942, p. 512.
† See p. 129. Even daylily fields are called steppes. See p. 295.

134

Climate

The prairie region, being located farther south than the woodland, has a warmer climate. Summers are hot and dry; precipitation varies from 17 inches to 12 inches. In parts adjacent to the semidesert region it may drop to 8 inches. Most of the precipitation falls in the form of rain. The snow cover in winter is not very deep; in the northern part of the European steppes it is from 7 to 10 inches, whereas near the Black Sea it is 3 or 4 inches. The potential evaporation is considerable, actually exceeding precipitation. At Semipalatinsk, where the precipitation amounts to 11 inches, the evaporation is 33 inches. Summer droughts, often accompanied by dry wind, known as Sukhovei (i.e., dry blower), are frequent. They cause a great deal of damage to the grain fields.

In the steppes of Western Siberia, winters are especially cold and long. The average January temperatures may be as low as 2°F, and

TABLE 9. TEMPERATURE AND PRECIPITATION AT TWO STATIONS IN THE PRAIRIE REGION

Jan.	Feb.	Mar.	Apr.	May	June	July	Aug.	Sept.	Oct.	Nov.	Dec.	Year

Saratov, elevation 197 feet, eastern Europe
Temperature, degrees Fahrenheit — Mean

| 11 | 12 | 22 | 42 | 58 | 66 | 70 | 68 | 56 | 42 | 28 | 16 | 41 |

Precipitation, inches — Total

| 1.1 | 0.8 | 0.8 | 1.5 | 1.2 | 1.6 | 2.1 | 1.5 | 1.1 | 1.5 | 1.4 | 2.1 | 16.7 |

Akmolinsk, elevation 1148 feet, Western Siberia
Temperature, degrees Fahrenheit — Mean

| 2 | 4 | 12 | 34 | 56 | 66 | 70 | 65 | 53 | 35 | 20 | 8 | 34.5 |

Precipitation, inches — Total

| 0.8 | 0.7 | 0.8 | 0.7 | 1.2 | 2.2 | 1.4 | 1.5 | 1.0 | 1.3 | 0.8 | 0.7 | 13.1 |

occasionally the temperature drops to 60°F below zero. Table 9 gives temperature and precipitation data for Saratov (eastern Europe) and Akmolinsk (Western Siberia).

Topography

The crystalline shield found in the southern part of European Russia appears on the surface in the prairie region only near the Azov Sea and also in places where rivers cut their courses into it through sedimentary deposits. Where the River Dnieper cuts into the crystalline rocks, dropping about 110 feet within a distance of 40 miles, it forms a series of rapids.

Between the Dnieper and the Azov heights the crystalline rocks are located at a considerable depth, being covered with more recent sedimentary deposits. The Donetz Heights,* an island of woodland in the steppe region, are located northeast of the Azov.

Considerable deposits of coal are found in the Donetz Heights. In two places in the steppes rich deposits of iron are found near Krivoi Rog (i.e., Crooked Horn) on the Dnieper.

Extensive sandy areas are located east of the low reaches of the Dnieper. The country adjacent to the Black Sea and the Azov Sea is flat, though the monotony of the relief is interrupted by the valleys of several large rivers. These rivers derive their water from the northern parts of Russia. In the prairie region they have very few tributaries; therefore, the drainage pattern of the country is poorly developed. The country farther east in the Don region is dissected by ravines and is rather hilly in appearance.

The Volga Heights † in the prairie region have the form of a plateau. At the 51st parallel the elevations reach over 2000 feet, but farther south they decrease considerably; the watershed divide between the Don and the Volga is only 350 to 400 feet above sea level.

The Mugodjars (Mugodjary) are a low continuation of the Ural Mountains. Elevations here are very low. The Mugodjars are formed by two chains of low mountains. The western chain reaches about a 2000-foot elevation, whereas to the east the elevation is lower. These low hills are covered with prairie vegetation, and their southern extremity reaches into the semidesert region. In deep gullies there are some groves of aspen, birch, and willow.

---

* In Russian, Donetski Kriazh; kriazh means a flat-topped highland.

† The Russian name Pri-Volzhskaia Vozvyshennost means Pre-Volga Elevation.

East of the Volga the topography was formed by tectonic uplifting and is from 300 to 600 feet in elevation. It is called Obshchii Syrt.*

During the Quaternary period the Caspian Sea was connected with the Black Sea by a strait. At present this Quaternary strait appears as the Manych depression with a divide 85 feet above the level of the Black Sea. West of the divide the depression drains through a system of brackish or salty lakes to the River Don near the Azov Sea. The area east of the divide is drained by the Eastern Manych River, which disappears in the sands near the course of the River Kuma. A 364-mile irrigation-navigation canal (under construction in 1950) will connect the Black Sea with the Caspian Sea.

The northern part of the prairies in the Asiatic part of the Soviet Union belongs topographically to the Western Siberian lowlands and is extremely flat. Farther south, however, the steppes occupy a part of the Kazakh folded land—an area reduced by erosion into a series of separate low hills and ridges rising from 250 to 350 feet above the main part of the territory.† In some places, chiefly in the south, chains of severely eroded old mountains reach considerable heights, sometimes as much as 3000 to 4000 feet or even higher.

Geologically the Kazakh folded land is of the same origin as the northern part of the Tien Shan system. It is composed predominantly of Lower Paleozoic rocks; there are some Upper Paleozoic foldings and Tertiary dislocations of a fault type.

Soils and Vegetation

Soils of the northern part of the prairie region in Europe are of the chernozem type, containing about 8 to 10 per cent of humus. In the southern part of the region, where the climate is drier and vegetation is poorer, the humus content may drop to 5 or even 3 per cent; accordingly, soils here are lighter in color and are known as chestnut-colored soils. These soils are lumpy in texture as compared with the crumbly chernozem; the lower layers of the humus horizon lack the friability of the chernozem and are more packed.

In Western Siberia chernozems of the prairie region are poorer than those of the European part of the region and the chernozem area is

* Obshchii is a Russian word meaning, in this case, the united; syrt is a Turkic word meaning high plateau. The name is very common in the descriptive geography of Middle Asia.

† In Russian literature this territory is designated as melkosopochnick, a compound word meaning an area dotted with scattered small hillocks.

not too wide. Chestnut-colored soils are the most common in the Western Siberian prairies.

The vegetation of the prairie does not form a compact, continuous sod so typical of the dicotyledon steppe of the woodland region. It consists of drought-resistant grass species: feathergrass, needlegrass— both of the genus *Stipa;* fescue; and June grass. These form separate tufts or bunches,* leaving some bare ground between individual plants. Generally, however, the vegetative cover of the prairies is relatively dense. In early spring and late fall mosses and algae appear among the dry tufts of bunchgrass.

In the European steppes, spring vegetation consisting of tulips (*Tulipa schrenki*)—with their multicolored yellow, rose, but predominantly red flowers—*Iris pumila*, valeriana, star-of-Bethlehem (*Ornithogalum tenuifolium*), milkvetch, yellow buttercups (*Ranunculus*), and purple hyacinth (*Hyacinthus sarmaticus*) appears at the end of April. About the middle of May dark red peonies (*Paeonia tenuifolia*) open, soon to be followed by the blue flowers of the sage (*Salvia nutans*). In June the prairies appear as an endless undulating sea of silvery feathergrass (*Stipa stenophylla, S. lessingiana*), admixed with other, less conspicuous grasses such as fescue (*Festuca sulcata*), June grass (*Koeleria gracilis*), and crested wheatgrass (*Agropyron cristatum*). At the beginning of July the steppe vegetation is at its best. Towards the end of the summer needlegrass (*Stipa capillata, S. tirsa*) begins to dominate.

The time of flowering of the different species and their importance in the composition of the vegetative cover vary, of course, from one place to another. In the southern part of the region the growing season begins earlier than in the northern part. Generally speaking, however, feathergrass and needlegrass (i.e., several species of the genus *Stipa*, called in Russian the kovyl) are the main components of the steppe vegetation. The rest are subordinate, and even showy flowers of rather numerous species of dicotyledons are scattered and lost in the mass of prairie grass.

Most of the prairie region is under cultivation, and the patches of virgin steppe as they appeared before the intrusion of man are found only in a few preserves, of which Askania Nova † is the best known.

Closer to the Black Sea and in the areas of the North Caucasian region the climate is drier, the soil contains less humus, and the vege-

---

* Hence the American name bunchgrass for such species as fescue and June grass.

† The name of this once privately owned preserve has been changed to Chapli.

tation, mostly grasses, is relatively poor. In some places in the prairie are found brushfields of drought-resisting shrubs, such as ground cherry, Russian peashrub (*Caragana frutex*), spiraea, and Russian almond (*Amygdalis nana* or *Prunus tenella*).*

The Western Siberian prairies may be divided into two types: (1) the northern needlegrass-feathergrass-dicotyledon type and (2) the southern needlegrass-fescue type. The first is found on the chernozem soils, and its dominant plant is needlegrass (*Stipa capillata*), mixed with feathergrass (*Stipa Zalesski, S. stenophylla*), fescue (*Festuca sulcata*), and desert oats (*Avena desertorum*). The admixture of dicotyledonous plants, although not so generous as in the woodland meadow type of steppe, is nevertheless quite pronounced.

Among the leguminous † species found are sickle alfalfa (*Medicago falcata*) and milkvetch (*Astragalus macropus*). Other dicotyledons are: *Jurinea linearifolia*, tuberous Jerusalem sage (*Phlomis tuberosa*), thyme (*Thymus marshallianus*), cinquefoil (*Potentilla bifurca*), veronica (*Veronica incana*), and several species of wormwood, such as *Artemisia glauca* and *A. latifolia*.

In low places where there is more moisture, dicotyledons almost dominate over the grasses. On patches of alkaline soil are found licorice (*Glycyrrhiza uralensis*), wheatgrass (*Agropyron ramosum*), prostrate summer cypress (*Kochia prostrata*), and Siberian statice (*Limonium gmelini*). Occasional brushfields, mostly found near the northern boundary of the steppe, consist of the same species as the shrubby patches of the east European steppe, i.e., ground cherry, Russian peashrub, and Russian almond.

In the southern part of the Western Siberian steppes, where soils are poorer and contain only 3 to 4 per cent of humus, dicotyledons are almost absent. In spring there may be found some short-lived flowering annual plants on the rocky outcrops. Wormwood, or sagebrush ‡ (*Artemisia frigida, A. incana*), is found, but the dominant plants of the south are needlegrass (*Stipa capillata, S. sareptana*) and June grass. The occurrence of feathergrass is limited. These needlegrass-June grass flatlands stretch for many miles without variation in the vegetative cover. Barley (*Hordeum secalinum*) and licorice grow on the alkali soils.

* Several drought-resistant shrubs of the southern Russian steppes have been used for planting on the prairies of the United States.

† Leguminous plants have the capacity for the fixation of atmospheric nitrogen. Their role in the ecology of any plant community is thus very important.

‡ A composite; not to be confused with sage (*Salvia*), which belongs to the mint family.

In the flood meadow vegetation, along the river courses, quackgrass (*Agropyron repens*) occupies an important place.

Apparently, Russian prairies were treeless even before the intrusion of man. All Russian geographers and botanists agree on that. As to the causes for the absence of woody vegetation, except, of course, along the rivers, opinions differ. Some consider lack of precipitation to be of paramount importance, whereas others emphasize the high concentration of various salts in the soil, such as sodium chloride and sodium sulfate. Berg * considers that the absence of forests in the steppes is a zonal phenomenon. It is caused by the climate of the region; more specifically, by the dryness of the air, a high rate of evaporation, and a relatively light precipitation.

Forests are found in the European steppes only in the immediate vicinity of rivers. Along the river courses grow groves of willow, alder, and cottonwood, and on higher places maple, elm, and evonymus may be found. On the slopes along the west bank of the Dnieper grow shrubby elms, pear, hawthorn, wild apple, oak, and blackthorn (*Prunus spinosa*). Occasionally, sandy terraces above the rivers are occupied by common pine (*Pinus sylvestris*) stands,† accompanied by such northern species as cowberry (*Vaccinium vitis-idaea*). A scrubby savin juniper (*Juniperus sabina* var. *radians*) may be found on the sands of the Don region. On the flood meadows quackgrass (*Agropyron repens*) is prominent.

In Western Siberia patches of birch and common pine forests penetrate rather deeply into the northern part of the steppe. Whereas birch groves may be considered a part of the woodland region, the pine forests are truly intraregional. Extensive strips of pine forests are found on sands in the Kulunda steppe, east of the Irtysh. Many northern plants, including sphagnum moss, the myrtle whortleberry (*Vaccinium myrtillus*), and cowberry are found there. Some pine woods are also found between Semipalatinsk and Barnaul. It is possible that these pine forests have not advanced from the north but rather descended from the Altai Mountains, which are located to the southeast.

Animal Life

Before the intrusion of man, the virgin prairies of eastern Europe maintained a large and diversified population of wild animals, includ-

---

* *Priroda SSSR*, 2nd ed., 1938, p. 94.

† Pine forests are intraregional and may be found from the northern taiga to the prairie, as well as in the mountains.

ing wild cattle (*Bos taurus primigenius*), saiga antelope (*Saiga tatar-ica*), wild horse (*Equus gmelini*), marmot (*Marmota bobac*), stag (*Cervus elaphus*), and boar (*Sus scrofa attila*). Wild boar still lives along the lower reaches of some rivers. Roebuck (*Capreolus*) still occurs occasionally in the forest areas of the region. At present, however, the steppe is extensively cultivated, and wild life has become much depleted. Wild horses and cattle have been completely exterminated, antelope migrated into the semidesert, and the marmot also disappeared. Bats do not adapt themselves very well to the prairie landscape and cannot be called typical steppe animals. At present the steppes of the Ukraine are populated by dormouse, hamster, mole-rat, ground squirrel (*Citellus pygmaeus, C. suslicus*), prairie fitch (*Putorius eversmanni*), jumping mouse (*Alactaga jaculus*), and such birds as lark (*Melanocorypha calandra*), rose-colored starling (*Pastor roseus*), demoiselle crane (*Grus virgo*), common partridge (*Perdix perdix*), and bustard, or strepet (*Otis tetrax orientalis*). Waterfowl consists of ducks, pelicans, and herons. Reptiles are represented by a common lizard (*Lacerta agilis exigua*), the prairie viper (*Vipera revardi*), and some harmless snakes (*Coluber, Elaphe*). Locust (*Locusta migratoria*) and several species of grasshoppers cause some damage to the crops of the region.

The animal life of the Western Siberian and Kazakhstan prairies also is quite sparse and is very similar to that of the eastern European prairies, although some Asiatic species appear here. Jumping mouse (*Alactaga saliens, A. elater*) and ground squirrel are common. Marmot also is still found. In the prairies of Kazakhstan the human influence on the animal life is not so noticeable as in the European part of the country, although the wild ass and saiga antelope no longer occur in the Kazakhstan steppes. Waterfowl (geese, ducks) are found in abundance in the numerous shallow lakes of the Asiatic prairies. Other birds of the Western Siberian prairies include cranes, bustards (*Otis tarda*), larks (*Melanocorypha leucoptera*), eagles (*Aquila heliaca, A. nepalensis*), and hawks (*Buteo rufinus*). In the pine forests that penetrate rather deeply into the Siberian steppe one may find a mixture of the prairie and the taiga birds.

People

Most of the prairie region of eastern Europe is populated by Ukrainians. In the western part of the region live Moldavians. Near the

Black Sea dwell some Greeks and Bulgars. The Russian population of the region is considerable. Along the Don and the Volga, Russians predominate.

In Western Siberia the population also is chiefly Russian, although there is a considerable admixture of Ukrainians and Kazakhs.

Chapter 14

Semidesert Region

The semidesert region, sometimes called the zone of dry steppes, occupies only a small area in the European part * of the Soviet Union in the lower Volga region. It includes the southeastern part of the Manych-Kuma depression and, roughly speaking, the area between the Don and the Volga, as far north as the 50th parallel. The area around the Volga delta and between this river and the Ural River, near the Caspian Sea, is considered by some geographers (Berg) as a part of the semidesert region, whereas others (Suslov) include it in the zone of deserts. East of the Ural River the southern boundary of the semidesert zone extends latitudinally from the upper reaches of the River Emba to Lake Zaisan, located in the southeastern corner of Kazakhstan, near the Altai Mountains. (Map 3, VI.)

Climate

Table 10 gives figures on the temperature and precipitation for Turgai at approximately 63°30′ longitude and 49°40′ latitude, at an elevation of 426 feet. Turgai is located in the heart of the semidesert area east of the Mugodjar Mountains and north of the Aral Sea.

TABLE 10. TEMPERATURE AND PRECIPITATION AT TURGAI

Jan.	Feb.	Mar.	Apr.	May	June	July	Aug.	Sept.	Oct.	Nov.	Dec.	Year
Temperature, degrees Fahrenheit												Mean
0	2	15	40	60	70	75	70	58	40	24	10	39
Precipitation, inches												Total
0.7	0.6	0.5	0.7	0.8	1.2	1.1	0.9	0.7	0.9	1.0	0.7	9.8

* In this book the River Ural is taken as the boundary between Europe and Asia.

As a whole the climate of the region is characterized by very cold winters and hot summers. Winter temperatures may drop to −40°F in the western part and to −57°F in the eastern part. The severe cold is accompanied by blizzards blowing from the northeast. The snow cover, except where accumulated by the wind, is scanty: about 25 inches in the north and between 7 and 8 inches in the south. The lack of snow leaves the grazing land open throughout the winter. Spring is very short; often winter cold is replaced by summer heat within the space of a few days. Summers are dry and hot; temperatures may occasionally reach 104°F. The prevailing summer winds are from the north and northeast. Though not so strong as the winter winds, they are exceedingly dry. In the fall of the year the temperature drops more gradually than it rises in the spring; therefore, the autumn period is longer.

The potential evaporation is great; it may reach 80 inches a year. Precipitation is light, not exceeding 12 inches a year and most of it occurring in summer in the form of cloudbursts. For that reason the runoff is great and the penetration of water into the soil, with its scanty vegetation, is slight. The climate is not conducive to agriculture, and most of the region is devoted to grazing. Where crops are grown irrigation is required.

Topography

The Volga Heights below Stalingrad change into a low plateau of meridional extension known as Ergheni (plural). The highest points of the plateau do not exceed 600 feet above sea level. In the east the plateau descends abruptly to the Caspian lowland, most of which is located below sea level.* The Caspian lowland was under water in the Würm glaciation period. Bench marks showing below-sea-level figures extend up the course of the Volga to a point between Kamyshin and Saratov.

East of Stalingrad are two large salt lakes—Elton and Baskunchak—at elevations of 57.4 feet and 59.0 feet below sea level, respectively. The surrounding country is about 30 to 45 feet above sea level. East of these lakes are found extensive sandy areas which, under uncontrolled grazing, have lost their vegetative cover and become moving sand dunes. Still farther east, between the Caspian lowland and the Mugodjar Mountains, is the Emba plateau, composed of Cretaceous and

* The Caspian Sea is 85 feet below sea level.

Tertiary rocks.   Characteristic of the Emba Plateau are salt domes, which are not found farther east.

The Mugodjars in the semidesert region are formed by two low, much eroded chains of hills, rising above the surrounding country 650 to 850 feet.   The hills are covered with a scanty growth of grass. Only in deep gulches may birch, chokecherry, aspen, and willow be found.   The slopes of these gulches may be covered with some xerophytic shrubs, such as blackthorn, peashrub, and Russian almond.

The Turgai tableland is located between the Mugodjars in the west and the Ulu Tau Mountains in the east (elevation 3729 feet).   In the central part, the tableland is depressed to absolute elevations of 250 to 325 feet.   During the Tertiary period this depression was under water, connecting the Western Siberian Lower Tertiary sea with the Turan Sea.   West and east of the central depression the elevations are higher, and on the watershed divide between the Turgai, of the inner basin, and the Ishim, which belongs to the Ob system, elevations reach 950 to 980 feet.   In the southern part the tableland is only 600 to 650 feet above sea level.   The whole area is composed of Oligocene (Tertiary) marine sediments and continental Miocene deposits.   Later the Tertiary sedimentary rocks were subjected to intensive water erosion and still later to wind erosion.   Thus the original, flat, plateau-like area was gradually cut by erosion so that now segments of the tableland are separated by rather broad depressions, remnants of old erosion channels.   Geologically the Turgai tableland differs a great deal from adjacent regions.

The Kazakh folded land is located between the Ulu Tau Mountains in the west and the Altai system in the east.   In the north it merges into the Western Siberian lowland and in the south extends to Lake Balkhash.   The northern part of the area is formed by low hills, described in the preceding chapter.   In the central part relatively high mountain chains—Ulu Tau, Karkaralinsk, and Chinghis Tau (highest peak 3080 feet)—extend from west to east.   These are of Paleozoic origin.   In the east the bordering mountains—the Tarbagatai and the Saur—rise high above the Zaisan depression, almost reaching the line of permanent snow.   The Kazakh folded land is very rich in minerals, especially copper; tin, nickel, tungsten, and manganese are also mined here.

The rivers of the semidesert region belong mostly to the inner basin. The larger ones, such as the Turgai and the Nura, flow throughout the year.   The smaller rivers, in their lower courses, are dry during summer.   In the spring of the year, however, their beds are filled with

running water. Lakes are quite numerous; some of them contain fresh
water, but the majority are either saline or alkaline.

Lake Zaisan is located in the eastern part of the semidesert region
in a fault trough surrounded by mountains. It is over 60 miles long
and about 15 to 20 miles wide and covers an area of some 700 square
miles. It is rather shallow, the average depths reaching only 15 feet.
The River Kara * Irtysh flows into the eastern part of the lake and,
after leaving the lake in the northern part, assumes the name Irtysh.
Lake Zaisan has certain possibilities as a large, natural reservoir for
future irrigation and power development.

Soils and Vegetation

In the semidesert region where rainfall is deficient the underlying
parent rocks begin to play a considerable part in the soil-forming
processes. More compact sediments, such as clays, are, as a rule, more
alkaline than the porous materials, such as sand and loess. Most soils
of the region belong to the light-chestnut type. They contain some
sodium and accordingly are somewhat alkaline. The humus content
of these soils is very low: from 1 to 3 per cent.

Besides this general type of light-chestnut soil in the semidesert
region, patches of alkaline soils, so-called solonchak † and solonets ‡
soils, frequently occur. Solonchak is the name given to an alkaline
soil containing easily soluble salts of sodium, calcium, and magnesium.
These salts may be carbonates, such as calcium carbonate, sulfates
(magnesium sulfate), and even chlorides (sodium chloride). Soil of
this type is formed in depressions where alkaline ground waters rise
by capillary attraction and evaporate from the surface, leaving salts
in the upper layers of soil or even as a crust on the surface. A soil
from which soluble salts, except sodium, are leached is called solonets.
Sodium remains absorbed by the soil particles and is gradually released
into the soil solution, increasing its alkalinity and thus causing leaching of humus. Soils from which both salts and humus are leached
are called solodi.

The solonchak soils are not well suited to agriculture because of
their alkalinity. Solonets soils, however, may be reclaimed by re-
placing sodium with calcium, i.e., by application of lime or gypsum.
Although the solonets and solonchak soils may be found in prairies,

* Turkic for black.
† Sol is Russian for salt.
‡ Both of these terms are used internationally in the soil science literature.

in woodlands, and even in the taiga region, in the Yakut area, they are more common in the semidesert and desert regions of the country.*

Vegetation of the semidesert region is fairly uniform all the way from the lower reaches of the Volga to the foothills of the Altai. The predominant type of vegetation is wormwood (*Artemisia*).† In the northern part of the region there are still a great many of the prairie species, such as feathergrass and needlegrass, June grass, wheatgrass (*Agropyron desertorum*), and especially fescue, but the wormwood-fescue type is the most common. On the slightly alkaline clay loam, white wormwood (*Artemisia maritima*) is common, whereas, on the more alkaline clay soils, black wormwood (*Artemisia pauciflora*) dominates. This type of vegetation is sometimes called in Russian literature dry steppes. In America this type of grassland probably would be called the steppe proper in contradistinction to tall-grass land, or prairie. As it was pointed out on p. 134, the terminology of grassland is rather confusing.

In the southern part of the region grass species gradually disappear, and there appear several genera of the family Chenopodiaceae, of which saltbush (*Atriplex*) species are most common.

Spring vegetation consists, as is usual in arid countries, of flowering annuals that complete their life cycle before the ground gets too dry. There are also a few perennials, such as tulips and buttercups, which possess underground storage organs.

Along the main chains of the Mugodjar Mountains is found prairie-like vegetation consisting of feathergrass (*Stipa kirghizorum, S. lessingiana*), fescue, and *Artemisia austriaca*. Along the foothills the wormwood-fescue type is common.

In the Turgai tableland, with its lower elevation and more alkaline soil, the vegetation is of a halophytic character. In the northern part of the tableland, the plant life consists of dry prairie species, such as fescue, feathergrass, desert wheatgrass (*Agropyron desertorum*), and white wormwood (*Artemisia maritima*).

* In America, desert soils containing sodium, such as sodium carbonate, are known as black alkali; those containing calcium or magnesium are called white alkali. For details see *Diagnosis and Improvement of Saline and Alkaline Soils*, U. S. Regional Salinity Laboratory, Riverside, California, 1947.

† European species of *Artemisia* are generally called wormwood, whereas the name sagebrush is retained for the *Artemisia* of the western part of the United States. The name wormwood is applied to the artemisias of the prairies and semi-deserts, but for the desert region and for the mountain regions of Middle Asia and southern Siberia the name sagebrush seems to be more descriptive.

Along the rivers the common wormwood-grass-saltbush type of vegetation is found, together with *Anabasis salsa* and a very useful coarse grass, *Lasiogrostis splendens,* which is employed throughout the arid part of Soviet Asia and beyond for making mats.

In the Kazakh folded land the prairie-like vegetation consists of needlegrass, feathergrass, wormwood, and fescue, whereas the higher watershed divides are covered with thickets of peashrub (*Caragana frutex*) and small birch groves. In deep gulches one may find such shrubs as viburnum, hawthorn, chokecherry, birch, aspen, and willow. On mountains common pine forests are occasionally found. Black-wormwood (*Artemisia pauciflora*), giant fennel (*Ferula caspia*), *Statice gmelini, Camphorosma,* and saltbush grow on the solonets alkaline soils. On solonchak soils, besides blackwormwood and *Statice suffruticosa,* many species of the saltbush family (Chenopodiaceae) appear, such as *Halocnemum strobilaceum, Nitraria schoeberi,* summer cypress (*Kochia*), and seepweed (*Suaeda*).

Animal Life

The animal life of the semidesert region is characterized by the presence of several species of ground squirrel (*Citellus fulvus, C. pigmaeus,* and others), jumping mice, and other rodents. Kit fox (*Vulpes corsac*) occurs throughout the region. Saiga antelope is found in the western part of the region, but it is not plentiful. Waterfowl inhabit the delta regions of the larger rivers. The delta of the Volga was especially rich in waterfowl, but early in this century there began a wholesale extermination of birds and even their eggs. Recently, however, a bird sanctuary was established near Astrakhan. Cormorant (*Phalacrocorax carbo*) is perhaps the most common bird in the Volga delta, where it may be found together with geese, egret, and a gallinule (*Porphyrio poliocephalus*) noted for its brilliant plumage. Wolf, lynx, ferret, and ermine are common in the mountains. In the reed thickets near Lake Zaisan is found wild boar. Reptiles are numerous. The Caspian Sea is very rich in fish.

The most important domestic animals are sheep and goats; cattle, horses, and camels are of secondary importance. Hogs are kept only by the Russian settlers; the native Kazakhs, being Mohammedans, do not keep hogs. On the other hand, horse flesh is preferred to beef by the native population. Fermented mare's milk is a favorite drink of the Kazakhs and of many other Soviet Asiatic peoples. The Kazakh horse is of Mongolian stock and is very hardy.

People

The semidesert region in its western part is populated by the Kalmyks, whatever is left of them after the abolishing of their republic located between the Lower Volga and the Caucasian foothills. Along the Volga the predominant population is Russian. Most of the region, however, is located in the land of the Kazakhs. The Russian population of the Kazakh semidesert is considerable, consisting of some settlers but chiefly of industrial workers.

Chapter 15

Desert Region

The deserts of the Soviet Union are located in the Asiatic part of the country—between the Caspian Sea in the west and the border mountains in the east and south—formerly known as Russian Turkestan and now generally referred to as Middle Asia (Map 3, VII). The northern boundary line of the deserts begins near the Caspian Sea, approximately at the 45th parallel, and then extends northeast, following the rim of the Ust Urt Plateau; northeast of the Aral Sea it includes the Kara Kum sands * and extends east, running somewhat north of Lake Balkhash to the foothills of the Tarbagatai Mountains and the international border. There are also patches of desert in the low reaches of the Kura-Araks basin, west of the Caspian Sea. These will be mentioned in the description of the Caucasian region.

Climate

Table 11 shows data for the temperature and precipitation for three stations located within the desert region: Kazalinsk, on the lower Syr Darya, in the northern part of the region; Tashkent, in the middle part; and Bairam Ali, in the southern part, in the Merv (Mary) oasis, located in the low reaches of the Murghab River.†

The climate of the region is extremely continental, with very hot summers, relatively cold winters, a great range in annual and daily temperatures, and a lack of precipitation. The deserts of Middle Asia are the hottest part of the Soviet Union. Their summer temperatures are comparable to those of North Africa.

At Kazalinsk the mean July temperature is 79°F; at Tashkent, 82°F; and at Bairam Ali, about 86°F. The absolute maximum temperature recorded at Kazalinsk was 108°F; at Bairam Ali it was 114°F. The highest temperature ever recorded in Middle Asia was 122°F at Ter-

---

* Not to be confused with the more extensive Kara Kum sands south of the Aral Sea and west of the River Amu Darya.

† The Murghab flows from the Paropamisus Mountains of Afghanistan—not to be confused with the River Murgab of the Pamir region (see p. 167).

TABLE 11. TEMPERATURE AND PRECIPITATION AT THREE STATIONS
OF THE DESERT REGION

Jan.	Feb.	Mar.	Apr.	May	June	July	Aug.	Sept.	Oct.	Nov.	Dec.	Year
				Northern part, Kazalinsk, elevation 206 feet								
				Temperature, degrees Fahrenheit								Mean
11	14	29	49	66	74	79	74	62	46	31	19	46
				Precipitation, inches								Total
0.4	0.4	0.5	0.4	0.5	0.3	0.2	0.3	0.3	0.5	0.5	0.5	4.8
				Middle part, Tashkent, elevation 1567 feet								
				Temperature, degrees Fahrenheit								Mean
32	35	46	58	69	78	82	78	67	54	44	36	57
				Precipitation, inches								Total
1.9	1.6	2.6	2.1	1.1	0.6	0.1	Tr.	0.1	1.0	1.4	1.7	14.2
				Southern part, Bairam Ali, elevation 750 feet, 37°40' latitude N								
				Temperature, degrees Fahrenheit								Mean
38	40	48	62	73	82	86	82	70	58	48	36	60
				Precipitation, inches								Total
0.6	0.5	1.5	0.7	0.3	0.1	0	0	Tr.	0.2	0.4	0.5	4.8

mez, in the southern part of the region. The surface of the desert soil, exposed to the sun, may reach a temperature of 175°F. However, the heat does not penetrate deeply below the soil surface, and at a depth of about 3 feet daily fluctuations of temperature are not noticeable.

In the northern part of the desert region winter temperatures are very low; at Kazalinsk the mean January temperature of 11°F is about the same as the mean January temperature at Archangel, located near the White Sea. At Kazalinsk the absolute minimum temperature ever recorded was about 28°F below zero; at Bairam Ali, 14°F below zero. As a whole, winters are much milder in the southern part of the region than around the Aral Sea.

At Kazalinsk the temperature remains above the freezing point for 172 days; and at Bairam Ali, for 215 days. Accordingly, the growing season is much longer in the south (Bairam Ali, 288 days) than the north (Kazalinsk, 204 days). The relative humidity is very low. For instance, in July at Kazalinsk it averages 50 per cent, and at Bairam Ali 30 per cent, though it may occasionally drop to 15, 10, and even 5 per cent.

Cloudy weather in the desert is very rare. The amount of sunshine in Middle Asia is comparable to that of the deserts of the southwest United States. At Bairam Ali the sun shines 94 per cent of the time.

Because of high summer temperatures and the dryness of the air, the potential evaporation of water from the soil and from water surfaces is very great, perhaps 10 times as much as the precipitation. The precipitation in the region is meager, varying from 4 to 8 inches a year. At Kazalinsk and at Bairam Ali it is about 5 inches a year, but in Tashkent, located higher than the two other stations and closer to the mountains, it is over 14 inches a year. From Table 11 it is observed that minimum precipitation occurs in summer. At Bairam Ali no rain falls during July and August and almost none during September. At Tashkent summers are very often entirely rainless.

Winds in the desert region are rather gentle, and still weather is common. In winter the prevailing winds are from the northeast, bringing cold air from Siberia. In summer, when the Siberian high pressure disappears, the winds shift to the northwest. Closer to the mountains the general direction of the winds is often changed by local conditions. In the southern part of the Uzbek country strong winds often blow from Afghanistan, bringing a great deal of dust. Dust is a real curse in Middle Asia. In summer it hangs over the cities, and during windy days the sun is obscured by a dry, dusty, whitish mist. This dust is composed of very fine loess particles and extends upward in the atmosphere as high as 20,000 feet.

At Osh, in the Ferghana Valley, an experiment station dealing with dust and the methods of controlling it has been established.

Topography

The most important characteristic of Middle Asian topography is the absence of mountain barriers in the north which would protect the area from the cold blasts of the Siberian wind. Another equally important feature is the high border range located to the south, which prevents the moist tropical air from penetrating into the region.

Berg divides the desert region into three large parts, or subregions, distinguished by their topography, soil, and vegetation. These subregions are (1) the northern Tertiary plateaux, (2) the sand areas of the central parts, and (3) the loess piedmont plains. Besides these three subregions, a part of the east coastal lowland of the Caspian lies within the desert region. Some parts of this area are even lower than the level of the Caspian Sea itself. The depression Batyr is 426 feet below sea level and 341 feet below the level of the Caspian Sea. This difference in the levels and the low elevation of the divide between the Caspian Sea and the depression—only 16 feet—offers certain possibilities for the development of hydroelectric power in the area.

The desert near the Caspian Sea is rich in oil. The best known oil fields are located on the island of Cheleken, near Krasnovodsk, and at Nebit Dagh (Oil Mountain). Scattered within the Caspian depression are isolated areas of higher elevations, such as Mangyshlak Mountains (1742 feet), Krasnovodsk Plateau (600 to 900 feet), and Big Balkhan (highest point 6117 feet). These uplands were formed during the Mesozoic era and subsequently eroded by water and wind. Little Balkhan, an isolated desert ridge about 2500 feet high, is composed of Tertiary rocks. North of the Krasnovodsk Plateau is a large gulf of the Caspian Sea—Kara Bogaz Gol—where sodium sulfate is obtained from the water in considerable amounts, as it is concentrated by the heat of the desert sun.

The northern subregion of the desert region includes two Tertiary plateaux: Ust Urt in the west and Bet-Pack-Dala in the east. A lesser plateau—Trans-Unghus—lies below the 40th parallel between the 60th meridian and the Amu Darya. Ust Urt Plateau is located between the Caspian Sea and the Aral Sea. The highest portions of the plateau reach 1000 feet above sea level, but generally the elevation is from 650 to 700 feet. The plateau is composed of horizontal Upper Miocene deposits and is well defined by abrupt rims, locally known as chinks, that separate it from the surrounding lowland. The eastern chink at the shores of the Aral Sea stands some 600 feet above the level of the lake.

There is no running water of any kind on the Ust Urt Plateau. Moreover, ground waters are located at considerable depths and are either brackish or saline. In the occasional sandy depressions, such as the Sam sands (elevation 250 to 300 feet) of the northern part of the plateau, water of good quality is found close to the surface.

North of the Aral Sea there are extensive sand areas, mostly covered with sand-binding vegetation. In places, however, where the vegetative cover has been destroyed by overgrazing, sand dunes have developed. The Russians call Bet-Pack-Dala Plateau the Northern Hunger Steppe (Golodnaia Stiep). Elevations here average about 1000 feet, and the plain-like plateau is either flat or gently undulating. The plateau ends in the west near the River Sary Su with cliffs 125 to 200 feet high. It extends as far south as the River Chu. To the east the plateau merges into the Kazakh folded land.

Lake Balkhash has been described previously in Chapter 4.

Sands occupy vast areas in the desert region between the Turkmenia-Iran international border and Lake Balkhash, and between the Aral Sea and the southern mountain ranges. The Kara Kum (black sands) extend southwest of the Amu Darya; northeast of this river lie the Kyzyl Kum (red sands), and farther northeast between the Chu River and the Kara Tau Mountains are the Muyun Kum. Apparently all these sands are of alluvial origin from the ice age, when large rivers, then numerous and now extinct, carried a great deal of sand to the plains and lowlands of Turkestan. The remains of the ancient rivers still exist in the sandy deserts. Of these the Uzboi is the best known. An old river bed connecting a series of depressions through which the waters of the Amu Darya flowed to the Caspian Sea was known by this name. Part of the Amu Darya water drained intermittently through the Uzboi to the Caspian Sea as late as the sixteenth century. Diversion of the Amu Darya waters through the old channel of Uzboi would open very large areas of the Trans-Caspian desert to cultivation and colonization.

The Kara Kum sands occupy an area of over 17,000 square miles. Some 10 per cent of this area consists of alkali depressions and clay flats. The sands are covered with sparse vegetation and are more or less stabilized. However, a small disturbance, such as a rodent burrow, may cause the formation of shifting sands and dunes, locally known as barkhans. The destruction of native vegetation or the cultivation of desert soil near oases may also cause the development of shifting sands. Barkhans are found mostly along the Amu Darya; usually they are 15 to 25 feet high, occasionally reaching 30 feet.

Along the Kopet Dagh foothills there are peculiar clay flats 20 to 25 miles wide and extending for considerable distances. These clay flats, locally known as takyr, in winter are filled with shallow water; in spring they are filled with clay mud; and in summer they appear as dry, hard, perfectly level flats with a shiny hard crust, entirely void of vegetation. Lower depressions, so-called sor or shor, equally extensive, are occupied with alkaline soil of the solonchak type.

The Kyzyl Kum sands are located between the Amu Darya and the Syr Darya. Most of these sands are well stabilized with native vegetation. Takyr clay flats also occupy extensive areas of this region. Occasionally, rather high chains of Paleozoic ridges rise above the sandy plains of the Kyzyl Kum. Ak Tau Mountains, south of the Kyzyl Kum, reach elevations of over 3000 feet. Copper, asbestos, tungsten, and other metals are mined here.

The Muyun Kum sands lie between the Chu River and the Kara Tau Mountains. They extend for a distance of over 300 miles, and their highest elevations reach 1246 feet.

It would be erroneous to assume that the sand deserts of Russian Middle Asia are entirely devoid of water. Several large rivers flow across the desert. Some of them disappear in the sand. The porous underlying strata, composed of Cretaceous and Tertiary deposits, readily absorb water both from the rivers and from the atmosphere. Under these sediments lie Paleozoic strata that are impervious to water. Therefore, enormous quantities of water are stored in these underground reservoirs. Occasionally this water may appear on the surface in the form of springs and lakes. In some places underground layers of water are found under such pressure as to permit construction of Artesian wells.

The plains south of Lake Balkhash are called by the Russians the Seven River Region (Semirechie). They are crossed both by rivers flowing into Lake Balkhash, the Ili River being the largest, and by ancient dry river beds. Extensive sand areas are found in this region.

The piedmont plains occupy the foothills of the southern mountain ranges of Middle Asia. The soil underlying these plains is loess, on which potentially fertile soils have developed. This is a region of an ancient agriculture and of an ancient civilization. In Turkmenia these plains are found at elevations of 300 to 1000 feet.

The Hunger Steppe (Golodnaia Stiep) * is a typical loess piedmont plain situated south of the Kyzyl Kum sands. Its elevations range from

* Not to be confused with another Golodnaia Stiep located west of Lake Balkhash and sometimes called Bet-Pack-Dala Plateau.

750 to 950 feet. This area, with its fertile soil and water from the Syr Darya available for irrigation, has been the scene of intensive reclamation projects.

The rich and densely populated Ferghana Valley is also located in the subregion of the piedmont loess plains. Elevations here are from 1100 to 1640 feet. The valley is surrounded by high mountain ridges. It is about 185 miles long and over 100 wide. Throughout its length flows the River Syr Darya. Several ancient cities are located in the valley, and the southern tributaries of the Syr Darya have been used for irrigation from time immemorial. In 1939 a very ambitious irrigation project was completed, which opened many thousands of acres for cultivation. Oil is being produced in the valley, and some valuable metals are mined.

Soils, Vegetation, and Animal Life

The Tertiary plateaux of the northern part of the desert region have poorly developed soils: the soils are gravelly on the surface and contain only 1 per cent of organic matter. These are the so-called sierozem, or gray, soils. Their calcium carbonate content is high, and they effervesce on the surface, but the amount of carbonates decreases with depth. Sometimes these soils have high alkalinity, and then they approach either a solonchak or even a solonets type when sodium carbonate is in excess. Gypsum is usually found at depths varying from 1 to 4 feet. At any rate these soils are more alkaline than the gray soils of the piedmont plains.

The vegetation of the northern plateau deserts, on the one hand, is similar to that of the dry steppes of the semidesert region, and, on the other, it resembles that of the Mongolian deserts. Perennial xerophyls, such as sagebrush (*Artemisia*), are common. Together with chenopodiaceous plants they form, in the rocky clay deserts, meager vegetation of the sagebrush-saltbush type. Dominant saltbush species are *Salsola arbuscula* and *Anabasis salsa*, with which are mixed *Nanaphyton erinaceum* and *Salsola gemmascens,** also of the saltbush family. Sagebrush is represented by three species: *Artemisia terrae albae*, *A. turanica*, and the endemic *A. maikara*. These species afford excellent browse for sheep. In places scrub thickets of a peashrub (*Caragana grandiflora*) are found.

Animal life of the subregion is as meager as the vegetation. There are some rodents, such as ground squirrels and jumping mice. Of

---

* *Salsola* is known in the United States as Russian. thistle.

birds, the houbara (*Chlamidotis undulata*) is perhaps the most noteworthy. Along the west and south chinks (see p. 153) mountain sheep
(*Ovis orientalis*) is found occasionally. Wild ass (*Equus hemionus*)
and saiga antelope (*Saiga tatarica*) are almost extinct and at present are
protected by law.

The sands of the northern subregion are also rather monotonous in
their vegetative cover. In the Muyun Kum sands winterfat (*Eurotia
ceratoides*) and milkvetch (*Astragalus brachypus*) grow, mixed with
some grasses, such as needlegrass and ryegrass.

In the sands adjacent to Lake Balkhash there are extensive areas occupied by white saxaul. There is also a great deal of grazing land
covered with sagebrush (*Artemisia songarica*) and Siberian wheatgrass
(*Agropyron sibiricum*). Extensive areas supporting grass species are
used for grazing. A species of threea (*Aristida pinnata*), camelthorn
(*Alhagi kirghizorum*), and seepweed (*Suaeda crassifolia*) grow in the
alkali depressions. A skeletonweed (*Chondrilla ambigua*) containing
considerable amounts of rubber grows in the sands of the Lake Balkhash region. This species, together with other native rubber-produc-
ing plants, such as kok-saghyz (a *Scorzonera*), and introduced ones,
such as guayule (*Parthenium argentatum*), is cultivated on a large
scale in the Soviet Union.

In the sand areas of the central part of the desert region are found
many interesting plants that are well adapted to this peculiar environment. On the shifting sands and dunes there is no vegetation. The
pioneer sand plants appear as soon as an opportunity is offered, as,
for instance, by a period of still weather and a sprinkling of rain.
Of these pioneers the most prominent is a grass species: threea (*Aristida pinnata*). It has the capacity to form runners from its stem.
These appear as soon as the plant is partly buried under the sand.

Threea has several companions: *Heliothropium*, *Tournefortia*, and
Jurinia. This group is followed by sprouting shrubs, such as *Calligonum arborescens* and *Ammodendron conollyi*, which have the capacity of keeping their heads above the encroaching sand. *Calligonum*
reaches a height of about 7 feet. It develops roots at any part of its
stem as soon as it is buried under sand. *Ammodendron*, a leguminous
shrub called sand acacia, has graceful pendulous branches, small gray-
ish silvery leaves, and dark violet flowers; it also produces adventitious
roots from the stem. In the course of time the dune is stabilized and
the shrubs begin to catch dust from the air, which settles on the now
protected surface of the sand. Other plants appear and contribute
to the addition of organic matter to the surface. With this addition

the sand becomes less porous and rainwater does not penetrate it so readily as before but evaporates from the surface or runs off to low places. The pioneer vegetation, because its superficial roots are then deprived of water in the upper layers of sand, soon begins to die, and presently more deeply rooted shrubs appear. Of these the white saxaul (*Haloxylon persicum*) is the most common. It, too, possesses the capacity of producing adventitious stem roots in case of emergency, and it reaches a height of 10 or 15 feet, sometimes having the appearance of a small tree.

Besides occasional shrubs such as saxaul, the completely stabilized vegetation of the sandy hills consists of sedge (*Carex physoides*) and short grasses, such as ryegrass (*Agropyron*) and cheatgrass (*Bromus tectorum, B. oxyodon*).

In the Kyzyl Kum sands the vegetation is composed of the more northern species, sagebrush (*Artemisia terrae albae*) and winterfat (*Eurotia ceratoides*) predominating. The Paleozoic ridges contain such xerophytic shrubs as *Ephedra intermedia* and *Cousenia pseudo-affinis*.

Animal life of the Kyzyl Kum is represented by rodents, such as jumping mice (of the genera *Dipus* and *Paradipus*) and a ground squirrel (*Spermophilopsis leptodactylus*), the latter being common from Turkmenia to Lake Balkhash. Saiga antelope and wild ass are almost extinct. Gazelle (*Gazella subgutturosa*) is still numerous. Saiga antelope possesses a rather ugly muzzle with an enlarged nasal cavity, developed apparently for warming up intaken cold air during fast running. Its original home was the tall-grass prairie, whence it was pushed by man to the wildest corners of the deserts of Middle Asia.

Birds are few. Typical of the saxaul scrub is the saxaul jay (*Podoces panderi*). In the mountains of Kyzyl Kum, as well as in the sandy areas, the chukar partridge (*Alectoris graeca*) is found. Smaller birds are represented by the warbler (*Sylvia nana*), the saxaul sparrow (*Passer ammodendri*), and a shrike (*Lanius excubitor*).

The reptile population consists of several genera of lizards, among which the varan (*Varanus griseus*) is the largest, sometimes reaching as much as 6 feet in length. There are also several species of snakes.

Insects are not numerous and are found mostly under the shade of shrubs. Scorpions are found throughout the desert sand areas.

Alkaline deserts of the solonchak type do not occupy large areas, occurring rather as patches among other types of landscapes. They are found mostly in depressions and near the river bottomlands. The vegetation there is similar in appearance to the solonchak areas of the dry steppes and is composed of saltbush family plants mixed with such grass species as *Aeluropus litoralis* and occasional tamarisk bushes. The vegetation of these alkaline patches is palatable to animals. Saltbush (*Atriplex*) is considered a very good forage plant for camels and sheep.

A remarkable tree known as black saxaul (*Haloxylon aphyllum*) grows on relatively mildly alkaline soils of the desert sand areas. It prefers ancient river valleys and washes, where it grows to a height of 6 to 10 and even 20 feet, forming peculiar open scrub forests of scattered trees. It has exceedingly hard wood, which serves as fuel in that region. Dead trees either standing or lying on the ground resist decay for a long time. The living trees look no better than the dead ones since they have no foliage (but spines) and furnish no shade. The grotesque appearance of the black saxaul "forests" has been commented upon by many travelers.

In the piedmont plains subregion of the southern part of the desert region, the subsoil is loess on which gray soils have developed. These gray soils, having been formed in the region of insufficient rainfall, contain even less humus than the gray soils of the northern plateaux. They contain considerable amounts of carbonates but some of these are leached from the upper horizons. The gray soils, however, are rich in minerals necessary for plant growth. The underlying loess is found at a depth of 30 to 40 inches. When irrigated, these piedmont soils are extremely fertile.

Although the precipitation is uniformly meager throughout the year in the northern part of the desert region, in the piedmont plains there is decidedly more rain in the spring. Accordingly, spring vegetation here is rather luxurious. The desert comes to life at the beginning of March, and in April the countryside is covered with a continuous carpet of flowering plants. The dominant species are bluegrass (*Poa bulbosa vivipara*) and a small sedge (*Carex pachystylis*). The bluegrass, which is 10 to 15 inches tall, forms, instead of seeds, little bulbs. Larger bulbs are formed at the base of the stem. The sedge has underground runners by which it reproduces itself. Thus, the two principal members of the piedmont vegetative cover possess provisions for vegetative propagation. Some perennial angiosperms are admixed with the bluegrass and sedge. They consist of buttercup, geranium, and some of the lily family. Annual species, such as red poppy and dark violet *Malcolmia turkestanica*, sometimes cover considerable areas with their flowers. By the end of April the vegetation has begun to turn yellow, and towards the middle of May the growing period is over.   One plant, however, the desert *Euphorbia*, remains green throughout the summer.   After the fall rains, the desert again turns green.

Two other noteworthy plants in the piedmont plains are a giant umbelliferous devilsdung (*Ferula foetida*), whose large roots produce medicinal resin, and Levant wormwood (*Artemisia cina*), used in medicine as an anthelmintic.*   Among the cultivated plants, cotton is the most important in this region.

Animal life of the piedmont loess plains is not very abundant.   The habits of many animals are dependent on the development of the vegetation.   The ground squirrel (*Citellus fulvus oxianus*) appears in March, feeds on the spring vegetation, breeds, and then retreats underground, where it remains dormant for 8 or 9 months.   The desert turtle (*Testudo horsfieldi*) follows a similar pattern.   The desert fox (*Vulpes vulpes caragana*) is now almost completely exterminated.

Birds are represented by the houbara (*Chlamidotis undulata*), which is still numerous, and vultures, which are found everywhere.   Of smaller birds the crested lark (*Galerida cristata*) is perhaps the most typical.

Lizards and snakes are numerous.   Noteworthy among the insects are termites.

Along the river courses, and especially in the lower reaches of the Syr Darya, Chu, Ili, and Sary Su and in the delta of the Amu Darya, lie alluvial meadows composed chiefly of a grass species, aeluropus (*Aeluropus litoralis*), accompanied by so-called Bermuda grass (*Cynodon dactylon*) and bunchgrass (*Atropis distans*).   Low places on the river bottomland are occupied by dark green reed thickets.   The reeds are utilized by the natives for making mats, and the young plants are used for hay.

The riparian forests of the desert region are known locally as the tugais.   The tugais follow the meandering courses of the desert rivers as a dark green strip of vegetation composed of cottonwood (*Populus euphratica, P. pruinosa*), so-called Russian olive (*Elaeagnus angustifolia*), tamarisk, willows, and other low-growing shrubs.   In the southern part of the Amu Darya tugais, there grows a giant reed (*Arundo donax*) reaching 20 or 25 feet in height.   Dogbane (*Apocynum scabrum*), a shrub with some possibilities as a fiber-producing plant, grows to a height of 6 feet or more in the deltas.   Tugai forests

---

* The active ingredient is santonin, an oxygen-containing sesquiterpene derivative.

are in very poor condition because of uncontrolled cutting, goat grazing, and burning.

The river bottomland forests of the Seven River Region, i.e., in
the area of the Chu, Ili, Lepsa, and others, have a somewhat different
composition. Cottonwood is not found here, but, on the other hand,
other species, such as birch, appear. Willows, hawthorn, barberry,
and rose form bottomland thickets. In more elevated places in the
Seven River Region, peculiar grassland areas are found covered with
a cheegrass (*Stipa splendens*), a coarse bunchgrass with stalks about
5 feet tall. Natives of Middle Asia and of the whole desert region of
Central Asia use this grass for weaving mats, hats, and baskets. In Russian literature it is known by the name of chii.*

Animal life of the tugais consists of mice, rabbits, and other rodents.
The wild boar (*Sus scrofa*) is still found in the reed thickets. Tigers
(*Felis tigris virgatus*) are numerous in the delta regions of the Amu
Darya and the Ili. The jackal is found in the tugais. The Bukhara
stag (*Cervus elaphus bactrianus*) may be found along the upper course
of the Amu Darya. This animal is protected from hunting. The
reed cat (*Felis chaus chaus*) also lives in the reed thickets. In the
Seven River Region it is replaced by the prairie cat (*Felis caudata*).
Including the tiger, there are seven species of cats in the deserts of
Middle Asia.

Pheasants (*Phasanius colchicus turkestanicus* and other species) are
plentiful in the southern tugais. The Mongolian pheasant also lives
in the Seven River Region. The ibis (*Plegadis falcinellus*) and other
water fowl, such as geese, ducks, and flamingo, are found along the
water courses. The deltas of the Amu Darya and Syr Darya, the
course of the Ili, the Aral Sea, and Lake Balkhash support multitudes
of seagulls, ducks, geese, cormorants (*Phalacrocorax carbo*), herons,
and spoonbills (*Platalea leucorodia*). Pelicans are also found here
(*Pelicanus onocrotalus*). The reed thickets are breeding grounds for
the locust (*Locusta migratoria*) and mosquitoes.

From time immemorial areas of cultivated land, cities, and centers
of ancient civilizations have developed in those places where water
was available. The old irrigation developments still feed numerous
oases of the region. Modern irrigation projects were started at the
end of the last century. Waters of many rivers, such as the Zeravshan
and Murghab, as soon as they emerge from the mountains, are used
completely for the irrigation of the piedmont plains.

* The author collected this interesting plant as far northeast as the Lake Baikal
region on the border of the Eastern Siberian taiga.

The total area of irrigated land in the desert region is about 8.6 million acres. Cotton is the main crop; grapes, sorghum, rice, wheat, barley, and melons are also grown, and in each oasis luxurious fruit orchards are found. Fruit growing was an ancient occupation of the peoples of Turkestan. Many varieties of fruit originated in that country. Apples and apricots grow in the region in the wild state. Peaches, apricots, figs, and pomegranates are grown in the oases orchards. Elms, sycamores, and even some American trees, such as magnolia and tulip tree, or yellow poplar (*Liriodendron tulipifera*), are planted for shade.

The fauna of any village (kishlak) in the desert region includes the usual mice and rats. *Nesokia huttoni*, a species of rat, causes a great deal of damage to the grain fields. This rat is distributed from Egypt to northeastern India.

The most typical bird in any kishlak is the Senegal turtledove (*Streptopelia senegalensis*). Hoopoe (*Upupa epops*), barn swallow (*Hirundo rustica*), hobby (*Falco subbuteo*), Indian oriole (*Oriolus kundoo*), and an Indian flycatcher (*Terpsiphone paradisi turkestanica*) are also found in the villages. In the rice fields white storks (*Ciconia ciconia asiatica*) may be seen. Sparrows are extremely numerous and very harmful to the fruit orchards and cereal crops.

People

The northern part of the desert region was originally populated by the Kazakh nomads. At present many Russians live there and also in mining districts and in the oases of the southern part of the region. The area along the Syr Darya and near the northeastern shores of the Aral Sea (along the Aktyubinsk-Tashkent railroad) recently was resettled by Koreans who moved from the Far Eastern Region. Apparently many people have resettled during and since World War II in the reclaimed parts of the Kazakhstan deserts. The Kara Kalpaks, a partly agricultural and partly cattle-tending people closely related to the Kazakhs, live along the lower reaches of the Amu Darya, around the southwestern part of Aral Sea, and in the adjacent desert areas. Some of them are fishermen. Their area is called the Kara Kalpak Autonomous Republic and is a part of the Uzbek Republic.

Chapter 16

Mountains of Middle Asia

Topography

The mountains of Middle Asia are located within the boundaries of all five republics of that region. The Kopet Dagh Range lies on the border of Iran and the Turkmenian Republic. The Uzbek Republic includes in its southern part the very high mountains of the Tien Shan system. The southeastern part of Kazakhstan contains several mountain ranges. The Kirghiz land and Tajikstan both are entirely mountainous areas.

The mountain region comprises the highest part of the Soviet Union and is a much dissected, geologically complicated territory. Tectonic processes begun here have not been completed, and earthquakes are very common. The snow fields of the high mountains and numerous glaciers feed large mountain streams, and these waters have been used from time immemorial for irrigation. The mountains of Middle Asia are located in a region of very ancient civilization where many varieties of fruit trees have originated and where many agricultural crops have been cultivated for thousands of years.

From the beginning of the Paleozoic era to the middle of the Tertiary period, there was an enormous geosyncline in the region now occupied by the mountains of Middle Asia, which was covered by a warm sea. However, some folding had occurred as early as the Lower Paleozoic epoch in the northern part of the region. Thus, in the northern part of the region mountain chains began to appear, causing the sea to recede to the south. At the beginning of the Devonian period the sea advanced to the north again. In the Upper Paleozoic era additional folding and orogenesis occurred in the central part of the region, and the sea retreated south again. During the Mesozoic era the sea penetrated the periphery of the Paleozoic mountain ranges, and a luxurious vegetation thrived in the coastal areas under a warm, moist climate.

After the Jurassic period, however, the climate became drier, and during the Lower Cretaceous the sea disappeared and the region was considerably desiccated, deserts taking the place of the sea. In the

163

Upper Cretaceous and during the earliest part of the Tertiary period the sea advanced again and the region received more marine deposits.

Towards the Neocene the whole country was reduced to a peneplain, and subsequently the southern part suffered extensive folding, while farther north considerable uplifting of peneplaned areas occurred. Then the mountains were subjected to water erosion. Large rivers carried a great deal of material to the lowlands, depositing large quantities of sediments.

The mountains of Middle Asia may be divided into three groups: (1) the Kopet Dagh-Pamir system, (2) the central arcs of the Tien Shan (meaning Celestial Mountains, in Chinese) system, and (3) the northern arcs of the Tien Shan system. (Map 21.)

The Kopet Dagh-Pamir system embraces the desert chain of the Lesser Balkhan, near the Caspian Sea; the Kopet Dagh Range; the Paropamisus, which lies in Afghanistan, only its foothills being found within the border of the Soviet Union; and the southern ranges of the Tien Shan system, including the Ghissar Range and Peter I Range. The whole system is of Tertiary origin, produced by tremendous mountain-forming folding. The Kopet Dagh Range lies mainly in Iran. In the west it is geologically connected with the Elbrus Range, located along the southern shores of the Caspian Sea, and in the east it merges into the Paropamisus Range. Elevations in the Soviet part of the Kopet Dagh reach 2940 feet (in Turkmenia). The range is of a desert character; there are no snow-covered heights and very few streams. However, at the foot of the range appear numerous springs, which soon disappear into the porous desert ground and feed an intricate system of underground water ducts or galleries of ancient origin. Some of these underground galleries extend for many miles. Even at the present time these play an important part in the water supply of Turkmenia.

The Kopet Dagh in Turkmenia is composed of Cretaceous and Tertiary deposits. The mountain-forming processes took place repeatedly during the Tertiary period. During the Pliocene, especially, intensive foldings and violent dislocations occurred.

East of the Amu Darya the Kopet Dagh system is represented latitudinally by the Peter I Range. Here, near the meridional Range of the Academy of Sciences, is located the highest mountain of the Soviet Union—Stalin Peak, elevation 24,584 feet. The second highest mountain in the Soviet Union, discovered in 1871 and named General Kauffmann Peak, but renamed Lenin Peak by the Soviets, is 23,377

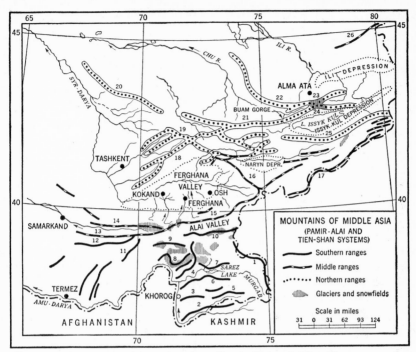

MAP 21. Mountains of Middle Asia. (Pamir-Alai and Tien Shan systems.)

A. Southern ranges, predominantly of Tertiary folding.

1. Sary Kol Range.
2. Vakhan Range.
3. Shugnan Range.
4. Yaz Ghulem Range.
5. Alichur Range.
6. Bazar Dara Range.
7. Mus Kol Range.

8. Darvaz Range.
9. Peter I Range.
10. Trans Alai Range.
11. Kara Teghin Range (of group B, according to Berg).
12. Ghissar Range.

B. Middle ranges, predominantly of Upper Paleozoic folding.

13. Zeravshan Range.
14. Turkestan Range.
15. Alai Range.

16. Ferghana Range.
17. Kokshal Tau.

C. Northern ranges, predominantly of Lower Paleozoic folding.

18. Chatkal Range.
19. Talass Ala Tau.
20. Kara Tau Mountains.
21. Kirghiz Range.
22. Chu-Ili Mountains.

23. Trans Ili Ala Tau.
24. Kungei Ala Tau.
25. Terskei Ala Tau.
26. Dzungarian Ala Tau (of group B, according to Berg).

Kopet Dagh Range, located west of the Pamir ranges, comprises a mountain system isolated from the Pamirs. As it was formed during the Tertiary, Berg considers it a part of the southern ranges (all belonging to the Kopet Dagh-Pamir system). (*After Suslov.*)

165

feet high. It is located in the Trans Alai Range, which extends latitudinally somewhat north and east from the Peter I Range.

The central arcs of the Tien Shan system were formed for the most
part by the Upper Paleozoic folding. Mesozoic and Cenozoic foldings
are poorly represented in this region. The Alai, Turkestan, Zeravshan,
Kokshal, and many other mountain ranges belong within this region.
Farther northeast and somewhat separate from the rest of the mountains of Middle Asia is the Dzungarian Ala Tau Range, and still farther towards the Altai system are the Tarbagatai Range and Saur
Range.

The northern arcs of the Tien Shan system were formed mainly
during the Lower Paleozoic epoch. The southern boundary of this
region extends along the north edge of Ferghana Valley and farther
up the River Naryn towards the Khan Tengri Mountains, where the
northern arcs are difficult to distinguish from the central arcs, i.e., from
the Upper Paleozoic region. The northern arcs of the Tien Shan system are formed of limestone, sandstone, and shales of the Lower, and
sometimes of the Middle, Paleozoic.

As a whole the Tien Shan represents a mountain system composed
of ranges and chains of different ages and located north of the Trans
Alai Range and east of the River Amu Darya. However, there is no
clear-cut boundary line between the Tien Shan and the Pamir-Alai.
The eastern part of the Tien Shan extends beyond the Soviet border
where the range separates Sinkiang from Dzungaria.

The highland of the Pamirs is located south of the Tien Shan Mountain system. It comprises the Gorno-Badakhshan Region of Tajikstan.* The Pamirs are a mountainous area situated between Trans
Alai Range, in the north, and Hindu Kush Mountains, which are south
of the border. On the west, the Pamirs are limited by the Panj (Py-
andzh), i.e., by the upper reaches of the Amu Darya (Oxus). The
Pamirs are divided into two topographically different parts. The eastern Pamirs are a high desert-like plateau in which broad valleys are
located at a 12,000- to 13,000-foot elevation and mountains reach
16,000 to 18,000 feet. The mountains in the eastern Pamirs are of a
gently rolling character and very little eroded. Near the Afghanistan
border at an elevation of 13,415 feet lies Victoria Lake (Zory Kul),
from which flows the Pamir River, one of the sources of the Amu
Darya.

* Here, as in many other Asiatic possessions of the Soviet Union, Russian names
and Russian endings are mixed with the native names. Gorno in Russian means
mountainous.

The high plateau of the Pamirs was crossed in the thirteenth century by Marco Polo, whose account of the country is still very interesting. Recently an automobile road has been built from Osh, in Ferghana Valley, across the eastern Pamirs to Horog, on the Panj near the Afghan border. The Kyzyl Art pass on the road between Alai Valley and Pamir plateau is located at an elevation of 13,389 feet above sea level. Generally speaking, communication between the different regions, especially in the southern mountains, is still extremely difficult. Ancient pack trails cross the most formidable passes and find their way along the most treacherous gorges. Where vertical cliffs block the passage, balconies were built a long time ago by driving wooden pegs into rock crevices, or man-made holes, and constructing some sort of corduroy path 3 to 3 ½ feet wide. These balcony trails, or ovrings, are sometimes over a mile in length, and travel over these shaky structures hundreds of feet above the bottom of the gorge is not always safe.

The western Pamirs are a much dissected area with deeply eroded gorges and rapidly flowing mountain streams. The northern part of the Academy of Sciences Range, located 4 or 5 miles from the River Mook Su, towers above it for more than 2 miles.

Ancient glaciation of the Pamirs was very extensive; traces of two and, in places, of three glaciations are in evidence.

Tectonic activity is still in progress in the mountains of Middle Asia. Earthquakes occur frequently; about 1000 earthquake shocks are recorded annually. The catastrophic earthquake of 1911, which destroyed the city of Verni (since renamed Alma Ata), ranks among the most violent earthquakes known. February 18, 1911, the gorge of the River Bartang, or Murghab, in the Pamir region was blocked by an enormous avalanche of earth (about ½ cubic mile) filling the valley with a dam 2600 feet high. Sarez Lake has formed behind this natural dam. In 1934 it was about 40 miles long and over 1600 feet deep.

At present the glaciers of the mountains of Middle Asia cover an area of about 4250 square miles, or about five times greater than that of the Caucasus. Some 1700 glaciers, mostly of a valley type, are scattered throughout the region, except of course for the Kopet Dagh system. But at the same time there exist several centers of very intensive glaciation. These are located in the Trans Alai, Khan Tengri, and Academy of Sciences mountains, and some others. The Fedchenko Glacier * is located east of the Academy range at the sources

* Named after A. P. Fedchenko, who explored the region in the 1870's.

of the River Mook Su. It is a valley type of glacier and descends from about 17,500 feet to 9500 feet. Its length is about 48 miles, and the volume of ice it contains amounts to 47 cubic miles. Another large glacier—Inylchek, near Khan Tengri Peak—is over 40 miles long. Its lower 12 miles are covered with 300 feet of glacial debris. At present the extent of glaciation in the region is rapidly decreasing and degradation of the glaciers is in evidence. From 1924 to 1935 the Fedchenko Glacier retreated a distance of 925 feet.

The snowline in the northern ranges of the Tien Shan system is generally located at an elevation varying from 11,000 to 12,000 feet, or approximately 3300 feet higher than in the Alps. The farther northeast one goes the lower the snowline is located. In Dzungarian Ala Tau it is found at an elevation of 10,500 feet. But to the south and east, from the central ranges of Tien Shan, the snowline is at higher elevations. For instance, in the western part of Peter I Range it is located at 14,000 feet and in the eastern part at 15,000 feet. In the Pamir region it is found at 16,500 feet and even higher.

An inventory of the mineral wealth of the mountains of Middle Asia has not been completed. Copper deposits are apparently larger than has been estimated. The iron range of western Ferghana Valley has not yet been fully investigated. Sulfur deposits near Kerki, on the Amu Darya, are said to be of the order of several million tons. Coal of fair quality is found on the periphery of Ferghana Valley. Towards the center of the valley, oil has been exploited since the beginning of this century.

Middle Asia is rich in silver, lead, zinc, arsenic, and bismuth. Antimony, tungsten, molybdenum, and other rare elements are found in Ferghana Valley. Uranium deposits of importance are found in at least two localities at the eastern end of Ferghana Valley. Uranium occurs here in combination with calcium and vanadium, forming a mineral tuiamuiunite $(CaO(UO_3)_2V_2O_5)$. Recently discovered potassium and phosphate deposits are of considerable importance for agricultural development of the region. Possibilities of using water power from the numerous large mountain streams for industrial development and for the manufacture of nitrogen fertilizers also are of paramount importance for Middle Asia.

Before the rivers of the mountains of Middle Asia reach the lowlands they are typical mountain streams, full-bodied and fed by the snowfields and glaciers. However, even before reaching the lowlands a great deal of their water is taken from them for irrigation purposes.

Some irrigation canals (or aryk, as they are called by the natives) have been in operation for many centuries.

Lakes of the mountains of Middle Asia are of several types. The largest lakes of the region—Issyk Kul and Kara Kul—are of tectonic origin. Some lakes have been formed by the damming of valleys by dirt avalanches; Sarez Lake has already been mentioned. There are also many small lakes in the high mountains. These are mostly of glacial origin.

Issyk Kul (meaning, in Kirghiz, Hot Lake) is located between Kungei Ala Tau on the north side and Terskei Ala Tau on the south. The lake is 5327 feet above sea level, and it is 2303 feet deep. Its shoreline is about 110 miles long.

The River Chu rushes towards Issyk Kul, but instead of emptying into the lake it turns suddenly north, cuts the deep Buam gorge through the Kirghiz Range, and flows into the desert. The nearest distance from the river to the lake is about 4 miles. Every year during high water some of the water from the Chu drains into the lake. The water in Issyk Kul is slightly saline (about 6 parts per thousand). The lake does not freeze in winter.

Kara Kul (Black Lake) is one of the highest lakes in the world, being comparable in elevation to the lakes of Tibet. It is located in the northern Pamirs at an elevation of 12,970 feet; it is 21 miles long and 774 feet deep. The water in the lake is brackish and not fit for drinking.

Climate

The climate of the whole mountainous region of Middle Asia is rather uniform. The general position of the region determines certain climatic characteristics that are far more important than any local modifications. The region is located at the same latitude as southern Italy, Greece, and Spain. This is the southernmost point of the Soviet Union territory (35° latitude N). There is an abundance of sunshine; summer temperatures are very high, and daily and seasonal amplitudes are very large. The climate thus is extremely continental, especially in the eastern part of the region. In winter the anticyclone is established over Central Asia. Its effects are felt in the mountains of Middle Asia. Winter cyclones from the Atlantic Ocean bring moisture which is deposited in the form of snow in the high mountains. Very little precipitation falls in the foothills, however. Unsettled weather, with variable winds prevailing in winter, is augmented by the cold masses of arctic air penetrating to the region from Siberia. Cold spells alternate with warm weather. At Alma Ata, elevation 2706 feet, the frostless period lasts 173 days.

The valleys of the southern part of the region, such as those of the Panj, Vaksh, and Kafirnigan, are well protected from the northeastern and northern winds, and the mean January temperatures there are in the neighborhood of 32°F. In the south the summer is very hot, the mean July temperature being above 88°F. The high-plateau temperatures are, in comparison with those of Siberia, rather mild. At Post Pamir (elevation 11,980 feet) the annual record is as follows:

Jan.	Feb.	Mar.	Apr.	May	June	July	Aug.	Sept.	Oct.	Nov.	Dec.	Year, Mean
1	5	19	32	42	50	56	55	45	32	18	4	30.4

Issyk Kul exerts a mollifying effect on the surrounding country. Przhevalsk (named after the famous explorer of Central Asia), at the east end of the lake, is located 3280 feet above Alma Ata, but its mean January temperature is 23°F, whereas at Alma Ata it is 16°F. On the other hand, the mean July temperature at Przhevalsk is 62°F, whereas at Alma Ata it is 72°F.

As a rule, for every 328 feet of elevation the precipitation increases 2.3 to 2.7 inches. The precipitation is greatest between 5000 and 10,000 feet; in this belt it may be as much as 40 inches a year, and in some western ranges, such as Talass, it may be over 50 inches. High plateaux surrounded by high mountain chains receive very little precipitation. At Post Pamir (elevation 11,980 feet) the annual precipitation amounts to only 2.3 inches. It is distributed throughout the years as follows:

Jan.	Feb.	Mar.	Apr.	May	June	July	Aug.	Sept.	Oct.	Nov.	Dec.
0.2	0.1	0.1	0.2	0.2	0.4	0.4	0.5	0.1	0.1	0	Trace

In the mountains, in contrast to the adjacent deserts, the maximum precipitation occurs in summer and the minimum in winter.

Soils and Vegetation

The mountains of Middle Asia have been inhabited for thousands of years. Intensive cultivation of accessible areas and continuous grazing of mountain meadows and high plateaus have changed the original vegetation considerably. Forests have been destroyed in many places, and mesophyll vegetation has been replaced by xerophyls. The region is notable for many varieties of wild fruit and nut trees, such as apple, apricot, walnut, and pistachio. Many widely cultivated varieties have originated in this region, especially in Ferghana and Tajikstan. The original forests, where still found, have certain outstanding characteristics. No pines or oaks are found here. Spruce and fir grow rather sporadically and only in the eastern part of the region.

Occupying a large area, the region possesses a very diversified vegetation and its vertical distribution is far from being uniform. Towards the south and east the vertical vegetation belts move higher and higher, so that at the same altitude, but in different parts of the region, one may find snowfields, deserts, prairies, and alpine meadows. Snowfields are found in some ranges of the Tien Shan system at the same altitude as highland deserts in the Pamir Plateau.

In the low foothills of the Tien Shan ranges, from 1100 to 1500 feet above sea level, the soil and vegetation are of a desert type. In the spring the usual desert flowers appear in profusion. Among them are crocus, tulip, iris, and hyacinth, intermixed with bluegrass (*Poa bulbosa*) and sedge (*Carex pachystylis*). Poppies, *Astragalus*, and buttercups complete their flowering period toward the month of April. The last to bloom is *Gentiana olivieri*. These few species form a dense cover, so that in 1 square yard there may be up to 5000 individual plants.

The composition of the foothill vegetation varies from one part of the region to another, although sedge dominates everywhere. In the eastern part sagebrush is common. Along the rivers are the usual giant reed (*Arundo donax*) thickets and groves of cottonwood.

Higher in the mountains, from 1500 to 5000 feet, is the semidesert region. The soils here are of a chestnut-colored variety of the prairie type. The vegetation is of the dry prairie type, composed chiefly of wheatgrass (*Agropyron popovi*) and barley (*Hordeum bulbosum*), with the usual admixture of dicotyledons, such as *Ferula badrakema* and *Inula grandis*. Sagebrush is absent. The spring vegetation appears early in April and is composed of tulips, yellow and purple iris, and other flowers. By the middle of June *Inula* and wheatgrass begin to bloom, and a month later the vegetation dries out.

In the mountains south of Lake Balkhash a needlegrass-sagebrush type of vegetation predominates. Pistachio scrub thickets are found all the way from Kopet Dagh to the west end of Lake Issyk Kul and especially near Kushka on the Afghan border.

A well-defined zone of dry mountain steppe is located at elevations ranging from 5500 to 6000 feet and is made up of chestnut-like soils. Fescue (*Festuca sulcata*), feathergrass (*Stipa kirghizorum*), needlegrass (*Stipa capillata*), and June grass form the vegetative cover. Occasional brushfields consist of spiraea, prickly almond, and rose.

Above the mountain steppe belt, at elevations from 4000 or 5000 feet to 7600 feet, lies a meadow-grassland zone with a great deal of woody vegetation. Herbaceous xerophytic vegetation usually occupies the southern slopes and watershed divides, whereas the trees are found in deep canyons and on the northern slopes in places where there is enough moisture to maintain their growth. Generally, however, even the northern slopes are occupied by mesophytic herbaceous plants. The grassy meadows of this zone can be divided into two types: (1) northern, found from the Dzungarian Ala Tau to the Talass Mountains and occasionally in the Ferghana Mountains, and (2) southern, in the Alai-Pamir area. The northern meadows bloom profusely in July. There are many legumes and species of grass (*Bromus inermis, Dactylis glomerata, Poa*). With these are admixed goldenray (*Ligularia altaica*), which may reach about 4 feet in height, a tall member of the lily family, *Eremurus, Delphinium confusum, Scabiosa alpestris*, and *Phleum pratense*. Occasionally grass species dominate.

The southern Alai and Pamir meadows are characterized by the presence of tall umbelliferous species, such as cha-ir (*Prangos pabularia*, which reaches 4 feet in height), giant fennel, and *Eremurus*. Many of these species shed their leaves in summer. Forests of walnut (*Juglans fallax*), admixed with wild apple, are occasionally found in this zone north of the Talass Range and east of Ferghana. Generally these forests are open and park-like in character, but sometimes they form a closed canopy. The trees may be 12 to 16 inches in diameter. Occasionally in the Ferghana region above these walnut groves there may be pure groves of maple (*Acer turkestanicum*). More often, however, walnut and maple are intermingled, and under these species is a shrubby understory consisting of apple, *Rhamnus, Lonicera hispida, Berberis heteropoda*, a plum (*Prunus divaricata*), and rose (*Rosa beggeriana*). Walnut forests do not reproduce themselves very well.

Walnut burls are an object of trade, thus contributing to the destruction of the walnut groves.

In the Tashkent region walnut is intermingled with pear, hackberry (*Celtis australis*), and grape. Scrubby juniper grows on rocky slopes. Scrub thickets of hawthorn, apple, and other shrubs are very common throughout the ranges of the Tien Shan system.

In central Tajikstan, forests of maple and walnut are found at elevations of 5000 to 7200 feet above sea level. From 7200 to 9000 feet there are scrubby groves of maple, juniper, plum, honeysuckle, and rose.

Walnut is absent from the Trans Ili Range, and woody vegetation is represented here by open scrub of apple, mountain ash,* Tien Shan birch, elm, aspen, cottonwood, and apricot. The capital of Kazakhstan, Alma Ata (in free translation, home of apples—alma means apple; ata means father), is the home of several varieties of apple and of innumerable forms of apricot, which is the most popular fruit of Central Asia. Dry apricots, called uriuk, are a common commodity in every grocery store in the Soviet Union, from Leningrad to Vladivostok.

Subalpine meadows are found at different elevations in different parts of the region. In the Trans Ili Ala Tau, they are located at 5000 to 5300 feet; in the Ferghana Mountains, between 8200 and 8900 feet; and in the Alai Range, at 10,200 to 10,500 feet. The soils here are of a meadow type, black in color, and rich in organic matter. The vegetation is more luxuriant than at lower elevations. It contains such species as *Phlomis tuberosa*, *Ligularia altaica*, and occasionally cha-ir (*Prangos pabularia*). A conspicuous grass species of this belt is *Trisetum*.

The woody vegetation found here consists of juniper scrub, and in the eastern part of the region are some forests of fir and spruce. Neither of these trees occurs west of the 72nd meridian.

In the Seven River Region, i.e., in the eastern part of the Tien Shan system, grows a beautiful Tien Shan spruce (*Picea schrenkiana*). It has a narrow columnar crown and attains a height of 150 to 160 feet and a diameter up to 7 feet. On the northern slopes of the Dzungarian Ala Tau and Terskei Ala Tau there are large areas covered with dense forests of Tien Shan spruce. Farther south, however, they assume a park-like character. Siberian spruce grows on the northern slopes of the Tarbagatai Range, which lies between the mountains of Middle

---

* Mountain ash is not an ash but a rose family species, *Sorbus*.

Asia and the Altai system. Siberian fir grows in Dzungarian Ala Tau; in other ranges of the eastern Tien Shan is found a closely related fir, *Abies semenowi.*

The Siberian spruce forests maintain the gloom of the Siberian taiga. Under the dense canopy formed by their branches are found occasional bushes of *Sorbus tianshanica*, *Lonicera hispida*, and *Euonimus.* The ground is covered with moss and such taiga plants as *Pyrola secunda* and an orchid, *Goodyera repens.* Dense conifer forests, however, are found only occasionally in the mountains of Middle Asia. Generally, the mountain ranges are bare or covered with scattered juniper trees that can hardly be called forests or with scrub composed of *Sorbus tianshanica*, *Euonimus*, *Rubus*, or rose. Moses' staff (*Abelia corymbosa*), which reaches a height of about 15 feet, covers considerable area. Its trunks are used for making staffs.

Juniperus semiglobosa forms real forests in Turkestan and the Alai ranges; although these forests are of a park-like character, they are of considerable value in controlling erosion on the mountain slopes.

The alpine zone is located at about 10,000 or 11,000 feet, which is above the scrubby shrubs and timberline. The vegetation here is only 4 to 6 inches tall and consists chiefly of compact perennial plants. Here are found *Saxifraga alberti*, *Acantholimon marmoreum*, and *Androsace villosa.* Gentians cover the ground with a mass of blue color. Buttercups grow in bright golden yellow masses. Alpine poppies supply pale yellow color and asters a delicate rose. Several species of *Cobresia* sedge cover considerable areas, and there may also be scattered woolly *Leontopodium alpinum*, the much prized edelweiss of Switzerland, which grows in profusion as far east as the mountains of Eastern Siberia. Among the rocks grow *Crepis tenuifolia*, *Astragalus nivalis*, and *Oxytropis pagobia.* In the Zeravshan Mountains flowering plants grow at as high an elevation as 12,500 feet, but in the Pamirs some of them may be found as high as 14,750 feet. The trailing alpine juniper (*Juniperus pseudosabina turkestanica*) occasionally occurs in the alpine zone.

For the southern and central Tajikstan, Berg gives the following scheme of vertical distribution of vegetation (after Goncharov):

Desert, semidesert, and steppe
   Brushfields, predominantly with rose   6000 to 6500 feet

Forests
   Maple forests, with walnut and pearlbush   6500 to 7200 feet
   Maple thickets, with shrubs   7200 to 8900 feet

Subalpine vegetation
[1] Herbaceous meadows, with cousinia and bentgrass   8900 to 9800 feet
Highland steppe, with cousinia and fescue   9800 to 11,500 feet

Alpine vegetation
Short grass * meadows   above 11,500 feet

*It should be kept in mind that in Russian the term grass also includes herbs, i.e., dicotyledons.

The Kopet Dagh is a desert range, and its vegetation differs considerably from the vegetation of other mountain ranges of Middle Asia. The foothills, up to an elevation of a little over 1000 feet above sea level, support a typical desert vegetation, already described in Chapter 15.

Above the deserts the vegetation changes into the semidesert type, with a predominance of sagebrush (*Artemisia maritima*). In the spring, however, many other flowering plants appear, such as tulips and glorybind (*Convolvulus*), and the hillsides become covered with a good stand of sedge (*Carex stenophylla*) and bulbous blue grass. On rocky slopes mountain xerophytic perennials, such as *Cousinia stephanophora*, *Acantholimon*, and *Acanthophyllum*, begin to appear.

At elevations from 1500 to 5000 feet the soils become better, with a higher humus content, and vegetation becomes better suited for making hay and for grazing. Prairie grass species, such as wheatgrass and feathergrass, are intermixed with dicotyledons.

At elevations from 3500 to 5500 feet above sea level on dark chestnut-colored soils occur steppes with needlegrass, feathergrass, fescue, and June grass. These steppes resemble very much the Ukrainian prairies. Central Asiatic elements are absent. *Acantholimon* and *Acanthophyllum* develop here at their best, and to these xerophytes are added a compact caryophillaceous plant (*Gypsophyla aretioides* *), *Astragalus tragacantha*, and *Onobrychis cornuta*. The higher the elevations the more dominant are the mountain xerophytes. Occasionally fair open groves of juniper (*Juniperus polycarpos turcomanica*) occur in the mountains at elevations of 3500 to 8200 feet, admixed with maple. At 5000 feet juniper is at its best, reaching 50 or 60 feet in height.

In canyons and gulches may be found scrubby vegetation of hawthorn, honeysuckle, barberry, *Cotoneaster*, and wild plum, and along those stream bottoms which in summer are usually dry there may even be walnut (*Juglans regia*), desert maple (*Acer monspessulanum*),

* *Gypsophyla* is used in this region as fuel.

cottonwood, ash, elm (*Ulmus densa*), juniper, *Arum elongatum* (in shade), and numerous wild fruit trees, including the fig (*Ficus carica*).

In the western part of the Kopet Dagh many species are found which grow in the Caucasus but which do not occur east of the Kopet Dagh. These are Christ's-thorn, pomegranate, sycamore, and others.

The Pamirs, in the eastern part especially, are noted for poor desert-like vegetation. *Eurotia ceratoides*, called by the native Kirghiz the teresken, grows here with a few other plants, such as *Oxytropis chiliophylla* (a legume), *Christolea pamirica* (a crucifer), some bluegrass (*Poa attenuata*), and some fescue (*Festuca violacea*). Sagebrush (*Artemisia skorniakowi*) and *Stipa orientalis* grow on better soils. Cobresia meadows, where *Cobresia schoenoides* is mingled with a sedge (*Carex microglochin*), are found in wet valleys along the streams.

The western Pamirs are not so desolate as the eastern Pamirs. They contain herbaceous highland meadows, tall umbellifers, and birch and cottonwood along the streams. Alai Valley, situated between the Alai Range and the Trans Alai Mountains, is a high mountain steppe with gentle slopes and meandering stream courses. High slopes are covered with cobresia, which is replaced in lower elevations with alpine meadows. There is an abundance of food for cattle; the summer climate is cool and pleasant. Alai means, in Kirghiz, Paradise. Some agriculture is practiced in the western part of the valley.

South of Lake Issyk Kul are found highland desert flats similar to the eastern Pamirs. Their Turkic name is syrt. The soils here are slightly alkaline because of the presence of carbonates, and the vegetation is of a dry prairie or mountain desert type. In moister places cobresia grows, and in drier situations the vegetation consists of feathergrass, needlegrass, wheatgrass, June grass, and desert oats, with some admixture of leguminous species and woolly edelweiss. The syrt highlands of the upper Naryn, with their stunted sagebrush (*Artemisia rodantha*) and tufts of *Acantholimon*, are very similar to the eastern Pamirs.

Common cereals, such as barley and wheat, grow in desert foothills without irrigation; rice and cotton, as well as fruit trees and grass, need irrigation. In the Uzbekistan foothills there remain large areas that can be irrigated. In the mountain area of Tajikstan all land suitable for irrigation and cultivation has already been in use for a long time. Improvement in crops is of more importance here than expansion of cultivated land.

The zone of dry mountain steppes contains some valuable wild fruit and nut trees that may yet contribute to horticulture: pomegranate, almond, jujube (*Zizyphus jujuba*, a plant with edible fruit, sometimes called Chinese date), and pistachio.

Wheat, oats, and barley grow at Issyk Kul, elevation 5312 feet. Barley is cultivated at elevations as high as 6000 feet. Apples, apricots, corn, tomatoes, and cucumbers are also grown at Issyk Kul, but no melons or grapes are raised.

In Alai Valley wheat is sown up to 8900 feet and barley fields are found as high as 9800 feet above sea level. Oats and alfalfa are also grown. In places it is necessary to resort to irrigation. Attempts have been made to grow Yakut spring rye in the valley.

In Zeravshan Valley rice is cultivated up to 3800 feet above sea level; corn up to 4200 feet; peaches up to 4500 feet; grapes up to 6000 feet; millet up to 6400 feet; apricots up to 7000 feet; and barley as high as 8200 feet. Occasional apricot trees may be found at 9800 feet above sea level.

In the Pamirs (Gunt Valley) white mulberry and apricot and pear are grown up to about an 11,000-foot elevation. It is of interest to compare this area with the Alps, where agriculture is practiced not much higher than 6000 feet above sea level.

Animal Life

In the lower foothills of the mountains of Middle Asia one may find the usual array of semidesert rodents and an occasional desert kit-fox (*Vulpes korsak*), saiga antelope, and partridges (*Perdix perdix* and *Perdix dahurica*). Lizards are numerous, and in summer the country-side is infested with locusts. In the desert mountains of Tajikstan are found wolf, fox, porcupine (*Hystrix hirsutirostris*), and hyena. A mountain sheep (*Ovis vignei*) lives in the highland desert.

The broadleaf forests shelter porcupine, boar, and badger (*Meles meles tianshanicus*); also Siberian deer, or roebuck (*Capreolus pigargus tianshanicus*). Birds living in the broadleaf forests include *Thitrea paradisea turkestanica*, *Columba oenas tianshanica*, and *Carduelis carduelis*.

Common inhabitants of the spruce-fir forests of the eastern part of the region are Siberian deer; Siberian wapiti, or maral (*Cervus canadensis sibiricus*); occasional lynx; ermine (*Mustela erminea ferganae*); weasel (*Mustela nivalis pallida*); pika (*Ochotona rutila*); bear; and wild cat (*Otocolobus manul*).

Many birds of the Siberian taiga, such as the nutcracker (*Nucifraga caryocatactes rothschildi*), crossbill (*Loxia curvirostra*), bullfinch

(*Pyrrhula*), three-toed woodpecker (*Picoides tridactylus tianshanicus*), pine grosbeak (*Pinicola enucleator*), and a bullfinch (*Uragus
sibiricus*), nest in the spruce forests of the southeastern part of the
region, i.e., in the Seven River Region. The last two birds, as well
as *Pyrrhula*, fly there from the north for the winter. A dove (*Streptopelia orientalis meena*) is rather abundant in the spruce forests. The
black grouse (*Lyrurus tetrix*) also occurs occasionally. Juniper groves
are inhabited by chukar partridge (*Alectoris graeca*), a bird that has
been introduced into the southwestern part of the United States.
Finches nest in the spruce forests but descend for winter to the broadleaf groves below. The hawk owl (*Surnia ulula tianshanica*) has a
similar habit.

Marmots (*Marmota caudata, M. menzbieri, M. baibacina centralis*)
live in the high mountains. A ground squirrel (*Citellus relictus*)
makes its burrows in mountain prairies, where there are also mouflon
(*Ovis vignei*), and magnificent Marco Polo sheep (*Ovis poli*). Pika
(*Ochotona rutila*) is common in the high mountains.

The mountain goat (*Capra sibirica*) is found from 8000 feet up to
the snowline. The alpine habitat of the mountain goat is shared by
the snow leopard (*Leopardus uncia*). The Tien Shan bear (*Ursus
arctus leuconyx*) feeds in the alpine zone on marmots and wild buckwheat, but towards autumn, when apples and apricots are ripe, the
bear descends to the lower elevations.

The red wolf (*Cyon alpinus*) occurs in the southeastern mountain
ranges and is also found in the Altai Mountains. Common wolf and
fox also occasionally visit the alpine habitat. Mountain sheep and
goat live in the high mountains, together with a grouse (or rather a
partridge) (*Tetraogallus himalayensis*) and the common Eurasian
chough (*Pyrrhocorax graculus*). *Pyrrhocorax pyrrhocorax* is found
in somewhat lower altitudes. Also typical of the alpine zone are horned
lark (*Eremophila alpestris*), water pipit (*Anthus spinoletta blackis-
toni*), accentor (*Prunella collaris rufilata*), and *Leocosticte nemoricola
altaica*. The house martin (*Delichon urbica meridionalis*) does not
live in cities and towns as it does in Europe but rather nests in the
alpine zone and in the forests of the foothills. Birds of prey represented in the alpine zone include the bearded vulture (*Gypaetus bar-
batus grandis*).

Recently attempts have been made to introduce the South American llama and the chinchilla into the alpine zone.

Fauna of the Pamirs is similar to that of Tibet and also to that of
the syrt highlands of the upper Naryn. The biggest of all mountain

sheep, *Ovis poli*, can be found all year round in the mountain deserts.
Marmot, *Ochotona*, and hare (*Lepus europeus tibetanus*) also occur
there.

Birds of the Pamirs include a snow partridge (*Tetraogallus tib-etanus*), a small grouse (*Syrrhaptes tibetanus*), and a couple of species
of wheatear (*Oenanthe deserti* and *O. isabellina*). The last two spe-cies occur also in the lowland desert region of Middle Asia. Other
birds of the Pamirs include the griffon vulture (*Gyps fulvus him-malayensis*), a species of goose (*Anser indicus*) that spends its winters
in India, and a Tibetan raven (*Corvus corax tibetanus*).

The most important domestic animal in the Pamirs is the Tibetan
yak (*Poephagus grunniens*). It provides excellent wool, good meat,
and rich milk and is used as a beast of burden.

Among the animals of the Kopet Dagh Mountains are many Iranian,
Afghanistan, Caucasian, and Asia Minor forms. There are mountain
goat (*Capra aegagrus*), mountain sheep (*Ovis orientalis cycloceras*),
leopard (*Leopardus pardus*), and cheetah (*Acinonyx jubatus;* noted
for its easy taming). Natives throughout Central Asia and parts of
India use the cheetah for antelope hunting. The bear of the Kopet
Dagh is an Asia Minor variety (*Ursus arctos syriacus*). There are also
encountered a species of pika (*Ochotona rufescens*); a Caspian par-tridge, or grouse (*Tetraogallus caspius*); and honey badger, or ratel
(*Mellivora indica*). In dark canyons and caves one may find a large
cobra up to 6 feet in length (*Naja naja coeca*). In the foothills termites
(*Hodotermies turkestanticus*) are common.

People

The population of the region includes Uzbeks, living in the foot-hills of the mountains and in adjacent irrigated plains. There is a
great admixture of various peoples, such as Chinese Moslems from
Sinkiang, Baluchi, Arabs, many Ukrainians, and a great many Russians.
The foothills of the Kopet Dagh are sparsely populated by Turkmen,
who live mainly in the irrigated oases. Along the Afghanistan border
of the Pamirs live different Afghan tribes. The high plateaux of east-ern Tibet serve as grazing ground for cattle of the Kirghiz nomads,
some of whom live in nearby Kashmir. The Kirghiz Republic, as
well as the Tajik Republic, is predominantly mountainous. The
southeastern part of the region is populated by Kazakh cattlemen and
also contains a considerable admixture of peoples who were moved
during and after World War II from the European part of the Soviet
Union.

Chapter 17

The Caucasus

The Caucasus is located between the Black Sea and the Caspian Sea. The northern boundary of the region may be drawn along the Kuma-Manych depression (see Chapter 14, "Semidesert Region"), which in late Quaternary times served as a connecting link between the Black and Caspian seas.

Geographically, the Caucasus belongs to western Asia. Administratively, the Caucasus is divided into several regions. The country north of the crest of the main range, including Daghestan, belongs to Russia proper. South of the crest is the region generally referred to as Transcaucasia. It consists of Georgia in the west, Azerbaijan in the east, and Armenia, occupying parts of the Lesser Caucasus and the Armenian Volcanic Plateau. Armenia has a common border with Turkey and Iran.

Topography

The Caucasus is a mountain region. Its main range, known as the Greater Caucasus, extends northwest to southeast from the Black Sea to the Caspian Sea. South of the Greater Caucasus are the ranges of the Lesser Caucasus, bordering the high Armenian Plateau on the north. The Greater Caucasus is connected with the Lesser Caucasus by the Suram Range. (Map 22.)

Although the Caucasus is predominantly a mountainous region, nevertheless within its limits also are extensive prairie-like stretches, semi-deserts, and deserts, some of which lie below sea level, and two areas which are referred to in Russian literature as subtropical lowlands.

The Greater Caucasus is a complicated and extensive mountain region that originated as the result of Tertiary foldings and that was subjected to a post-Tertiary uplifting.

The main Caucasian range extends from Anapa, on the Black Sea Coast, east-southeast to the Apsheron Peninsula, on the Caspian Sea. The range consists of several folded chains. It is about 700 miles long and at its widest part is a little over 100 miles wide. The chain, which constitutes the watershed divide, consists, in its highest part, of a skyline of snowclad peaks of an average height of about 12,000 feet. The highest peaks—Elbrus, 18,450 feet, and Kazbek, 16,557 feet—are located not on the watershed divide but somewhat north of it. In its northwestern part, near the port of Novorossisk (i.e. New Russian), the main range consists of three low parallel chains of an average height between 1100 and 1600 feet. Farther down the coast of the Black Sea, north of Sochi, the Caucasus appears as a gently sloping forest-clad range of medium height. In the vicinity of Sochi the mountains are higher. Snow-covered peaks can be seen from the coast; the skyline of the main range here is about 7000 feet high.

Farther southeast the main range recedes from the coast; it also widens, and the mountains look rugged and high, with deeply cut canyons, and snowfields and glaciers on the summits. The elevations of the crest here run about 11,500 feet. The entire area between the main range and the sea is filled with high mountain chains that extend from the main range to the south and southwest. On the north side of the main range also there are many subsidiary chains; some run parallel to the main range and are separated from it by valleys, whereas others branch from the main range and do not appear as separate ranges.

The highest peaks of the Caucasus are located on one of these ranges, known as Peredovoi Khrebet (Advanced Ridge). Generally, three major chains of mountains are distinguished north of the main range: Skalistye Gory (Rocky Mountains), 6000 to 10,000 feet high; Black Mountains, 3000 to 5000 feet high; and a foothill chain, which is not over 3000 feet. All these three ranges are of a cuesta type; their southern slopes are steep, and their northern slopes are gentle.

The central part of the Caucasus, from Elbrus to Kazbek, appears as a formidable chain of snow-clad mountains with peaks towering above 14,000 feet and with a few passes crossing the mountains at about 10,000 feet elevation. Only Marmison Pass, on the Ossetian Military Road, is located at an elevation of 9548 feet. At the southeastern side of Kazbek the elevation drops, and through the saddle at a 7813-foot elevation passes the renowned Georgian Military Road.

From the central part of the main range high chains of mountains, such as the Svaneti Range, run south and southwest. These chains gradually decrease in altitude and form the foothill country of western Transcaucasia.

In the vicinity of Kazbek the southern slope of the main range is wider than the northern slope. At this point two chains of mountains

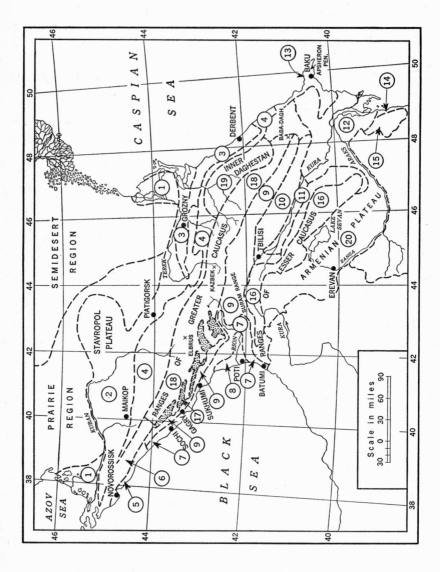

Map 22. Natural regions of the Caucasus.

1. Delta swamps of the Kuban and the Terek rivers.
2. Woodland with patches of grassland and oak groves; more xerophytic to the east.
3. Foothills of the eastern part of the main range, predominantly with prairie vegetation and with xerophytic shrubs.
4. Broadleaf forests.
5. Xerophytic vegetation of the Mediterranean type.
6. Broadleaf forests of medium-height mountains of the west end of the main range.
7. Foothill forests of the Colchis type on broad terraces along the Black Sea coast.
8. Colchis lowland with swampy alder forests.
9. Beech forests of middle elevations. Some oak forests in the central and eastern parts.
10. Plateau-like foothills of Transcaucasia with brushfields, patches of grassland, and semidesert.
11. Kura plains with semidesert types of vegetation.
12. Kura-Araks lowlands.
13. Sagebrush, saltbush, and sandy semideserts of Apsheron Peninsula and adjacent parts of Transcaucasia.
14. Talysh or Lenkoran lowlands.
15. Talysh Mountains.
16. Ranges of the Lesser Caucasus with hornbeam-beech forests.
17. High mountain valleys and cirques with spruce and fir forests.
18. Subalpine meadows, patches of alpine vegetation, snowfields, and glaciers of the main range.
19. Inner Daghestan. High mountains and deep valleys. Predominant vegetation types are grasslands and xerophytic shrubs.
20. Armenian Volcanic Plateau. Dry prairies, semideserts, alpine meadows in high mountains, sagebrush semideserts, and, in the southeastern part, oak forests.

extend from the main range to the south and southeast. They are the Kakhetia Range and the Kartali Range. These two, however, decrease rapidly in height and soon appear as plateau-like foothills extending parallel to the main range.

Farther southeast the main range of the Caucasus enters the region known as Daghestan (in Turkic, the Land of Mountains). The mountain skyline here is from 10,000 to 11,500 feet high with few passes accessible except to pack trains; Kodor Pass is 7849 feet, Vant Lashet 9236 feet, and Salavat Pass 9236 feet. There are several glaciers in this region. The northern slope of the main range in this area forms an intricate, extensive, and very isolated highland country known as Inner Daghestan. Several parallel chains of mountains in Inner Daghestan run from 6500 to 8200 feet in height.

After leaving Daghestan, the main range narrows considerably but it still consists of very high mountains of the alpine type. Southwest of Mt. Baba-Dagh (11,909 feet) elevations drop rapidly, and the main range of the Caucasus soon changes to mountains of medium height, which, farther southeast, towards the Caspian Sea, branch into three chains of low foothills separated by the rivers Sumgait Chai and Persagat.

Geologically, the core of the main range is composed of pre-Cambrian granite and gneiss. On both sides of the core are metamorphic rocks. The primary folding of the region took place during the pre-Cambrian period. There are no traces of Lower Paleozoic tectonic activity, but Upper Paleozoic dislocations can be clearly seen. The region was peneplained at the beginning of the Mesozoic era, with subsequent foldings at the end of the Lower Carboniferous epoch and again at the end of the Triassic and the beginning of the Jurassic periods. Further dislocations occurred at the end of the Cretaceous period. Tertiary deposits are characteristic of the foothill regions. Extensive dislocations occurred at the end of the Tertiary and continued throughout the Pleistocene epoch. Quaternary deposits are found along the river valleys and on the mountain flats. It is interesting to note the indications of considerable volcanic activity through various periods of the geologic past. Both Elbrus and Kazbek are dead volcanoes. Elbrus was still active during the Upper Pliocene epoch. In the northern foothills the volcanic activity during the Upper Pliocene is evident in the Piatigorsk volcanic region in the form of several laccoliths. The highest of these is Mt. Beshtau, 4723 feet.

Present glaciation in the Caucasus is very extensive, especially in the central part of the main range. The snowline in the western part of the range is found at 8800 to 9800 feet. Eastward it gradually ascends. In the central part the snowline is located at 9800 to 11,500 feet, and farther east, where the climate becomes drier, it does not descend lower than 11,500 feet. The area covered with permanent ice is about 800 square miles. Twenty-two glaciers that descend from Elbrus have a total area of 56 square miles. There are 1400 glaciers in the Caucasus. Nevertheless, the Caucasian glaciation is only about half as extensive as the glaciation of the Alps, since, generally speaking, there is less precipitation in the Caucasion region.

The northern portion of the Caucasian region can be divided into three parts: (1) The Kuban-Azov plain, which is low and flat. It is crossed by the southern tributaries of the Kuban and is covered with loess-like sandy loam. (2) The Caspian depression, the greater part of which is below sea level. (3) Between the two is the Stavropol Plateau, composed of Tertiary clays, sandstones, and limestones. In its southern section elevations run up to 2700 feet. Its central section is lower—about 2000 feet above sea level. From the Caucasus proper the plateau is separated by a dip of slightly lower elevation.

South of the main range there are also areas of plains and lowlands, but they are not so extensive as the northern plains.

The Kura-Araks plains of Transcaucasia are drained by these two rivers. Along the middle reaches of the Kura the plain is rather narrow, gradually sloping and widening to the southeast. Farther towards the Caspian Sea these plains become lowlands that are mostly below sea level. At almost the central part of the lowland the Kura joins the Araks, which has its sources in Turkey and which flows along the international border before reaching the lowlands. These areas along the Kura-Araks are known to the Russians as steppes. Among the better known are the Karabakh Steppe, Saliany Steppe, and Shirvan Steppe. These steppes, as we will see later, are in reality of a semidesert type.

On the Black Sea coast of the Caucasus, in the lower reaches of the River Rion, is the lowland of Colchis, known in Greek mythology as the home of Medea, daughter of Aeetes, and destination of the Argonauts in their search for the Golden Fleece.

During the Miocene epoch both the Kura-Araks plains and the Colchis lowland were under water. Subsequent uplifting of the country separated the two regions and elevated them above the water level. At present both the Kura-Araks and the Rion valleys appear as areas of alluvial sediments, but they are of tectonic origin.

The Lesser Caucasus consists of mountain chains bordering the Armenian Plateau on the northeast. It is separated from the main range of the Caucasus by the Rion and the Kura valleys. The Suram Range connects the main range of the Caucasus with the Lesser Caucasus. This range (Suram Pass, 3926 feet) together with Imeritin Range (Mt. Kara-Kaia, 9335 feet) forms a watershed divide between the Kura and the Rion systems.

Geologically and tectonically the Lesser Caucasus differs a great deal from the main Caucasian range. In the northwestern part of the system the oldest rocks are Upper Cretaceous deposits overlain by considerable Tertiary rock; in the southeast, in addition to Cretaceous rocks there are prominent Jurassic deposits, but Tertiary rocks are not found there. In the northwestern part, uplifting occurred during the Oligocene and Upper Miocene epochs. Then followed a period of erosion and peneplainization of the region. At the end of the Pliocene epoch there was considerable tectonic disturbance, which manifested itself in faulting and rupturing. Remains of the ancient peneplain are still noticeable in places on the tops of the mountains. The southeastern portion of the Lesser Caucasus apparently was folded much earlier than the northwestern part.

The Talysh Mountains are located near the Caspian Sea, forming several chains of a folded and faulted nature, extending from southeast to northwest along the Iranian border. (Highest point, 8029 feet.)

The Armenian Plateau is located between the ranges of the Lesser Caucasus and the Iranian and Turkish borders. It is predominantly of volcanic character. Volcanic activity took place during the Tertiary and continued throughout the Quaternary period. The highest mountain of the region is the extinct volcano Alaghez (13,405 feet). Mt. Ararat is located about 60 miles south of Alaghez in the territory of Turkey. The Armenian Plateau is composed mostly of Quaternary volcanic rocks: andesites and basalts. Of considerable importance in the tectonic structure of the Armenian Plateau are down-faulted troughs (grabens), such as the Araks trough, which is apparently still in the process of formation, and the Lake Sevan trough, which is occupied by this large (575 square miles) body of water, located at an elevation of 6284 feet above sea level, and surrounded by mountains towering to 12,000 feet. Lake Sevan is considered an excellent source of hydroelectric power.

The Caucasus is a region of considerable seismic activity. Though earthquakes are sometimes general in character, there are definite centers where violent earthquakes have occurred repeatedly. Earthquakes occur most frequently on the south slope of the main range and also in the vicinity of Tbilisi and on the Armenian Plateau. The town of Shemakha, located on the southern slope of the eastern part of the main range on a fault extending from northwest to southeast, was destroyed by an earthquake in 1902.

The Caucasus is rich in economic minerals. Oil is found in large quantities on the Apsheron Peninsula and all over Azerbaijan. The oil occurs mostly in a Pliocene sandy-clay layer, which is over 6500 feet thick. It is also found in other Tertiary strata. Oil fields of the northern foothills of the main range are located near Maikop, at Grozny and in Daghestan. Iron is found in Azerbaijan; coal of fair quality is mined in Georgia. The Chiatura manganese deposits located on the west slope of the Suram Range are among the richest in the world.

Marl from the large deposits in the Novorossisk region is used in the manufacture of cement. Some copper and building stone are mined in Armenia.

Numerous mineral springs (some of which are radioactive) located in the Piatigorsk volcanic region of the northern foothills have been used as spa resorts since the Russian conquest of the Caucasus. Great importance is attached to the Caucasian mineral springs, and their disease-curing properties are much discussed in Russian geographic books. Some mineral springs are also found in Transcaucasia. The Black Sea coast of the Caucasus between Anapa in the northwest and Sochi in the southeast has numerous resorts, sanatoriums, and summer homes. Along with the South Coast of the Crimea it may be considered the most popular vacation area of the whole country, comparable to the resort regions of the Mediterranean coast.

Climate

The Caucasus is located between Europe and Asia. On one hand, it is under the influence of moist air masses moving from the Atlantic; on the other hand, it is subject to the influence of the dry continental climate of Asia. The main Caucasian range exerts a great influence on the climate of Transcaucasia, which is considerably warmer than the regions located north of the great range. Besides being subject to the influence of the Atlantic air masses and the Siberian winter anticyclone, the Caucasian region possesses, so to speak, a climate of its own, determined by the proximity of the two large bodies of water the Caspian Sea and the Black Sea and by conditions existing on the

high Armenian Plateau. In winter the plateau is cooled considerably;
a local anticyclone is formed with pressures reaching 30.3 inches. At
the same time a relatively low pressure prevails over the Caspian and
Black seas.

In summer the Armenian Plateau is heated so that relatively low
pressures develop there. This tendency is augmented by the Central
Asiatic cyclone with low pressure prevailing over northwestern India
and Afghanistan and extending to Transcaucasia. Over the Caspian
Sea and Black Sea local centers of high pressure are established during
the summer.

The distribution of centers of high and low pressure over the Caucasus determines the direction of the wind and the amount of precipitation throughout the year. In winter, for instance, in the plains
of the Kura, air currents move from the Armenian Plateau, and the
prevailing winds are from the northwest. Along the Black Sea coast
Armenian anticyclones cause winds from the southwest, which are
especially pronounced in the southern part of the coast near Batumi.
On the Armenian Plateau itself calm weather prevails in winter. In
summer, in the Kura plains southeastern winds are common, and on
the Black Sea coast the winds are of a westerly direction.

The cyclones moving from the west bring changeable winds and a
great deal of precipitation. Besides these major movements of air
masses, the Caucasus, with its high mountain ranges and deep canyons,
possesses all sorts of local air currents, such as valley winds, foehns,
and sea breezes. In the summer western Transcaucasia enjoys mild
weather. On the Armenian Plateau, however, summers are hot, the
mean July temperature being from 80° to 86°F. The hottest spot is
in the Araks trough region.

For the whole Caucasian region, winters are the warmest along the
Black Sea coast from Gagry to Batumi (see Table 12). Mean January
temperatures vary here from 43° to 45°F. Mean January temperatures
of the Armenian Plateau, reduced to sea level, are 25° to 28°F.

The region of Colchis, being protected from the northeastern winds,
possesses very mild winters. The mean temperature of the coldest
month is always above 40°F. Summers are hot and humid. Colchis is
the warmest spot in the entire Soviet Union. In the foothills of this
region such crops as tangerines and tea are grown.

In western Transcaucasia, along the Black Sea coast, the climate is
similar to that of Colchis. At the resort city of Sochi day temperatures in summer fluctuate between 76° and 82°F. At night the temperature very seldom drops below 68°F.

The growing period along the Black Sea coast of Transcaucasia is almost continuous throughout the year, but frosts may occur in winter. At Sochi there is an average of 15 days with frost during the year; occasionally there may even be snow, but it does not stay on the ground for more than 4 or 5 days.

In the Talysh lowland, summers are hot and sultry and winters are rather mild. At Lenkoran the average July temperature is about 80°F and the mean January temperature is 38°F. However, a sudden drop in temperature may occur occasionally in winter. Berg * narrates an interesting account of a cold spell that occurred in the Talysh lowland in January 1925. The temperature dropped to 5°F, inlets and swamps of the Caspian Sea region froze, and many of the waterfowl perished, including thousands of flamingos.

The precipitation in the Caucasus, generally speaking, decreases from west to east. Its distribution is influenced a great deal by the topography of the region. The Caspian Sea contributes but little to the precipitation pattern of the Caucasus except in those places where high mountains stand close to the sea, as in the Talysh region.

High elevations of the main range receive a great deal of rain. At the Krestovoi Pass of the Georgian Military Road, the annual precipitation amounts to 66 inches. The northern foothills of the Caucasus, in their western part, receive from 16 to 24 inches of precipitation annually. In the eastern part, however, the precipitation decreases to 16 inches and near the Caspian Sea even to 8 inches. On the north slope of the main range, as a rule, the precipitation increases with altitude, but in some places, such as in Inner Daghestan, the high valleys and flats may be exceptionally dry. In Transcaucasia, east of the Suram Range, there is much less precipitation than on the west side of the range. Very little rain falls in the Kura-Araks lowlands: from 16 to 8 inches and even less than that. The average annual precipitation on the Armenian Plateau varies from 15 to 30 inches; i.e., it is adequate for the growth of many agricultural crops.

The Talysh lowlands receive a great deal of precipitation—47 to 55 inches per year. In this region, however, the precipitation decreases with the elevation. There is a definite dry period in June. The greatest amount of rain falls in September and October.

The country west of the Suram Range slopes to the Black Sea as a large amphitheater, protected on the north, west, and south by high mountains. This region of Colchis lowlands and the adjacent moun-

* *Priroda*, 2nd ed., Moscow, 1938, p. 170.

tains receives a great deal of precipitation. More rain falls here than in any other part of Russia.

TABLE 12. TEMPERATURE AND PRECIPITATION DATA FOR BATUMI,
ELEVATION 10 FEET

Jan.	Feb.	Mar.	Apr.	May	June	July	Aug.	Sept.	Oct.	Nov.	Dec.	Year
Temperature, degrees Fahrenheit												Mean
43	44	47	52	60	68	73	73	68	62	54	48	58
Precipitation, inches												Total
9.3	7.3	5.4	4.9	3.3	6.4	6.4	8.7	12.4	9.5	11.8	9.3	94.7

There is no dry period in the Colchis region. The minimum rainfall occurs in May; maximum, in the fall. Cloudbursts are frequent; once in Poti 8.2 inches of rain fell during 24 hours.

The Black Sea coast in the Novorossisk region (i.e., at the northwestern end of the Caucasus) has a Mediterranean climate, characterized by dry, hot summers. At Novorossisk 3.5 inches of precipitation falls in January and only 1.3 inches in August. The annual precipitation is 27 to 28 inches.

In Daghestan summers are warm; winters are not too cold but very dry and sunny. At Gunib (elevation, 5192 feet) the mean July temperature is 63°F. The rainfall amounts to 15 to 30 inches.

Soils and Vegetation

Approaching the Caucasian region from the north, one passes through the prairies of the lower Don and the Kuban river region. The prairies all are under cultivation, the chief crop being wheat. Towards the Caspian Sea the country takes on a semidesert or even desert character. Closer to the Caucasus elevations increase. On the Stavropol Plateau and in the foothills of the main range of the Caucasus, the prairie vegetation changes to the woodland type. Woody vegetation is represented here chiefly by oaks (*Quercus robur* and *Q. sessiflora*), hornbeam, ash, maple, elm (*Ulmus campestris*), wild pear, and wild apple. The shrubby species here are the usual dry environment species, such as wild myrobalan plum (*Prunus cerasifera*) and hawthorn (*Crataegus monogyna*), with which is admixed Pontic azalea (*Rhododendron luteum*).

In the prairie patches of the woodland, feathergrass and needlegrass (i.e., species of the genus *Stipa*) predominate. The soils here are also similar to those of the woodland region. In the prairie patches they are of a chernozem type; under the forests they are slightly modified, resembling brown forest soils of the woodland region. On the Stavropol Plateau, at about 2000 feet elevation, where annual precipitation may be as high as 28 inches, there are oak-ash forests with admixed hornbeam, linden, maple, and elm with underbrush of viburnum, privet, dogwood, and occasionally such northern trees as aspen and birch. On northern slopes there are hornbeam-beech forests of good quality. Both east and west of the Stavropol Plateau and the central part of the foothills, the vegetation is poorer. In the Novorossisk region brushfields are common. In the eastern foothills the woodland belt is very narrow. The patches of forest that occur are composed of rather scrubby oak, ash, elm (*Ulmus campestris*), and pear. Wild grape vines occasionally climb on the trees.

Brushfields of the deciduous type of the eastern Mediterranean region, which perhaps may be described as deciduous chaparral, cover considerable areas. On the Balkan Peninsula this type is known as shiblak,* which is different from the true Mediterranean evergreen chaparral called maquis. The deciduous chaparral of the eastern Caucasian foothills consists of such shrubs as blackthorn (*Prunus spinosa*), so-called Scotch rose (*Rosa spinosissima*), and hawthorn (*Crataegus monogyna*), with the addition of Christ's-thorn (*Paliurus spinachristi*), a thorny shrub that does not occur farther north and that often forms impenetrable thickets in the lower elevations of the Caucasus.

Above the woodland on the north slope of the Caucasus grow chiefly broadleaf forests. At low elevations of the forest belt rainfall amounts to 20 to 30 inches; higher up, it is from 30 to 45 inches. There is an abundance of snow in the mountains; at Klukhor Pass, elevation 9236 feet, the winter snow pack is over 8 feet. In the western part of the belt, near Maikop, there are many trees which are typical of the warmer part of the Black Sea coast (i.e., Colchis), such as boxwood, yew, laurel cherry (*Prunus laurocerasus*), and *Ostrya*,

* Lujo Adamovic, "Die Sibljak-Formation—Ein wenig bekanntes Buschwerk der Balkanländer," *Botanische Jahrbücher für Systematik, Pflanzengeschichte und Pflanzengeographie*, edited by A. Engler, Vol. 31, pp. 1–29 (1901). (In German.)

with underbrush of *Rhododendron ponticum* * and Caucasian blueberry. The general type of low-elevation forests (2600 feet to 4600
feet), however, is oak (*Quercus sessiflora*). At higher elevations
beech forests predominate. Occasionally on dry slopes there are pine
forests (*Pinus sylvestris* var. *hamata*). Fir-spruce forests, with *Rhododendron ponticum* and ivy climbers, are located above the broadleaf
forests at elevations ranging from 4600 to 6300 feet. In the western
part of the main range the timberline is located at 6600 feet; in the
eastern part it is 600 feet higher. At the timberline are found scrubby
maple (*Acer trautvetteri*) and birch thickets (*Betula pubescens*). An
interesting plant of these conifer forests is sweetroot (*Osmorhiza
brevistylis*), which has close relatives in Siberia, Japan, and the eastern
United States. Near the timberline open groves of *Acer trautvetteri*
are mingled with alpine meadows. Above the timberline there may be
either Pontic azalea thickets or trailing juniper (*Juniperus depressa*),
scrubby laurel cherry (*Prunus laurocerasus*), or even beech scrub.

East of the 42nd meridian the climate becomes drier. Fir and spruce
forests gradually disappear, and forests are mostly composed of beech,
sometimes with linden, elm, maple, hornbeam, ash, and occasionally
yew. After removal by fire or by cutting, these beech forests are replaced by the oak-hornbeam scrub.

High valleys and flats between the mountain ranges are very dry.
The common pine (*Pinus sylvestris* var. *hamata*) grows here on the
northern slopes, whereas the southern slopes are covered with xerophytic thickets of barberry, sage (*Salvia canescens*), thyme, astragals,
various compositous shrubs, and savin juniper (*Juniperus sabina*).
The upper limits of the forests here are formed of birch scrub and
Caucasian rhododendron. Along the Georgian Military Road they
are found at elevations between 4600 and 8000 feet. The woody vegetation of the subalpine zone is represented by birch and maple groves
and by low junipers, and the meadows are covered with tall (up to
10 feet) luxurious herbaceous vegetation. Higher up, grasses begin
to predominate. Grasses and herbs here decrease in their height, being only about 3.5 feet tall.

The alpine zone occupies elevations between 7000 and 10,000 feet.
Vegetation here varies in height from 4 to 12 inches and is composed
chiefly of *Cobresia* sedge, some grass species, and such flowering plants
as gentian, primrose, forget-me-not, violet, and dryad (*Dryas caucasica*). In drier places alpine pastures are composed of xerophytic

* A species often seen in American gardens.

grasses. Rocky slopes are occupied by various plants, such as saxi-frage, draba, arenaria, and *Gypsophila*, and moist patches between the rocky ledges are covered with June grass, brome, fescue, and various dicotyledons, including several endemic species of *Campanula*.

The tops of the mountains in the main range are covered with snow-fields. If one were to cross the crest of the range, in the vicinity of Elbrus, and descend towards Poti on the Black Sea coast of Abkhasia, he would encounter alpine and subalpine zones of the same character as those on the northern slope, although the vegetation here might consist of different species. The subalpine zone in Abkhasia is found at 5500 to 7000 feet elevation. Birch groves, with an understory of *Rhododendron ponticum*, redbud maple (*Acer trautvetteri*), and mountain ash (*Sorbus caucasica*), alternate with tall herbaceous vegetation of the mountain meadows used by the natives for summer pastures.

A zone of fir forests is located at an altitude of 4000 to 6300 feet. The Caucasian fir (*Abies nordmanniana*) has an admixture of beech, maple, hornbeam, and occasionally spruce (*Picea orientalis*). The underbrush consists of Caucasian blueberry (*Vaccinium arctostaphy-los*), laurel cherry, *Rhododendron ponticum*, and holly (*Ilex*). The herbaceous vegetation in these forests is luxurious, containing such tall species as Caucasian heracleum (*Heracleum pubescens*) and milky bellflower (*Campanula lactiflora*). The fir forests do not form a continuous belt. In some places they occupy a considerable area, whereas in others they are completely lacking so that the broadleaf forests of lower elevations reach all the way to the subalpine zone.

Pinus sylvestris var. *hamata* grows on dry slopes. Beech forests are found below the fir zone. Generally these occupy the slopes from 2000 to 4000 feet elevation, but in places they may extend from sea level to the subalpine zone. These beech forests are almost always pure stands. Only occasionally is chestnut admixed.* The ground cover and underbrush is generally absent except for occasional holly, azalea, Caucasian blueberry (*Vaccinium arctostaphylos*), and hazelnut.

The soils under these forests are of a lateritic type; i.e., they are enriched with hydroxide of iron and depleted of silicates. Such soils are reddish in color and are not very fertile. Tea, however, grows very well on these lateritic soils, and many acres of cleared forest land of this region now are tea plantations.

* Once in the thirteenth century these chestnut trees provided beams for the Rheims cathedral.

Beech forests are not the only type found in this region. A common forest type near Sochi and in Abkhasia is the Imeretin oak (*Quercus imeretina*) with azalea undergrowth. On higher terraces Iberian oak (*Quercus iberica*) is dominant. With the oaks are admixed hornbeam, elms, linden, zelkova, beech, chestnut, maple, laurel (*Laurus nobilis*), boxwood, and *Ostrya*. Climbing plants are common. Such mixed oak forests occur up to 2000 or 3000 feet above sea level.

All these broadleaf forests of the Black Sea slope of the main Caucasian range are generally described by Russian geographers as Colchis type of liana * forests. Yew, which occurs here occasionally, is called Krassnoie derevo, i.e., redwood.

Near the Black Sea coast, where the climate is very mild, the growing season extends throughout the year. Near Sukhumi, violets flower in December, apricots begin to bloom at the end of February, and peaches blossom at the middle of March. Many exotics have been introduced into this region, such as magnolia, acacia, camellia, several species of palms belonging to the genera *Chamaerops, Livistona, Washingtonia, Phoenix*, and many other foreign plants. Although lemons do suffer from low winter temperatures, the Satsuma (unshiu) oranges, or tangerines, are hardy on the southern part of the Black Sea coast of the Caucasus.

An endemic Pitsunda pine (*Pinus pithyusa*) occurs on the limestone cliffs, and the swampy low reaches of the rivers are covered with dense thickets of alder (*Alnus barbata*).

The Colchis lowland is located along the Black Sea coast from Sukhumi in the north to Batumi in the south and up the river Rion to Kutaisi. This area, somewhat triangular in shape, is very swampy and covered with rank vegetation of alder, willow, and Caucasian wingnut (*Pterocarya fraxinifolia*), all tangled with sarsaparilla. A tall fern, *Osmunda regalis*, grows in swamps. Oak (*Quercus hartwissiana*) grows on slightly elevated places, also hornbeam, and sometimes Caucasian beech and *Zelkova crenata;* the last furnishes very durable wood suitable for construction in the damp climate of Colchis.

There are many Tertiary relict plants closely related to the species in the Russian Far East and those in the eastern United States. On the other hand, during the glacial period many northern species, such as

---

* Russian geographers attach great importance to the presence of climbing plants in the Caucasian, as well as the Crimean and Far Eastern, forests, in contradistinction to their absence in the more northern forests. The most common climbers are: ivy, grape, clematis, sarsaparilla. All climbing plants are always referred to as lianas.

sphagnum moss, migrated to this region. In recent times the Colchis swamps have been the subject of a very intensive reclamation, and considerable areas are now being cultivated. Although many acres of swamp have been reclaimed, malaria still causes a great deal of trouble in the region.

The geographic landscape of the northern part of the Caucasian main range facing the Black Sea is quite different from that of the southern part. Here, in the vicinity of Novorossisk, the mountains are not very high, reaching 2500 to 3000 feet. Their vegetative cover resembles that of the Balkan coast of the Mediterranean Sea, being characterized by the presence of many Mediterranean species. The slopes, up to 500 or 700 feet, are covered with deciduous xerophyl scrub, similar to the shiblak of the Balkan peninsula. Typical components of these brushfields are a scrub oak (*Quercus pubescens*), oriental hornbeam, *Paliurus,* and occasional pistachio (*Pistacia mutica*). Much of this scrub has been converted into vineyards.

Above the scrub growth, up to 1000 feet elevation, there are scattered junipers, and still higher are oak forests composed of *Quercus sessiflora,* with the usual admixture of various broadleaf trees and occasional beech (*Fagus orientalis*). Climbing plants occur only in moist places. At an altitude of about 1500 feet, however, the forests give way to the grassland, which extends to the northeastern slope of the mountains.

The forests of the eastern part of the south slope of the main Caucasian range, i.e., of the region generally referred to as Transcaucasia, are poorer in composition than the Colchis forests. In this region, below the subalpine zone and the birch-rhododendron thickets, occur beech forests, and below these are oak forests. The vegetation here is not very luxuriant; climbing plants, such as holly, and rhododendron shrubs disappear. East of the South Ossetian Autonomous Region fir-spruce forests do not occur.

In Kakhetia and farther east, at elevations between 2300 and 6000 feet, there are beech and beech-hornbeam forests with oaks (*Quercus iberica* and *Q. macranthera*) and Persian velvet maple (*Acer velutinum glabrescens*). Forests of the ranges bordering the Armenian Plateau, i.e., the ranges of the Lesser Caucasus, are of a similar composition, but since it is drier in that region they contain more xerophytes. Oak-hornbeam forests are common, whereas mesophytic beech forests are relatively rare.

Below the forest belt of Transcaucasia, at elevations ranging from 1500 to 2600 feet, is a woodland belt. The relatively mild climate of this belt permits cultivation of grapes and fruit trees. Vineyards are located as high on the slope as the 3000-foot level. Kakhetia is famous for its red wine. The capital of Georgia, Tbilisi, is located in this belt. The original forest vegetation of the Transcaucasian woodland was long ago destroyed and has been replaced either by cultivated fields or by Christ's-thorn thickets. Along the river bottoms grows alder intermingled with brambles.

The Armenian Plateau is also mostly under cultivation. The main crops are wheat and barley. The original vegetation of the plateau, where it still exists, is of a prairie type: feathergrass, needlegrass, and fescue are intermingled with such dicotyledons as silene, nepeta, and milkvetch. In the grassland there are occasional patches of the Armenian variety of common pine (*Pinus sylvestris*).

The mountains of the plateau possess vegetation of a xerophytic character. Near Mt. Alaghez there are park-like oak forests with grass cover underneath, and above these grow scrub juniper (*Juniperus depressa*) and *Astragalus tragacantha*.

Along the middle reaches of the Araks are stretches of semidesert and desert. The precipitation here drops to 6–12 inches and the summer temperatures are high, 77°F being the average for July. With irrigation it is possible to grow such crops here as cotton, rice, grapes, peaches, and wheat. The natural vegetation of the middle Araks region is xerophytic, represented by such plants as astragals, camelthorn (*Alhagi pseudoalhagi*), *Atraphaxis spinosa*, and hormel peganum (*Peganum hormala*).

Along the middle Kura, between Tbilisi and Evlakh, elevations run from 2600 to 2300 feet. With rainfall amounting to 16–20 inches a year, the vegetation here is of a dry prairie character. In spring there is an abundance of showy flowering plants. During the summer, which is hot and dry, the vegetation is represented by such semidesert species as *Salsola verrucosa* and *Artemisia hanseniana*. Cotton is grown on irrigated land. Towards the mountains the soil is better and more suitable for growing wheat. Near Evlakh large areas are under cultivation; guayule (*Parthenium argentatum*) is grown here as a source of rubber. On dry sites along the rivers there are occasional brushfields of terebinthinous pistachio (*Pistacia mutica*). In the lower Kura-Araks region, below Evlakh and towards the Caspian Sea, are extensive desert areas. The soils here are of alluvial origin, with occasional patches of gray desert and alkali soils. In this region winters are mild and summers are very hot (at Saliany the mean January temperature is 36°F; mean July temperature, 81°F). The annual precipitation amounts to only 12 inches. With irrigation many valuable crops are grown in the Kura-Araks lowlands, such as sesame, cotton, and grapes.

Towards the end of April the spring vegetation has already completed its cycle, and in May perennials, such as sagebrush, begin to dominate. On alkali soils *Halocnemum strobilaceum* is common. Large areas of alkali flats are covered with thickets of a tall (up to 4.5 feet) chenopodiaceous plant, *Halostachys caspica*. The composition of the vegetation in this region varies a great deal with the degree of alkalinity of the soil. Slightly alkaline soils may be characterized by the presence of *Salsola verrucosa*, whereas more alkaline soils can be recognized by the growth of such species as *Salsola crossa*, *Petrosimonia brachiata*, and *Gamanthus pillosus*. *Salsola ericoides* grows on the most alkaline soils. Where there is more moisture, depressions locally known as chal are covered with a rather thick cover of camelthorn (*Alhagi pseudoalhagi*) with licorice (*Glycyrrhiza glabra*) and *Statice meyeri*.

In the swamps of the low course of the Araks Hindu lotus (*Nelumbium nuciferum*) is found.

On the Apsheron Peninsula, where oil is the principal resource, summers are slightly cooler than in the low Kura region. At Baku the mean July temperature is 78°F. The precipitation amounts to slightly over 7 inches a year. The vegetation on the Apsheron Peninsula, however, is much better than one would expect under such dry conditions. There is not much sagebrush but a great deal of needlegrass, bluegrass, and some leguminous plants, such as milkweed (*Astragalus humilis*) and sainfoin (*Onobrychis vaginalis*). On the slopes wild oats, goatgrass (*Aegilops*), and a grass species closely related to wheat predominate. A great deal of land here is used for dry farming.

The region south of the lower Kura, between the Caspian Sea on the east and the Talysh Mountains on the Iranian border on the west, is referred to by the Russian geographers (together with Colchis) as a subtropical region. Geographically it belongs to the Hyrcan or Mazanderan region of Iran, and it may be considered the easternmost region of Mediterranean flora. This narrow strip of lowland, a little over 60 miles long and from 3 to 20 miles wide, is also known as the Lenkoran region.

The soils in the Lenkoran lowland are alluvial, changing with elevation to the lateritic and the brown forest soils. The vegetation is similar to that of the Colchis lowland, although no evergreen broadleaf understory species are encountered here. The dominant species in this

area is *Parrotia persica*, a small tree 20 to 60 feet tall; mixed with it
are a slender chestnutleaf oak (*Quercus castaenefolia*), hornbeam, and
the now almost completely absent *Zelcova crenata*. Climbers are represented by an endemic ivy, sarsaparilla, and escaped American grape-
vine (*Vitis labrusca orientalis*). The original forests, however, are
almost completely gone, having been replaced with rice fields,
orchards, and grainfields. Swampy spots are covered with alder
(*Alnus barbata*) and an endemic bramble (*Rubus raddeanus*). Close
to the shore of the Caspian Sea sand dunes are common. These are
covered with sparse vegetation consisting of grasses and brambles
(*Rubus sanctus*). In the northern part of the region one finds *Ephedra
vulgaris* on the sand; farther south pomegranate (*Punica granatum*) is
more common. The meandering sluggish streams, bayous, and swamps
are overgrown with reeds (*Phragmites communis*).

Above the strip of lowland (which is below sea level) are the towering Talysh Mountains. In the foothills, up to some 2000 feet, the
vegetation is very similar to that of the lowland. *Parrotia* is still dominant. With increased elevation, the precipitation decreases, more and
more chestnutleaf oak is found, and in shady places occur small groves
of persimmon (*Diospyros lotus*). In the southern part of the foothill
forests there is a small and exceedingly beautiful silktree acacia (*Al-
bizzia julibrissin*); it has been introduced in the warmer parts of the
United States, especially in Florida. The underbrush of these foothill forests consists of boxwood, butcher's-broom (*Ruscus hyrcanus*),
and medlar (*Mespilus germanica*). The climbing species include sarsaparilla and brambles (*Rubus*).

Along the river courses are alder (*Alnus subcordata*), wingnut
(*Pterocarya carpinifolia*), and Caspian honeylocust (*Gleditschia caspica*), whose large pods are used as winter fodder for cattle. The
common fig (*Ficus carica*) grows in abundance in places, and in deep
canyons there is majestic Persian velvet maple (*Acer velutinum glabrescens*). Above a 2000-foot altitude parrotia disappears and is replaced by the Caucasian beech. The chestnutleaf oak is here at its best.
The underbush consists of holly and yew. Above 4000 feet and up to
6000 feet the forests consist chiefly of a drought-enduring oak
(*Quercus macranthera*), scrubby Hyrcan hornbeam, and juniper scrub.
A great deal of the forest in this zone has been cleared for wheat
fields.

Alpine meadows are absent in the Talysh Mountains; instead, the
vegetation in the high mountains is of a xerophytic character. In the
northwestern part, at elevations of 4000 to 6000 feet, are compact tufts

of *Acantholimon hohenackeri* and prickly *Astragalus* shrubs. On gentle slopes at 6000 to 8000 feet the vegetation is a dry grassland type—mostly June grass and fescue.

The country between the crest of the main Caucasian range in the southwest and the Caspian Sea in the northeast is known both geographically and administratively as Daghestan. In the south the boundary of the region follows the line from Bazardiuze Mountain to the mouth of the River Samur. In the north the boundary extends from Diklos Mta Peak northeast to the Terek and then along this river to the Caspian Sea.

Geographically, Daghestan may be divided into four major parts: * (1) lowlands, (2) foothills, (3) highlands of Inner Daghestan, and (4) high mountains. The lowlands stretch along the Caspian coast as a narrow strip interrupted in the vicinity of Derbent and extending farther inland, in the southern part, on both sides of the River Ghurgen-Chai. Soils here are semidesert in character, with frequent occurrence of the alkali type. Vegetation on such soils is sparse, consisting of wormwood and camelthorn. In the northern part sand dunes stretch along the coast. But in the above-mentioned area there are shrubs and broadleaf forests of oak, hornbeam, walnut, and other deciduous trees, with hazelnut underbrush and many species of climbing plants, such as sarsaparilla, clematis, grapes, and ivy.

The coastal area is used only for sheep grazing in winter. In the southern part, however, near Derbent and in the delta of the Samur, winter wheat and rice are cultivated, as well as fruit. The mild climate permits cultivation of such fruits as grapes, pomegranates, figs, almonds, and olives.

The foothills occupy a belt 15 to 30 miles wide and over 150 miles long. The altitudes range from 650 to about 4000 feet. Near Derbent the mountains come close to the sea. The narrow strip of land between the sea and the mountains, known as Derbent Gate, was used in ancient times for defensive purposes.

In the lower foothills soils are the chestnut-colored type usually found in semideserts and in dry prairies. Higher up the soils contain more humus and may be classified as chernozems. Low elevations are covered with deciduous chaparral, or rather brushfields of the shiblak type (see p. 191). At altitudes between 1300 and 1600 feet, large areas are covered with dense growths of *Paliurus spina-christi*. Other species

---

* B. F. Dobrynin, *Landscapes of Daghestan*. *Zemlevedenie*, Vol. 36, Nos. 1–2, pp. 93–113, 1924. (In Russian.)

in these brushfields are buckthorn (*Rhamnus pallasi*), dwarfed *Quercus pubescens*, dogwood, pear, scrubby hornbeam, rose, spiraea, barberry, and an admixture of juniper. The scrub vegetation is intermingled with brambles (*Rubus discolor*). Occasionally such brushfields extend up to the highlands of Daghestan.

Vegetation of a different type, known in northern Greece by the name of phrygana, is found on dry rocky slopes. This name recently has been introduced into Russian geographic literature by Dobrynin to designate a similar plant association in the Caucasus and Crimea. Phrygana is a plant community of an open type composed of xerophytic herbaceous plants and of low semiwoody species such as thyme, asphodeline, sage, and many other woolly or prickly xerophytes. Phrygana is not a synonym for chaparral, as is sometimes thought.* Phrygana of the Daghestan foothills consists of many mountain xerophytes, such as caper (*Capparis herbacea*), viper's bugloss (*Echium violaceum*), sage (*Salvia aethiopis*), thyme (*Thymus*), *Centaurea*, and thistle (*Cirsium*), but there are no grass species save in some open areas on the southern slopes which are covered with feathergrass (*Stipa pulcherrima*).

The low foothills are suitable for cultivation. Winter wheat and corn are the main crops. Fruits and grapes are also cultivated. The higher foothills and mountains, from 2600 to 3200 feet, are covered with dense forests of Iberian oak, beech, hornbeam, and other broadleaf trees. In the forest openings grows luxurious herbaceous vegetation including tall monkshood, sage, and others. Above 3000 feet the forests become thinner, and at 4000 feet they are absent. In the higher foothills spring cereals are sown.

The highlands of Inner Daghestan occupy upper reaches of the Samur and the Sulak with its four tributaries, all four of which are known by the same name, Koisu. The parent rocks here are predominantly limestone. Inner Daghestan is very dry; the vegetation is of a xerophytic character, and forests are absent save for occasional mixed pine forests on northern slopes and rare birch and hornbeam groves. But these forests are exceptions. Usually, the vegetation on the slopes and flats consists of xerophytic shrubs, such as astragal (*Astragalus marshallianus*), sainfoin (*Onobrychis cornuta*), sage (*Salvia canescens*), Christ's-thorn (*Paliurus spina-christi*), caper (*Capparis herbacea*), and thistle (*Cirsium sinuatum*). The last is used for fuel.

* H. L. Shantz, *Water Economy of Plants*, leaflets of the Santa Barbara Botanic Garden, Vol. 1, No. 6, Santa Barbara, Calif., December 1948.

The high mountains of Daghestan are, in general, of the same character as the main range of the Caucasus. This is a region of shale
rocks rather than of limestones. The climate here is drier than farther
northwest and is very severe. Subalpine and alpine vegetation predominates. In deep canyons occasional pine forests are found.

Animal Life

In the Caucasian region the Mediterranean fauna and the Central
Asiatic fauna meet. Moreover, during the glacial period many northern animals migrated to the Caucasus. The grasslands of North Caucasus are similar to those of the Russian prairies and Caspian semideserts. Many animals near the Caspian Sea are of Central Asiatic origin.
Here are found saiga antelope, the desert kit fox (*Vulpes korsak*),
jumping mouse, and other rodents. Insectivorous animals, such as
mole and hedgehog, are widely distributed. Bats are numerous. Pika,
a widely distributed rodent in all mountains east of the Caspian Sea,
is absent in the Caucasus. Marmot and mole rat are not found in the
region.

The forests of the Caucasian north slope are inhabited by animals
commonly found in any paleoarctic forest, such as bear, roebuck
(*Capreolus*), stag or elk (*Cervus elaphus*), boar, common red fox,
marten, badger, lynx, and wolf. Squirrel, however, is not found here.
Bison (*Bos bonasus caucasicus*) was formerly found in the forests but
has been completely exterminated. As late as 1928 there were some
bison in the higher elevations, but they were slaughtered for food by
the local population. Wildcat (*Felis silvestris*) and leopard (*Leopardus pardus tullianus*) are found at the timberline. The leopard, an
animal living throughout Africa and southern Asia, finds its northern
limits of distribution in the Caucasus.

Birds of the forest zone are the common crossbill (*Loxia curvirostra*), bullfinch (*Pyrrhula pyrrhula*), and great black woodpecker (*Dry-
ocopus martius*).

Boar and bear live in the subalpine meadows, as does the Prometheus
mouse (*Prometheomys schaposchnikovi*), which belongs to an endemic genus.

The Georgian black grouse (*Lyrurus mlokosiewiczi*), a snow partridge (*Tetraogallus caucasicus*), the mountain sheep or mouflon (*Ovis
ophion*), several species of ibex or mountain goat (*Capra cylindricor-
nis* and others), the Caucasian chamois (*Rupicapra rupicapra caucas-*

ica), and a ground squirrel (*Citellus pigmaeus musicus*) are found in the alpine zone.

Animals of the Transcaucasian broadleaf forests include bear, stag, roebuck, and others. The jackal is found all along the Black Sea coast. There are several species of endemic frogs, the Caucasian salamander, and a species of triton (*Tritonus vittatus*).

Animal life of the Colchis lowland is not very abundant. It is Mediterranean in character and contains some endemic forms, such as hedgehog, Caucasian pheasant (*Phasanius colchicus*), a woodpecker, numerous endemic snails, two species of scorpions, Colchian gecko lizard, fireflies, and cicadas.

The Armenian Plateau has fauna resembling the fauna of Asia Minor. Here are the Kurdistan fox, wild goat (*Capra aegagrus aegagrus*), Armenian mountain sheep (*Ovis ophion armeniana*), chamois, bear (*Ursus arctos syriacus*), badger, wolf, and hyena (*Hyaena hyaena*). Among the rodents found are the jumping mouse and ground squirrel.

In the region of the low Kura live typical Central Asiatic animals, such as gazelle antelope (*Gazella subgutturosa*), jackal, hyena, reed cat (*Felis chaus*), jumping mouse, many species of lizards, and snakes. Birds worthy of note include flamingo and Caucasian francolin (*Francolinus orientalis caucasicus*), related to the partridge.

Camel and buffalo are common domestic animals in the lower Kura country.

Tiger, leopard, reed cat, and wild boar are found in the Talysh lowlands. Birds of this region include gallinule (*Porphyrio poliocephalus*), pheasant, pelican, flamingo, cormorant, and other waterfowl.

Stag (*Cervus elaphus*), roebuck, bear, leopard, and lynx (*Lynx lynx orientalis*) are found in the Talysh Mountains. Pheasant, jackal, hyena, and wild boar live in the reed thickets of the Caspian coast of Daghestan.

The coast of the Caspian Sea is not very hospitable, being malarial and otherwise unsuitable for cultivation, except near Derbent and in the delta of the Samur. The coastal area of Daghestan is very important as winter pasture for sheep.

Fishing is of some importance along the coast of Daghestan.

In the highlands of Inner Daghestan are animals usually found in the Caucasian forests, such as bear, roebuck, stag, some game birds, and rodents.

In the foothills of Daghestan oxen are used as draft animals. In the southern part buffalo are used both for work and for milking.

Table 13, adapted from Bobrinski et al., gives a list of typical Caucasian animals, showing their relation to the adjacent faunistic regions.

TABLE 13. THE MOST TYPICAL ANIMALS OF THE MAIN CAUCASIAN RANGE AND OF
WESTERN AND CENTRAL TRANSCAUCASIA

(After Bobrinski et al., *Animal Geography*, 1946)

West Caucasian mountain goat (*Capra severtzovi*)	
Daghestan mountain goat (*Capra cylindricornis*)	
Prometheus mouse (*Prometheomys schaposchnikovi*)	Endemics
Caucasian grouse (*Lyrurus mlokosiewiczi*)	
Snow partridge or ular (*Tetraogallus caucasicus*)	
Chamois (*Rupicarpa rupicarpa*)	
Snowy fieldmouse (*Microtus nivalis*)	
Wild cat (*Felis silvestris*)	
Forest marten (*Martes martes*)	
Dormouse (*Glis glis*)	Common with western Europe
Mole (*Talpa europea*)	
Stag (*Cervus elaphus*)	
Nightingale (*Luscinia megarhynchos*)	
Tree frog (*Hyla arborea*)	
European hare (*Lepus europeus*)	
European hedgehog (*Erinaceus europeus*)	Common with eastern Trans-
Caucasian pheasant (*Phasanius colchicus colchicus*)	caucasia
Caucasian turtle (*Testudo graeca*)	
Leopard (*Leopardus pardus tullianus*)	
Mouflon (*Capra aegagrus*)	
Snowy fieldmouse (*Microtus nivalis*)	Common with Kopet Dagh
Caspian partridge (*Tetraogallus caspius*)	
Bear (*Ursus arctos*)	
Lynx (*Lynx lynx*)	
Fox (*Vulpes vulpes*)	Widely distributed
Badger (*Meles meles*)	
Ermine (*Mustela erminea*)	
Fitch (*Putorius putorius* and *P. eversmanni*)	
Pika (*Ochotona*)	Animals absent in the Caucasus
Marmot (*Marmota*)	
Snowshoe rabbit (*Lepus timidus*)	
Squirrel (*Sciurus vulgaris*)	

People

The population of the region is very diversified. In the Georgian Republic, besides the Georgians proper, who call themselves the Kartveli, live several other mountain peoples of the Kartveli group: the Pshavs, Imeritians, Ghurians, Mingrelians, Svanets, Kakhetians. High in the mountains lives an Iranian people, the Ossets. These peoples inhabit the inner valleys of the republic and engage in agriculture. On the Black Sea coast of Georgia live Abkhasians and Adjarians. Georgian Jews, amounting to 25,000, are called Ebraeli; they are a picturesque people, resembling the Near Eastern Jews; they speak Georgian. In the southeast of the Caucasian region live Armenians, forming the Armenian member-republic of the Soviet Union. Along the Caspian coast of Transcaucasia is the home of Iranian Turks, known as Azerbaijanis; they form the Azerbaijan member-republic. The part of the region north of the main range of the Caucasus is under the jurisdiction of the Russian republic. Here live many small groups of peoples: the Adighe (Cherkess or Circassians), Kabardians, Chechen, Ingush, and Ossets. Numerous tribes, such as the Avars, Andians, Lezghians, and Lak, inhabit Daghestan. So-called Dagh-Chufut Jews, who speak a Tat-Hebrew, also live in Daghestan. This group differs a great deal from the Ebraeli. There also live in the Caucasus many Ukrainians and other European groups. Early in the nineteenth century the Abkhasian merchants brought a few Negro slaves from Africa. Apparently descendants of these Negroes are occasionally, though very rarely, found along the Black Sea coast of the Caucasus.

Chapter 18

Carpathian Mountains

The Carpathian Mountains belong to western Europe. (See Map 23.) The region was acquired by the Soviet Union only recently (1945). The mountains extend from northwest to southeast, forming a continuation of the Alps and in the south merging into the northwestern extremity of the Balkan Mountains. To the Soviets belongs the middle part of the Carpathians, which is rather narrow and relatively low. The elevations vary from 1500 feet to 6500 feet, rarely exceeding 5000 feet. The mountains have a rather monotonous character and are covered with forests. The geological foundation of the Carpathians is composed of Cretaceous sedimentary rocks intermixed with sandstones, conglomerates, clay, and marl deposits. In the Tertiary period these masses of rock were folded contemporaneously with the folding of the Alps. The Carpathians were formed during the late Oligocene and early Miocene epochs, but during the Miocene they were already eroded to a peneplain. The present appearance of the Carpathians was caused by uplifting of the previously leveled mountains during Pliocene and Pleistocene epochs. Subsequently, rivers cut their valleys in the soft clay and marl rocks; the more resistant sandstones and conglomerates remained, appearing now as a series of parallel ridges.

During the ice age, glaciation in the Carpathians was only partial, covering merely the highest places. The Carpathians are not very rich in minerals; considerable deposits of oil are found only in the northwestern foothills in two places, and potash is mined to some extent.

The Carpathian Mountains of the Soviet Union are divided into three parts: The northwest and southeast ones are rather low with broad lengthwise valleys. The central part is more mountainous. Most of the passes to Hungary are in the northwest region, although in the southeast is found the famous Magyar Pass (3054 feet), through which the Magyars invaded the steppes of the Danube. The convenient passes make an easy communication between Russia and west-

Map 23. Carpathian Mountains.

1. Beech foothill forests.
2. Mixed conifer and broadleaf forests of medium elevations (1000 to 2000 feet altitude).
3. Spruce-fir forests of high elevation, with subalpine meadows above the timberline.
4. Broadleaf forests of medium and low elevation of the Transcarpathian Ukraine, composed chiefly of beech.
5. Broadleaf forests of foothills of the middle-Danube lowland, composed chiefly of oak.
6. Mixed forest region of eastern Europe.
7. Woodland region of eastern Europe.

206

ern Europe. This newly acquired region is of considerable strategic importance to the Soviet Union.

The foothills possess a rather mild climate, with an annual precipitation of 20 to 28 inches. Higher up the climate gets cooler and the precipitation increases to 30–48 inches a year; the winters are snowy. The abundance of precipitation is favorable to the development of many rivers. Such rivers as the Dniester and the Prut originate here.

Soils in the northwest and southeast foothills are partly of a chernozem type developed on the loess deposits but mostly of the gray forest type. Higher up the soils are of the brown forest type and the podzol type, and still higher of a mountain meadow type.

The natural vegetation is of a forest type. In the foothills and in the mountains of the lower northwest and southeast parts, the forests have been considerably cut over to give room for agriculture, but in the central, less accessible part the mountains are still covered with excellent broadleaf forests.

Foothill forests, where they still remain, are composed of oak, hornbeam, and beech. Higher up, from about 1000 feet to 2000 feet, are found excellent forests of oak, hornbeam, beech, linden, maple, and elm, with an admixture of fir and spruce. At higher elevations the conifers and beech begin to predominate. At about 4000 feet spruce forests prevail in the central and southwestern parts of the region and reach the upper limits of the forest zone at a little over 5250 feet. Above the timberline are found subalpine meadows and thickets of *Pinus montana*, alder, and rhododendron. On the other hand, the upper limit of the forests in the northeast, where the climate is drier and the elevations lower, is found surprisingly low, not higher than 4000 feet. Even at as low an elevation as 3000–3500 feet the spruce does not appear too healthy.

Animal life of the Carpathians is similar to that of the mixed forest region of eastern Europe. In the mountain forests there are still found bear, wolf, roebuck, lynx, boar, badger, marten, ferret, squirrel, and wild cat. Of game birds are found a grouse (*Tetrao tetrix*), black cock, and hazel hen. The black woodpecker is common.

On the southwestern slope of the Carpathian Mountains is located the Transcarpathian Ukraine. The lower and middle elevations of this area are covered with broadleaf forests; above are found mountain meadows. To the northwest and the southeast, just as on the opposite slope, the mountains are low, whereas in the central part the mountains are higher with a well-defined high crest. The whole southeastern slope of the Carpathian Mountains is cut by the system of the Tissa River. The climate of the foothills of the Transcarpathian Ukraine, as well as of the adjacent, hilly parts of the Middle Danube plains, is temperately warm and rather dry; summers are hot. In the mountains the precipitation is higher and the temperature is lower. In the plains and the foothills are found oak forests. In the middle elevations predominate beech forests; the spruce and fir belt above is not very broad. In the high mountains vegetation consists of brush-fields and meadows used by the natives as summer pastures.

The inhabitants of Carpathian Mountains are Ukrainians.

Chapter 19

Crimea

The Crimean Peninsula, located in the northern part of the Black Sea, was known in the days of ancient Greece as Tauric Chersonesus. The Phoenicians, Romans, and Greeks established their colonies there, and the Genoese traded there in the thirteenth century. In 1475 it became part of the Ottoman Empire, and at the time of the Mongol invasion of Russia (see Chapter 5) Crimea was invaded by the Tatars, who until very recently comprised 23 per cent of its 412,000 inhabitants (see Chapter 6). To the Russians, who annexed it in 1783, the peninsula is known by its Tatar name, Krym.

The peninsula, roughly, has the form of a lozenge to the eastern part of which is attached the Kerch Peninsula (Map 24). Crimea, together with its Kerch appendage, separates the Black Sea from the Azov Sea.

The peninsula covers an area of about 10,000 square miles and is connected with the mainland by a 5-mile-wide neck of land called, by the Russians, Perekop, a name conveying the idea of a place where one can defend himself by entrenching. In the old days of Greek colonies, and later during the Turkish rule, the isthmus was crossed by a moat and an embankment and was guarded by a fortress.

Topography

The part of the Azov Sea adjacent to the northeastern shores of Crimea is cut into numerous inlets and sloughs, forming part of a shallow gulf separated from the sea by a long, narrow stretch of land known as Arabatskaia Strelka (i.e., arrow).

Most of the Crimean Peninsula is flat or gently rolling prairie. The southern part is mountainous. The narrow strip of land beyond the mountains, facing the Black Sea, is one of the warmest parts of Russia. It is a resort area, the playground of the whole country.

The Crimean Mountains are remnants of a once large land that was connected to Asia Minor and to the Balkan Peninsula. Most of this land has sunk, and parts of the Black Sea near the southern shores of Crimea are still in the process of sinking.

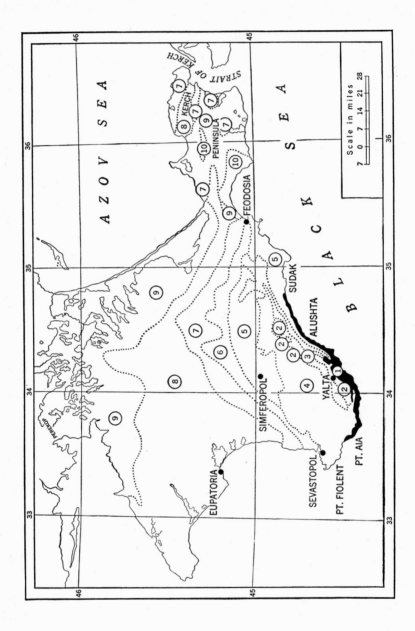

MAP 24. Natural Regions of Crimea. (*After Dobrynin, modified.*)

1. Coastal vegetation consisting in the west of mixed forest with evergreen understory, of Crimean pine, and in the east of mixed forest again but without evergreen understory.

2. Meadows and pastures of the Yaila plateau-like tops of the mountains.

3. Broadleaf forest, mostly beech.

4. Broadleaf forest, mostly oak.

5. Xerophytic shrubs with patches of grassland (in the east) and scrub oak.

6. Woodland.

7. Prairie with herbs (i.e., dicotyledons).

8. Prairie with needlegrass and feathergrass.

9. Dry steppe of semidesert type with wormwood.

10. Wormwood semideserts.

The northern, prairie part of Crimea is composed of marine Neocene and continental Tertiary deposits. On Kerch Peninsula the terrain was folded during the Upper Tertiary period. The Crimean Peninsula can thus be divided into three parts: (1) the Crimean Mountains, (2) the plains of northern Crimea, and (3) the folded land of the Kerch Peninsula.

The Crimean Mountains extend from Sevastopol to Feodosia, a distance of some 100 miles, and have a width of not more than 30 miles. They appear as an uplifted arch extending from southwest to northeast. One side of this arch drops abruptly to the Black Sea, and the other, the northern side, gradually descends to the plains, which were uplifted during the formation of the mountains. In the southwestern part the mountains consist of three parallel ranges, whereas in the northeastern part only two ranges are discernible.

The main southern range is the highest (Roman Kosh Mountain, 5062 feet). It is formed of Mesozoic sedimentary rock, predominantly Jurassic sandstones and limestones, which were subjected to Jurassic folding and subsequently leveled to a peneplain. This ancient peneplain later underwent further changes. Some parts were uplifted; others were sunk. The ancient peneplain areas appear now as flats on top of the range. These flats of the main range are at an elevation of about 3000 feet above sea level and extend in width for 2 or 3 miles. The flats have been used for grazing from time immemorial and are known by the Tatar name Yaila, meaning a pasture.*

As the south slope of the main chain drops abruptly to the Black Sea, it forms the narrow strip of the renowned South Coast of Crimea.† The whole coast is rugged, very picturesque, and of a rather complicated geological structure. Some volcanic structures form rocky points protruding into the sea, such as Point Fiolent or the dioritic laccolith, Aiu-Dagh (1784 feet, Bear Mountain in Turkic). The coastal strip is generally from 4 to 5 miles wide but narrows to 3 miles west of Alushta. From this point west to Yalta is the best part of the South Coast of Crimea.

The mountains of the western part of the South Coast of Crimea, from Point Aia to Alushta, are composed of so-called Tavrida sedimentary rocks forming a not-too-steep step-like slope. In some places,

---

* Many American geographers do not consider the flat tops of mountains as being necessarily the ancient peneplains. Russian geographers, however, apparently agree on this point. Cf. subsequent chapters.

† The South Coast of Crimea has the same fascination for Russian northerners as the Côte d'Azur for a Frenchman or as Florida for a midwesterner.

however, the limestones of the main chain drop abruptly from the Yaila top to the coast, forming cliffs several hundred feet high.

In the central part of the South Coast, east from Alushta to Kapsykhor, the main chain of mountains is located farther inland. The topography here is more monotonous, without abrupt cliffs at the edge of the water. The coastal strip of land is from 3 to 5 and even more miles wide. East of Kapsykhor the mountains again approach the coast, and the topography again becomes more interesting. Limestone formations, protruding into the sea near Sudak, are especially picturesque. On the extreme east end of the Crimean Mountains towers the ancient Jurassic volcano Kara Dagh (Black Mountain in Turkic), 1883 feet high. Its much-dislocated and eroded, grotesque buttresses drop abruptly to the Black Sea, forming many pretty little coves. West of Sevastopol and east of Feodosia the mountains disappear, and instead the foothills descend to the seashore.

The two northern ranges, or rather foothills, composed of Jurassic and Tertiary rocks were uplifted but not folded. The separation of these two ranges from the main range was caused by erosion.

The second range is separated from the main range by a valley 10 to 15 miles wide. It is lower than the main chain, reaching heights of 1500 to 2000 feet. The third ridge is still lower: 500 to 800 feet high. It is separated from the second ridge by an eroded valley 2 or 3 miles wide.

The tectonic movements in the mountains of Crimea have not stopped yet, and earthquakes occur frequently on the coast. In 1927 a severe earthquake took place in the vicinity of Yalta.

Because of the porous nature of the limestones of the main range, water percolates through the upper strata very readily and so the Crimean Yailas * lack running streams. Water sinks through the porous rocks until it reaches the impervious Middle and Lower Jurassic rocks, and then it appears on the surface of the valleys in the form of numerous springs and rather large streams. The river valleys of the main range are of a tectonic character, being cut along the fault lines, sometimes forming deep canyons.

The south slope of the main range, because of the soft, porous nature of the rocks, is notorious for its landslides, which are caused sometimes by earthquakes but mostly by melting snow or cloudbursts. The landslides cause a great deal of trouble to communication along the highway connecting the coast towns.

* Russian geographers often use the plural in speaking of the mountain flats of the Crimea.

The plains of northern Crimea are low and flat. Only in the northwestern part in the Tarkhankut region is the terrain slightly elevated.

The Kerch Peninsula, formed by folded Tertiary marine deposits, was subjected to much erosion and leveling so that at present it appears merely as an undulating plain. The Kerch Peninsula is rich in iron ore, conveniently found near the surface and near the shore of the Azov Sea. There are some indications of the presence of oil. Numerous shallow salt-water lakes are exploited as a source of various chemicals, such as common salt, epsom salt, and bromine.

Climate

Being protected from the north winds by the chain of mountains, the South Coast of Crimea, especially its western part, possesses a mild climate. Mean annual temperatures along the coast vary from 54°F to 56°F. In January the mean temperature is about 40°F. The absolute minimum of record was 6°F; the absolute maximum, about 100°F. The precipitation is not too abundant, and most of it occurs in winter. Cloudbursts are frequent. There is an abundance of sunshine throughout the year. The growing period at Yalta is long, with only 43 frosty days during the year. Temperature and precipitation data for Yalta, located in the western part of the South Coast of Crimea, are given in Table 14.

TABLE 14. TEMPERATURE AND PRECIPITATION AT YALTA, ELEVATION 13 FEET

Jan.	Feb.	Mar.	Apr.	May	June	July	Aug.	Sept.	Oct.	Nov.	Dec.	Year
Temperature, degrees Fahrenheit												Mean
39	40	44	51	61	69	76	75	66	58	48	43	56
Precipitation, inches												Total
2.6	1.9	1.7	1.2	1.1	1.8	1.5	1.1	1.4	1.8	2.4	2.8	21.3

The Yaila, i.e., the region of the flat tops of the main range, has a climate intermediate between the Mediterranean climate and that of the broadleaf forests of Europe. The mean annual temperature here varies from 40°F to 43°F, the mean of January being 24°F.

The climate of Crimea north of the mountains resembles the climate of the European prairie region; perhaps it is slightly milder. The absolute minimum recorded in the northern part of the peninsula was −30°F. Mean annual temperatures here are from 50° to 52°F. The mean January temperatures in the northeastern part of the Crimean prairies are 28° to 30°F and are slightly higher (34°F) in the northwestern part.

The precipitation generally is moderate, varying from 12 to 20 inches a year. The driest parts of the peninsula are located on the eastern coast, in the Kerch region, and in the northwest. On the western part of the coast the annual precipitation varies from 20 to 30 inches. On the western Yaila flats the annual precipitation may reach 40 inches or more, but farther east it drops to one-half that amount. As a whole, only the western part of the South Coast of Crimea has a distribution of precipitation resembling that of the Mediterranean region, i.e., predominantly winter precipitation. In the rest of the peninsula most of the precipitation falls during the summer.

Soils and Vegetation

Soils of the northern part of Crimea and on the Kerch Peninsula are the chestnut-colored prairie type. Farther south, in the foothills, the soil contains more humus, thus approaching the chernozem type. On the Yaila pastures of the main range the soils are either a mountain meadow type or a chernozem-like prairie type.

The slopes of the main range are composed of russet-brown forest soils in which iron oxide is not fully removed from the upper horizons, as it is in northern forests; hence the podzol layer is not very conspicuous in these soils. The russet-brown forest soils occur generally in warmer climates. Farther south they display a more intensive red color. Russian soil specialists call such soils krasnozem, i.e., red soils. This type of so-called lateritic soil is extremely rare within the borders of Russia but rather common in the warmer parts of the United States, for example, in the forests of low elevations in the Sierra Nevadas of California and in Oregon and Washington. On the South Coast of Crimea the soils are poorly developed but well suited for growing grapes and tobacco.

In comparison with eastern Europe, the vegetation of Crimea is very rich, totaling about 2000 species as compared with 3500 species for the whole of eastern Europe. The number of endemic plants is very small, however, amounting to only 13 species. There are many plants closely related to those found in Asia Minor, on the Balkan Peninsula, and in the Caucasus. Also, there are some northern species that migrated to Crimea during the glacial period.

Along the South Coast of Crimea, particularly in its western part, between Point Aia and Alushta, the vegetation approaches the Mediterranean type. To be sure, there are not the extensive xerophytic evergreen thickets of the Mediterranean maquis type—similar to the chaparral of southern California. There are, however, some evergreen shrubs, such as madrone (*Arbutus andrachne*), rockrose (*Cistus tauricus*), and butcher's-broom (*Ruscus aculeatus*), but they do not form maquis-like thickets, appearing only as an undergrowth of bushes in the open coastal oak and juniper forests. This type of evergreen scrub does not extend up the slope higher than 1000 feet. Neither does it extend much to the east along the coast.

East of Alushta the vegetation assumes the aspect of xerophytic grassland, inasmuch as it consists of needlegrass, wormwood (*Artemisia maritima taurica*), harmel peganum, and nitraria. The vegetation between Sudak and Feodosia is decidedly of the steppe type. Because of the mild climate of the South Coast of Crimea, there have been introduced many exotics that cannot be grown in other parts of the country except perhaps in some parts of Middle Asia and Transcaucasia. Among these are wistaria, magnolia, myrtle, Italian cypress, and some cold-resistant palms. Palms, especially, have a peculiar fascination for the people of Russia, which is predominantly a cold country, and when they are mentioned in geographic books it is always with a mixed feeling of reverence and admiration.

The Nikitski Botanical Garden, where many exotics, such as California's Jeffrey pine, are grown, is located near Yalta. Nut trees growing on the south coast include pistachio, walnut, almond, and chestnut. Fruit trees and grapes are also being cultivated, as well as tobacco.*

The natural vegetation of the South Coast of Crimea, where it still exists, consists, from seashore to 800–1000 feet, of open groves of juniper (*Juniperus excelsa*) and oak (*Quercus pubescens*), with an occasional admixture of terebinth pistachio (*Pistacia mutica*), a tree reaching 50 feet in height, and ash. In the understory are hornbeam (*Carpinus orientalis*) and hackberry (*Celtis glabrata*). Evergreen

---

* In the colder regions of Russia only ill-smelling tobacco, *Nicotiana rustica*, can be grown. Better varieties of cigarette tobacco succeed only in Moldavia, Crimea, and the Caucasus, although some cigar tobacco is cultivated in Saratov and Chernigov provinces.

shrubs of the maquis type are also found in the juniper-oak forest. Such deciduous shrubs as Christ's-thorn (*Paliurus spina-christi*), smoketree (*Rhus cotinus*), and Sicilian sumach (*Rhus coriaria*) form extensive thickets. In places patches of Pitsunda pine (*Pinus pithyusa Stankevitchi*) * are found.

Growing above the oak-juniper belt and often from sea level to the rim of the Yaila are forests of Crimean pine (*Pinus nigra pallasiana*), a form of Austrian pine. These pine forests have been badly cut over and in places replaced by oak, hornbeam, and dogwood. In the east part of the coast range and in its extreme west part, pine forests are absent. They reach their best development near Yalta. Above the pine belt, generally at 2600 feet above sea level, occur beech forests with an admixture of Austrian and common † pines, maple (*Acer hyrcanum*), hornbeam (*Carpinus*), and *Euonimus latifolia*. In the upper part of the beech forests one may encounter solitary old specimens of yew (*Taxus baccata*). The beech of the Crimean Mountains is apparently a hybrid of the European *Fagus sylvatica* and the Caucasian *Fagus orientalis*, both parent species also being found there. Juniper thickets of trailing *Juniperus depressa* form an upper fringe of the beech forests, above which are the Yaila flats.

The Yaila flats are generally treeless. Only in protected sites are thickets of maple (*Acer campestre*) to be found, together with mountain ash (*Sorbus aucuparia*),‡ ash (*Fraxinus*), hornbeam, and scattered old pines and yews. In a few places beech forests are found. In dry places in the Yaila the vegetation resembles that of the prairie, consisting of gray-green grasses, such as fescue, June grass, and brome. In low-lying meadows, where there is more moisture, the vegetation is more luxuriant, bright green, and consists of many angiosperms like those in the herbaceous steppe of the woodland region. A few examples are lady's-mantle (*Alchemilla*), clover (*Trifolium ambiguum*), dropwort (*Filipendula hexapetala*), and sedge (*Carex humilis*). Rocky places support northern alpine species such as rockjasmine (*Androsace villosa*), draba (*Draba cuspidata*), and violet (*Viola al-*

---

* *Pinus pithyusa* is generally considered a form of Aleppo pine (*P. halepensis*). Biochemically, however, it does not resemble this tree. Cf. N. T. Mirov, "The Terpenes (In relation to the Biology of the Genus *Pinus*)," *Ann. Rev. Biochem.*, Vol. 17, 1948, p. 533, Annual Reviews, Inc., Stanford, California.

† *Pinus sylvestris* var. *hamata*, which also grows in the Caucasus.

‡ *Sorbus* is a tree or a shrub with bright red bitter berries. It belongs, as many fruit trees do, to the rose family. Its English name, mountain ash, is misleading. The berries are used by Russians all over the country for making a bitter and rather dry alcoholic cordial or liqueur.

taica). These species are considered remnants of the glacial period, when the climate in Crimea was colder than now.

The Yaila region has been used for sheep grazing for many centuries, and the natural vegetation that covered the flats has been changed considerably. Some botanists believe that once the flat tops of the Crimean coast range were covered with forests, that the activities of man destroyed these forests, and that continuous overgrazing has prevented their regeneration. Berg,* however, maintains that the chernozems found in the Yaila pastures could not have developed under forests, and hence the Yaila always has been a grassland rather than a forested area.

The north slope of the Crimean main range is covered with forests. Just below the Yaila flats, at elevations of about 3600 to 4200 feet, the mountainside is covered with rather poor beech and patches of common pine (var. *hamata*). But below that belt at elevations ranging from 1900 to 3600 feet beautiful beech forests are found, sometimes in pure stands and sometimes with admixture of hornbeam, linden, maple, elm, and solitary old yews. The forests of this belt are of high value for watershed protection. Their use for other purposes is restricted. One of the best watershed protection forests is located in the upper reaches of the rivers Alma and Kacha. Of interest is the occurrence in these forests of such northern species as birch, sidebells, and dewberry, which again may be considered remnants of the glacial period when many northern species were pushed farther south than their present habitat.

Lower elevations of the north slope—1500 feet to 2000 feet—which can be considered foothills of the main range, are covered with oak forests (*Quercus sessiflora*) and hornbeam, together with evonymus, hazelnut, maple, ash, occasional aspen, and wild pear. Real forests, however, are found only in the western part of the foothills, where there are also patches of Austrian pine. In the remainder of the region the forests have the appearance of scrubby thickets or open groves.

Farther north, at low elevations, the countryside is of a woodland type, with patches of oak (*Quercus pubescens*), elm (*Ulmus campestris*), and such dry climate shrubs as blackthorn (*Prunus spinosa*) and hawthorn (*Crataegus monogina*).

At an elevation of 300 to 350 feet the woodland is replaced by the prairies of the Crimean Peninsula. The plains of northern Crimea are covered with prairie vegetation with a predominance of needlegrass

* *Priroda*, 2nd ed., 1938, pp. 214–215.

(*Stipa capillata*) and dicotyledons. In the lowlands of the northeastern part of Crimea, where alkali soils are found, the vegetation is almost a semidesert type, consisting of wormwood (*Artemisia taurica*)
and some chenopodiaceous species. Most of the prairies of northern
Crimea, i.e., almost the whole peninsula with the exception of the
southern mountains, is under intensive cultivation. Wheat is the main
crop.

Animal Life

The fauna of the prairie part of Crimea does not differ much from
the fauna of the Ukrainian steppes, described in Chapter 13. There
are the usual prairie rodents: jumping mouse, ground squirrel, field
mouse, etc. Birds are represented by the lark, hoopoe, bustard, eagle,
and crane. Certain animals that are common in the prairies of the
southern Ukraine are not found in the prairies of Crimea. These are
black fitch, ermine, otter, and field mouse.

Among the animals of the Crimean mountains many forms are identical, or very closely related, to those of the Caucasus, Asia Minor,
and the Balkan Peninsula. On the other hand, many animals of the
east European forests are absent in Crimea. There are no bear, boar,
or squirrel. In the Yaila flats such birds of prey as the griffon, eagle,
and vulture are conspicuous. Smaller birds noted are the blue thrush,
chaffinch, and chat. There are not very many species of birds along
the coast.

The fauna of the forests of the north slope of the main range is
more diversified. Elk, or stag (*Cervas elaphus*), and deer, or roebuck
(*Capreolus capreolus*), occur here, as well as badger and fox. The
wolf has been almost completely exterminated. Redbreast, tit, wild
pigeon, owl, and woodpeckers are found here.

In the foothills little wild life is left. One may occasionally find
Crimean fitch (*Mustela nivalis nikolski*) and such birds as starling,
eagle, owl (*Bubo*), jackdaw, and oriole.

Crimea has many endemic species of mollusks closely related to the
Mediterranean and Asia Minor species.

Of note among the lizards is an endemic gecko (*Gymnodactylus
danilewski*). In the mountains is the common blacksnake (*Elaphe
situla*). The whipsnake (*Coluber jugularis*) occurs in the prairies as
well as in the mountains of Crimea. Chirping cicada (*Cicada plebeia*),
absent in the north, adds to the fascination of Crimea. There are also
found scorpions and scolopendrids.

People

The population of Crimea is composed of Russians, Ukrainians, and many other, lesser groups. The Tatar population is considerable; until lately Crimea was listed as the Crimean Tatar Autonomous Republic. At present the peninsula is listed as one of the provinces of Russia.

Chapter **20**

Ural Mountains

Topography

The Ural Range, or as the Russians call it, simply the Ural,* separates Europe from Asia (Map 25). Its west slope merges gradually into the plains of eastern Europe; its east slope descends rather abruptly to the Western Siberian lowland. The dividing line between Europe and Asia, therefore, is drawn along the east slope of the mountains, leaving the Ural within the boundaries of eastern Europe. The Ural Mountains extend in an approximately meridional direction from the Arctic to the steppes of the south, a distance of about 1200 miles. The northernmost point of the Ural is Konstantinov Kamen,† not far from the Kara Sea, at the latitude 68°30′.

From the northern extremity of the Ural a low range, Pai Khoi, extends northwest towards the Yugorski Shar (Strait). The average height of Pai Khoi is about 1000 feet; the range is composed of crystalline and sedimentary rocks mainly of the Devonian period. The Ural Mountains are separated from Pai Khoi by a 30-mile stretch of lowland tundra. The northern continuation of the range is evident in the islands of Vaigach and Novaia Zemlia.

The Ural is formed by a series of parallel chains, composed of Paleozoic, predominantly marine deposits varying in age from Cambrian to Permian. The central axis of the range is formed by metamorphic rocks, dating partly from the pre-Cambrian period and partly from the Lower Paleozoic epoch. The most intensive folding along the extent of the present range occurred during the Carboniferous period.‡ Since the end of Paleozoic times the mountains have been leveled by erosion, and the resultant peneplain was uplifted at the end of the Tertiary period.

The Ural is very rich in minerals, such as iron, copper, gold, platinum, manganese, nickel, and precious stones. The whole range may

* Pronounced *oural*. The plural form is never used in Russian literature.
† Literally "stone," an obsolete name for any rocky summit in the region. In old days the Ural as a whole was referred to as "the Kamen."
‡ It may be classified as the Upper Paleozoic or Hercynian period.

221

be divided, more or less arbitrarily, into four parts: the Arctic Ural, Northern Ural, Middle Ural, and Southern Ural.* The Arctic Ural is a narrow range, only 15 to 20 miles wide, cut by transverse valleys

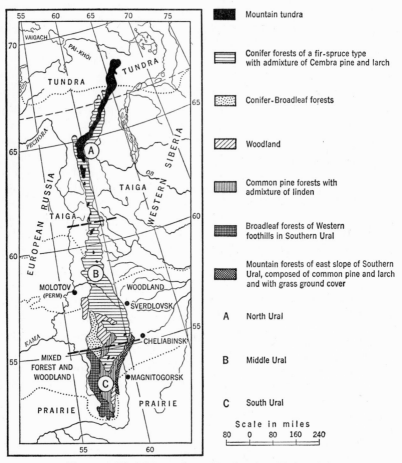

MAP 25.   Ural Mountains.   (*Partly after Dobrynin.*)

into separate mountain chains descending abruptly to the surrounding tundra.   Elevations here range from 2000 to 2600 feet.

The Northern Ural begins at 65°5′ latitude N and extends to Mt. Isherim, located at 61°04′ latitude N.   The highest peak of the whole

* It is interesting to follow the change of geographic names from Samoyed and Finno-Ugrian in the north to Russian in the central part and to Bashkir and other Turkic languages in the south.

Ural is located at 65° latitude N. It is Mt. Narodnaia,* elevation 6183 feet.

In the Northern Ural there are found considerable traces of glaciation; at present several very small glaciers are found on the highest peaks. Essentially, the Northern Ural consists of two chains of mountains, the eastern one being the watershed divide.

The Middle Ural extends south to Mt. Yurma, elevation 3448 feet, located at 55°25' latitude N. In this region the elevations are much lower than both north and south. The topography here gives an appearance of a very low series of mountains leveled to almost a peneplain. The railroad from Perm (Molotov) to Sverdlovsk crosses the region at a divide with an elevation of only 1350 feet.

The Southern Ural expands in width to about 100 miles and is composed of several parallel chains, the eastern one being the watershed divide. It is known as Ural Tau and is only 3000 feet high. The highest mountain in the Southern Ural is Mt. Yaman Tau (Goat Mountain), 5432 feet. Mt. Taganai, whose name in Bashkir means the Moon's Support, is 3503 feet high. The Southern Ural extends south to the middle flows of the Ural River, i.e., to 52° latitude N, but once south of the River Belaia (Russian for white, feminine gender), which cuts the western chains diagonally from northeast to southwest, the Ural loses its mountain character and is changed into a rolling plain 1500 to 1700 feet high, cut by deep river valleys. Only in the east the Irendyk Range, with its rugged rocky slopes, retains the character of a mountain chain. South and southeast of this region extends a vast rolling plain with occasional remnants of mountains, such as Mt. Magnitnaia (Magnet Mountain), with its enormous iron deposits. This plain was formed in the process of denudation during the Mesozoic era.

Climate

In comparison with the adjacent lowlands the Ural possesses a climate with lower temperatures and higher precipitation. Of course, extending from the northern tundras to the southern steppes, it possesses a great variation of climate, often complicated by the local conditions existing in any mountain country. In spite of its low elevations the Ural acts as a definite climatic barrier. It is colder east of the Ural than west of the range. Moreover, on the west slope more precipitation falls than on the east. The moist air masses moving from

* A new name, meaning People's Mountain.

the Atlantic are blocked by the Ural. Table 15 gives temperature and precipitation data for Zlatoust (Russian for Chrysostom), located almost on the borderline between the Middle and Southern Ural, on the railroad line between Cheliabinsk and Ufa.

TABLE 15. TEMPERATURE AND PRECIPITATION AT ZLATOUST,
ELEVATION 1502 FEET

Jan.	Feb.	Mar.	Apr.	May	June	July	Aug.	Sept.	Oct.	Nov.	Dec.	Year
				Temperature, degrees Fahrenheit								Mean
4	8	17	33	49	58	61	57	46	32	18	8	33
				Precipitation, inches								Total
0.7	0.5	0.6	0.9	2.1	3.0	4.1	2.8	2.0	1.5	1.3	0.9	20.4

Vegetation

The Pai Khoi Range and the Arctic Ural north of the 68th parallel are covered with lichen and moss tundra. Scrubby larch (*Larix sibirica*) begins to appear at the sources of the Kara River. At the 67th parallel above the tundra floor there are forests of larch with an admixture of spruce (*Picea obovata*) and birch (*Betula tortuosa*). The upper limit of forest vegetation in the Arctic Ural is located at an elevation of 650 to 1000 feet.

In the northern part of the Northern Ural birch often forms the timberline, above which tundra is found. At the latitudes of 63° to 64°, i.e., near the Telpos Iz Mountain, the conifer forests, which cover adjacent plains and which consist of spruce with an admixture of fir, cembra pine, and birch, extend as high as 1300 to 1600 feet. A transition zone is located at elevations of from 1600 to 2300 feet, where open birch groves with an admixture of fir, spruce, and larch alternate with the grass meadows. Above this alpine-woodland zone grow scrub thickets of dwarf birch (*Betula nana*), and still higher is found rocky lichen tundra with occasional patches of flowering plants, such as dryad (*Dryas octopetala*), geranium (*Geranium albiflorum*), veratrum (*Veratrum lobelianum*), and bistort (*Polygonum bistorta*). The timberline at 62° is found at about a 2400-foot elevation.

The Middle Ural, with its leveled and low topography, possessing only occasional rocky summits, is covered in its low elevations with conifer forests of the spruce-fir type, with an admixture of birch, aspen, and common pine (*Pinus sylvestris*). The rocky summits above the forest zone are covered with alpine vegetation in which arctic plants predominate. In the northern part the conifer forest (called taiga) ascends to about 3000 to 3100 feet. On the granites and perido-tites grow common pine-cembra pine forests with an admixture of Siberian larch. In the southern part the alpine zone is absent. Forests in this region are composed of larch, common pine, and occasionally some spruce. After fire or logging, the forests are temporarily re-placed by birch and aspen.

The Southern Ural rises above the surrounding woodland as a series of parallel ranges covered in the northern part * with either common pine-larch forests or with fir-spruce taiga. In the western part linden (*Tilia cordata*) is admixed.

The eastern watershed-dividing range, known as Ural Tau and hav-ing elevations up to 3135 feet, is covered with common pine-larch forests with a sprinkling of broadleaf trees. In the Southern Ural there are very few mountain summits that rise above the timberline. Mt. Iremel (elevation 5248 feet) is one of these. On its slopes, above the forest zone, are park-like spruce groves alternated with patches of meadows. Higher up the spruce assumes a scrubby, trailing growth habit. The flat top of the mountain is covered with tundra-like vege-tation.

The western foothills of the Southern Ural and adjacent plains, which are part of the mixed forest region, are covered with elm-linden forests having an admixture of maple, oak, and occasional birch and aspen.

On the east slope the Southern Ural merges into the west Siberian birch woodland. European broadleaf trees, such as oak and maple, are absent here.

Animal Life

Extending from the tundra through the forest region to the prairies, the Ural possesses a rather diversified animal life. In the taiga forests of the Ural are found moose, bear, roebuck, sable, squirrel, and

---

* It is interesting to note that in a description of the forests of this region the dense spruce-fir forests are referred to by Russian geographers as *taiga*, whereas the rather open pine-larch stands are described as *forests*.

marten, the last three named being subject to commercial hunting. Game birds consist of a capercaillie (*Tetrao urogallus*), black grouse (*Lyrurus tetrix*), and a small grouse (*Tetrastes bonasia*). Of interest is the occurrence of ptarmigan (*Lagopus lagopus*) in the Southern Ural.

Wild reindeer are found occasionally during the winter in the pine forests as far south as the 53rd parallel. Domestic reindeer, however, are tended only north of the 60th parallel. Accentors (*Prunella atrogularis* and *P. montanella*) and the arctic ptarmigan (*Lagopus lagopus*) are found in the birch thickets of the Northern Ural. In the alpine zone occurs another species of ptarmigan (*Lagopus mutus komensis*), together with a longspur (*Calcarius lapponicus*) and a plover (*Charadrius apricarius*), all three being common birds of the tundra region. In the spruce-cembra pine forests of the Northern Ural lives an Asiatic thrush (*Turdus ruficollis atrogularis*) that does not occur west of the Ural.

People

The population of the region is predominantly Russian. In the northern part of the Ural live some Samoyeds; south of them is the sparsely populated country of the Komi (Zyrians) and of the Voguls. In the Southern Ural, among the Russians live some Bashkirs.

Chapter 21

Altai System
and Kuznetsk Basin

Administratively, the Altai Mountains lie mostly in the Oirot Autonomous Province of the Altai administrative region; only the southwestern part of the Altai belongs to Kazakhstan. In the northeast the Altai (the Golden, in Turkic) system is connected with Kuznetsk Ala Tau; * in the east it is connected with the Sayan Mountains (Map 26). In the west the Altai merges gradually into the Kazakh folded land; in the north it is limited by an abrupt fault escarpment 600 to 1000 feet high; north of the fault are located the structurally simple, flat Western Siberian lowlands. The fault escarpment extends along the 52nd parallel; in the southwest it loses its definite character.

The structural center of the Altai system is located in Mongolia. Along the Russian border there extends the high range of Tabyn Bogdo Ola (i.e., Five Sacred Mountains) with the highest summit Mt. Keytyn, 15,262 feet. Southeast the Mongolian Altai extends deeply into the desert; † to the west are located the ranges of the southern Altai, which are wholly within the borders of Soviet Union; to the east lie the watershed dividing ranges between the Ob and the Yenisei drainage; this is the eastern Altai. Between the southern Altai and the eastern Altai is located the inner Altai. (See Map 27.)

The ranges of the southern or Greater Altai form a watershed divide between the drainage of Lake Zaisan and the Black Irtysh (or Kara Irtysh) to the southwest and the River Bukhtarma to the northeast. The southern Altai is a high chain of mountains: Tarbagatai is in the east, ‡ the Sarym-Sakty and Narym ranges are in the south. The eastern part of the southern Altai reaches elevations of over 12,800

* In the Altai region Turkic names of places are mixed with Russian names even more than in the mountains of Middle Asia. In the southeastern part Mongolian names appear.

† Explored by Russians toward the end of the nineteenth century.

‡ Not to be confused with the Tarbagatai Range of the eastern part of Middle Asia.

feet; the western part, about 11,000 feet.   The summits of the whole
chain are snow-covered throughout the year.   There are found extensive snowfields and numerous glaciers.   The chain is not much dissected;
its northern slope is steep, the southern slope is gentle; the passes are
high and difficult.   The eastern Altai consists of the Sailugem Range,

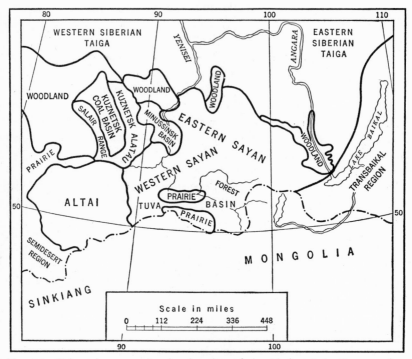

MAP 26.   Orientation map, showing location of the Altai and the Sayan regions
in relation to adjacent geographical regions.

the Chikhachev Mountains (a Russian name), and the Shapshal Range.
The Sailugem Range divides the Katun drainage (i.e., that of the
Ob) from the drainage of the Mongolian river Kobdo.   The elevations
of the eastern Altai run between 10,000 and 13,000 feet.   Northwest
of the Shapshal Range extend the Gorbu or Abakan Mountains.

Characteristic of the eastern Altai are level summits, gentle slopes,
and extensive rolling plateaux, such as the Chuia and Kurai "steppes"
and the Ukok (pronounced oucoke) Plateau.   These gently rolling
highland areas are situated at about 5000 to 8200 feet above sea level
and are very similar to the Mongolian high desert plateaux.

The inner or central Altai consists essentially of two chains of mountains. The southern chain is very high with extensive glaciers and snow-covered rugged peaks. This chain has an average height of 10,000 feet and is known as Katun Belki (i.e., Whites).* In the central part of the chain is located the double-headed Mt. Belukha (Russian for White Mountain). Its eastern peak is 15,154 feet high, and its western peak is 14,563 feet high. Belukha is the highest mountain in the Russian Altai; it is almost always surrounded with clouds and is very seldom seen clearly.

To the east of Katun Belki are located the Chuia Bielki. The two ranges are separated by the Argut gorge. To the west of Katun Belki, separated by the Katun Valley, lies the Kholzun Range, where elevations are lower, 7200 to 7900 feet. From the Kholzun Range and from the more northeasterly located Terektin Range there radiate towards the northwest numerous low ridges where elevations (of about 6000 feet) do not reach timberline and where no peaks are above the line of permanent snow.

Topography

The Altai Mountains are composed of Cambrian rocks, mostly limestones, and also of metamorphic schists and of Silurian and Devonian deposits. Lower Carboniferous marine strata are found only in the southwestern part of the system, the so-called Rudnyi (i.e., Ore-bearing) Altai. Granite intrusions are common, especially in the eastern part. During the Upper Devonian epoch the sea retreated from most of the area now occupied by the Altai system, excepting the southwestern part. During the Carboniferous period a great deal of erosion took place, and towards the Permian epoch the Altai region became completely peneplained. Metamorphic schists of greenish color (due to chlorite) are widely distributed in most of the Altai; of these are composed the Katun Range, Chuia Range, and many other ranges of the system. There are no Mesozoic rocks in the Altai Mountains. During the Tertiary period the Altai did not exist as a mountainous region. At the end of the Tertiary and the beginning of the Quaternary period considerable dislocations of a fault type took place, accompanied with cleavages and tectonic rupturing. At that time the Altai Mountains achieved their present shape. The contemporary Altai is a folded mountain system modified by the action of ice and water. In it the old peneplain areas are very conspicuous. These ap-

* Belok, plural belki, means egg white; proteins are also called belki.

pear as high plateaux on the tops of the mountain ranges, sometimes
swampy, with meandering, sluggish streams; when the streams reach
the brim of a plateau, they rush downward, cutting deep gorges and

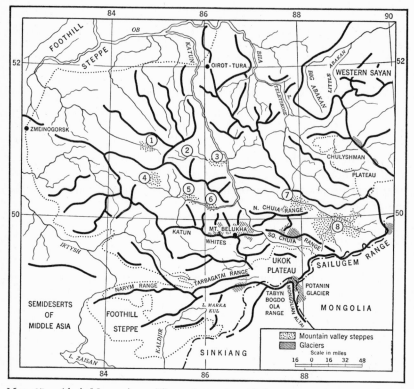

MAP 27. Altai Mountains. Throughout the Altai system are scattered open
grassland areas occupying flat-bottomed broad mountain valleys and called locally
the steppes (cf. p. 134). The largest steppe valleys are shown on the map as
follows: 1. Kan steppe. 2. Tenghin steppe. 3. Ursul steppe. 4. Abai
steppe. 5. Uimon steppe. 6. Kotandin steppe. 7. Kurai steppe. 8. Chuia steppe.
(*After Suslov.*)

forming high waterfalls. The landscape in the middle elevations, say
between 1600 to 3300 feet, is that of forest-clad, well-drained, and moderately eroded mountains, gradually merging into prairie foothills.

The snowline in the Altai Mountains is located between 8500 and
9800 feet; in the eastern part of the region, where the climate is drier,
it is found at somewhat higher elevations. In the Katun and Chuia
ranges on north slopes the zone of permanent snow begins at about

8000 to 8500 feet, whereas on the south slopes it begins at elevations of 8500 to 9800 feet.

The total area covered with glaciers is about 175 square miles, and the total number of glaciers amounts to 569. Glaciers of a hanging type are by far the most important. There are no extensive firn fields, and the masses of ice feeding glaciers generally hang from the surrounding cliffs.

There are five major centers of glaciation in the Altai: the Katun Range, the south Chuia Range, the north Chuia Range, the east part of the southern Altai, and the Tabyn Bogdo Ola center. The Katun Range comprises the most intensively glaciated part of the Altai. The glaciers are concentrated chiefly around Mt. Belukha. In the vicinity of this mountain are located some thirty glaciers, occupying a total area of 27 square miles. The most prominent glaciers of the valley type descending from Mt. Belukha are Mensu Glacier, about 7 miles long and covering an area of 4.6 square miles; Katun Glacier, which is about 5 miles long and which covers an area of 4.25 square miles; Berelski Glacier, which is also about 5 miles long but covers only 3 square miles. The glaciers descend to 6600–6400 feet. On the northern slope of the Katun Range are found 133 glaciers, covering a total area of 45 square miles; on the southern slope there are only 69 glaciers, with a total area of 21 square miles. The velocity of the ice movement of the Katun Glacier is 4 to 10 inches a day. As a whole the Altai glaciation is diminishing; since 1925 the Katun Glacier has retreated a distance of 36 to 56 feet and its western part has completely separated from the main body of the ice.

In the south Chuia Range the glaciers are distributed more uniformly; there are many valley-type glaciers, but generally they are not very long. The largest glacier of this area is the Big Taldurin Glacier, which descends the north slope of the range to an elevation of about 7700 feet. The glacier is 4.6 miles long, and it occupies an area of about 7 square miles.

In southern Altai there are located about 100 glaciers. The largest of all is the Alakhinski Glacier, 5 miles long and covering an area of about 8 square miles. Apparently it is the largest glacier within the Russian Altai.*

In the Mongolian Altai, south of the Soviet border, are found the greatest glaciers of the whole Altai system. Potanin Glacier is 10

* S. P. Suslov, *Physical Geography of the USSR*, 1947, Moscow, p. 90.

miles long and about 20 square miles in area.* It is located in the Tabyn Bogdo Ola Range and with other, lesser glaciers feeds streams flowing to Dzungaria.

During the ice age there occurred at least two, perhaps three or even four, glaciations. The first one covered the whole mountain region with a continuous thick cover of ice with occasional tongues of ice extending far into the adjacent plains; such was Bukhtarma Glacier, about 100 miles long.

The second glaciation was, however, of a strictly valley type in which glaciers descended for many miles, leaving after their retreat numerous terminal moraines. Mountain lakes are numerous in the upper parts of the ancient glacial valleys. Of the lakes of the Altai region the largest is Teletskoie Ozero (a Russian name; ozero means lake),† located along the west slope of the Gorbu Range. The lake is located at an elevation 1550 feet and is 1065 feet deep; it is about 50 miles long and only about 2 miles wide, covering an area of 90 square miles. The mountains tower above both sides for more than 6000 feet, and the lake has an appearance of a Norwegian fiord. The River Chulyshman flows into the southern (upper) end of the lake; the Biia, which together with the Katun forms the Ob, flows from the northern end of the lake. Teletskoie Lake has mainly a recreational value; some commercial fishing is practiced there; its possibilities as a source of water power are considerable. There are no commonly accepted theories as to the origin of Teletskoie Lake; some consider it a fault trough, whereas others believe that it was formed by glacial action with subsequent moraines damming the northern end of the valley.

Marka Kul, the largest alpine-type lake of the region, is located in the southern Altai, not far from the international border, on an elevation of 4700 feet in the bottom of a structural valley between the Kurchum and Azu ranges. The area of the lake is 175 square miles; its southern shores are rocky and abrupt; its northern shores are low. The largest stream flowing into the lake has a Russian name, Topolevka, meaning Cottonwood Creek. From the lake flows the River Kaldjir (a Turkic name), a tributary to the Kara Irtysh.

Considerable mineral deposits are found in the southwestern part of the region along the River Irtysh. This area during the end of the

* Named after G. N. Potanin (1835–1920), explorer of Central Asia. In 1876–1879 he explored northwestern Mongolia; in 1884–86 he traveled in Tangut country bordering Tibet and Central Mongolia; in 1892–93 he visited Szechuan.

† The Turkic name of the lake is Altyn Kol, i.e., Golden Lake.

Permian epoch was the scene of a rupturing and breaking of a southeast to northwest extension, several hundred miles in length. Rich deposits of rare elements have been discovered along this line of rupture. Sixty-two per cent of the lead and 46 per cent of the total production of the zinc of the Soviet Union is mined here. Rare metals are also found here, together with some gold and silver.

Climate

Because of its position almost in the center of Asia, the Altai region possesses a definitely continental climate; whereas warm and moist air masses from the Atlantic barely reach the region, the cold and dry air of the Arctic finds no obstructions on its way towards the Altai Mountains. Accordingly, winters in the region are much more severe than would be expected at the relatively low latitudes of the Altai. However, the Altai system lies as a warm island in the midst of much colder lowlands. The cold Siberian air does not penetrate too far beyond the foothills. In February, for instance, the mean temperature at the Zyrian mine of the southwestern Altai, elevation 1476 feet, is −8°F, whereas at Altai Stanitsa,* which is located at 2876 feet, or 1400 above the former station, the mean February temperature is 10°F. On the other hand, in summer, the Altai region is cooler than the surrounding lowlands. The high plateaux cool off considerably during winter; at Kosh Agach in the Chuia steppe, elevation 5538 feet, the mean January temperature is −24°F; the absolute minimum ever recorded was −55°F. As the snow cover there is negligible (less than 3 inches), permanently frozen ground is found only 3½ feet below the surface. On the high plateaux and in the alpine zone of the mountain ranges, even in summertime, blizzards are not unusual; in July the temperature may drop to 20 or 25°F, and small lakes and swamps may be covered with ice, and snow may fall instead of rain.

In winter dry southern and southwestern winds prevail; in summer the winds are of a northwestern and western direction and they bring rains. Maximum precipitation occurs in August and September. Generally, in the Altai region, the annual precipitation is above 12 inches. At the middle elevations it may reach 40 inches. In the western Altai (at Zmeinogorsk, a Russian name meaning the town of Snake Mountain) the annual precipitation amounts to 20 inches, but farther west, near the dry steppes, it drops to 16 inches. In some places in the western Altai the annual precipitation may be as high as 60 inches.

* Stanitsa is a Russian name for Cossack settlements.

The fault trough areas of high elevations (the so-called steppes), being surrounded with high mountains, are exceedingly dry. Ukok Plateau receives only 11 inches of annual precipitation. Most of the precipitation occurs in summer; in winter there is not enough snow for sled travel, and wheel vehicles are used throughout the year. Remains of ancient irrigation ditches have been found in this area.

The southern part of the Altai also is very dry. In the lower reaches of the Bukhtarma, the annual rainfall amounts to less than 12 inches. In the northeastern part of the region, where relatively high ridges protrude far north, catching a considerable amount of moisture, the annual precipitation is high, up to 35 inches, and snow in winter is deep.

In the central Altai the precipitation is lighter, generally 20 to 24 inches a year.

Vegetation

Tertiary vegetation of the Altai region, with its moist and warm climate, was similar to the North American and east Asiatic Tertiary vegetation, but not to the European. South of Marka Kul have been found fossil remains of *Sequoia langsdorffi, Taxodium dubium, Ginkgo adiantoides, Liriodendron tulipifera, Pterocarya densinervi.* The present vegetation is typically Siberian; of European broadleaf trees only linden is found in the Kuznetsk Ala Tau. The influence of man on vegetation in the Altai is not so pronounced as in the mountains of Middle Asia and is of a rather recent origin. With the intrusion of Russian colonists considerable areas have been depleted of forests, partly by cutting, partly by burning. Some travelers of the beginning of this century record a puzzling destruction of forests by girdling in places neither suitable for cultivation nor accessible for logging.* As in all newly settled countries, forests were considered a menace and a nuisance.

The prairie region touches the Altai in the west and goes up in the foothills to an elevation of 1100 to 1500 feet. A mixture of shrubs, including *Rosa acaulis, Spiraea hypericifolia, Lonicera tatarica, Caragana arborescens, Amygdalis nana,* forms a strip between the flat prairie and the Altai foothills. In the low foothills the soils are better than in the adjacent steppes and the vegetation is more luxurious, of a

* S. Grigoriev, "Severnyi Altai," *Zemlevedenie,* Vol. 36, Nos. 1–2, pp. 180–210, 1924. [In Russian. German summary.]

woodland prairie type, i.e., having a considerable admixture of dicotyledons, such as dropwort (*Filipendula hexapetala*) and sainfoin
(*Onobrychis sativa*). On rocky slopes the vegetation is of a xerophytic character, with many leguminous species of the genera *Astragalus* and *Oxytropis;* there are over 100 species of the latter in the
Altai region.

Steppe vegetation of the Central Asiatic type penetrates deeply into
the southern Altai from Zaisan depression and from the Irtysh valley
and occasionally goes up as high as 5000 feet. Mountain steppes are
found occasionally in the medium elevations (3000 feet to 3500 feet)
of the forest area of the Altai as discontinuous stripes and patches;
the vegetation here is similar to that of the western Altai foothills.
After the usual outburst of spring flowering of buttercups, adonis,
anemone, and other perennials, there appear feathergrass (*Stipa jo-
annis*) and needlegrass (*Stipa capillata*) and other prairie grasses and
herbs. On the rocky spots grow xerophyls like winterfat (*Eurotia
ceratoides*), summer cypress (*Kochia prostrata*), and lichens. Thus
the vegetation here is of a semidesert character.

Steppe vegetation is also found in the broad glacial valleys; the
broader the valley the more steppe-like is the vegetation; the higher
a valley ascends the shorter and the more xerophytic is the vegetation.
Here are found a species of needlegrass (*Stipa consanguinea*), crested
wheatgrass (*Agropyron cristatum*), and small globethistle (*Echynops
ritro*). In the upper reaches of the valleys the vegetation of the
prairies assumes a decidedly Mongolian character.

In high elevations of the southeastern part of Altai are located ancient broad fault trough valleys covered with dry steppe vegetation
similar to that of the adjacent gravelly and rocky mountain steppes of
northern Mongolia. Along the River Chuia at 5500 to 5900 feet lies
the Kurai steppe. Vegetation in this and similar steppes is very monotonous, consisting of xerophytic astragals, *Stipa glareosa, Dontoste-
mon perennis, Lasiogrostis (Stipa) splendens*, peashrub (*Caragana
bungei*), and sagebrush. The Kurai steppe has a predominance of
prostrate forms of astragals and oxytropis, whose underground parts
are much more developed than the aboveground parts.

The Ukok Plateau, which has an average elevation of about 8000
feet, is a rocky steppe with poorly developed, sometimes saline, chestnut-brown soils and is covered with sagebrush, wildrye (*Elymus dasys-
tachis*), and crested wheatgrass. Closer to the mountains grow edelweiss (*Leontopodium alpinum*) and alpine poppy (*Papaver alpinum*).

Glaciers descending towards the plateau terminate at 8500 to 8200 feet; i.e., they almost touch the slopes of the dry steppe.

In the northeastern part of the Altai the forests merge into the Kuznetsk region fir forests and then into the Siberian taiga. In the west and southwest of the Altai system the forest belt begins at about 1000 or 1200 feet above sea level and it extends up to elevations ranging from 6500 feet to 8000 feet.

Altai forests differ from those of the adjacent Siberian taiga in their absence of extensive swamps and in their more luxurious herbaceous vegetation. Broadleaf trees are represented only by birch and aspen, and even these two species are of a rather secondary importance. Of the shrubs sometimes reaching the size of small trees mountain ash and chokecherry (*Prunus padus*) are important, small berries of both being of value as food for birds and human beings. Birch and aspen usually appear in the places where the climax conifer type of forest was cut or burned. Coniferous species of the Altai are the same as in the Siberian taiga, consisting of cembra pine, fir (*Abies sibirica*), spruce (*Picea obovata*), common pine (*Pinus sylvestris*), and larch (*Larix sibirica*). Towards the northeast the first three species predominate, forming a dark, gloomy type of forest, locally called chern (meaning black or dark). Towards the south and southeast larch predominates, forming open, light groves. Common pine does not grow up the mountains higher than 2300 feet, and it never occurs in pure stands but is mixed with birch and aspen and, in higher elevations, with larch. Pine forests have underbrush of *Rhododendron dahuricum*. In the openings, in spring, grow anemones (*Anemone altaica, A. caerulea, Pulsatilla patens*) and, later, *Iris ruthenica* (called violet in southern Siberia) whose dark blue-violet flowers possess a very delicate odor, peony (*Paeonia anomala*), martagon lily, dark blue gentians, sky-blue forget-me-nots, orange-colored *Trollius,* and other showy Siberian summer flowers.

Above 2300 feet larch forms pure park-like forests with numerous openings covered with such shrubs as spiraea, rose, barberry, honeysuckle, red currants and the usual array of bright flowers, persisting throughout the summer. Red currants grow in such a profusion that very often a whole hillside is covered with the solid color of red berries. Larch grows up to an elevation of 6500 feet and often forms a timberline of rather straight trees, unlike the timberlines of cembra pine, which always looks weatherbeaten, crooked, and even scrubby. Cembra pine apparently endures greater heights than the other conifers; solitary pines may be found as high as 8500 feet.

Conifer forests with a predominance of spruce occur in the north-eastern Altai to an elevation of 3500 feet. Higher up, cembra pine begins to dominate and often forms pure stands. The cembra pine forests are rather dense and dark, and in such forests the underbrush of the usual Altai shrubs is rather sparse. At higher elevations in the forests is found an abundance of large-leaved saxifrage, or badan (*Bergenia crassifolia*), a common border plant of American gardens. Locally it is used as a source of tannin.

In deep, moist valleys, forests consist of a mixture of larch, cembra pine, spruce, and fir. The bottoms of deep, cold canyons are usually covered with pure spruce stands. Herbaceous vegetation in the openings of these forests is exceptionally tall; it consists of *Delphinium*, *Aconitum*, burnet (*Sanguisorba alpina*), some tall umbellifers, and many other plants.

Fir and spruce extend almost to the timberline, but birch is not found above 4500 feet; aspen disappears at a somewhat higher elevation.

As has been already mentioned, large areas of forests have been destroyed by fire. Larch forests endure fire well, because the trees grow fairly far apart and because their thick bark protects them from heat damage. Dense cembra pine forests suffer much more. Reproduction of these forests is exceedingly slow. The burned-over area is invaded by tall, pink-flowering, and rather attractive fireweed (*Epilobium angustifolium*), as happens in many other temperate parts of the world including North America. Then birch and aspen take possession of the area, and gradually the conifers are reproduced under their canopy. Occasionally, burned-over country is covered with thick raspberry brambles; the berries are gathered by people of the area for food.

Above an altitude of 4500 feet there is no birch or aspen, nor will fireweed grow there. Burned forests are replaced by cembra pine and larch reproduction without going through the birch-aspen stage.

Forest meadows are covered with herbaceous vegetation reaching over 3 feet in height. Near places of habitation these meadows are used as hayfields. Open areas of southern slopes (called by the Russian settlers the elani, a word that is not understood in European Russia) also are covered with tall herbaceous plants, such as monkshood (*Aconitum septentrionale*), cowparsnip (*Heracleum dissectum*), and thorowax (*Bupleurum aureum*).

The transition area between the forest and the alpine zones is occupied by dwarf birch (*Betula nana*), low-growing willows, *Cotoneaster*, honeysuckle, and fragrant currant (*Ribes fragrans* var. *infracanum*).

Subalpine meadows are covered with herbaceous vegetation (up to 5 feet tall) of delphinium, cowparsnip (*Heracleum*), *Saussurea*, and *Swertia obtusa*. The higher is the elevation the shorter are the plants; the alpine zone is located at 6500–7900 feet to 9200–9800 feet above sea level. The vegetative period here is very short. Toward the end of May snow melts on the slopes; as early as August the first snow covers the ground. Silvery frost on the alpine meadow vegetation in full bloom is quite a common sight of a summer morning.

The alpine vegetation consists of columbine (*Aquilegia glandulosa*, which is also found at much lower elevation), *Viola altaica*, saxifrage, gentian, buttercup, a small sedge, and other plants.

Above the alpine meadows and especially on the summit flats of the ancient peneplain is found tundra. Here grow an occasional scrubby birch (*Betula rotundifolia*), dryad, and many herbaceous species common to the tundra zone of the north. Among patches of lichen, such as *Cladonia alpestris* and moss, are found *Crepis chryzantha*, alpine sweetgrass (*Hierochloe alpina*), June grass (*Koeleria atroviolacea*), sedges, cottonsedge (*Eriophorum altaicum*), and rush (*Juncus*).

On the rocky stretches of tundra near the patches of permanent snow grow *Braya rosea*, *Dryadanthe bungeana*, and *Saussurea sorocephala*.

The most cold- and wind-enduring plants of this environment are stonecrop (*Sedum quadrifolium*), a gentian (*Gentiana tenella*), veronica (*Veronica densiflora*), and a woolly *Senecio frigidus*.

Above 11,000 feet only lichens are found. On the snowfields occasionally a red alga *Sphaerella nivalis* may be seen.

The upper limit of agriculture in the northeastern part of the region is found rather low, at 1500 feet. In the south and in the east, fields are cultivated to an elevation of 4000 feet. In the Chuia steppe, at an elevation of 5740 feet successful attempts have been made at growing alfalfa, Abyssinian strains of barley, peas, and some other vegetables. In lower prairies under irrigation millet, wheat, and melons are produced. The highland steppes are used mostly for grazing; a great area, however, is under cultivation, but above 4500 feet grain crops do not mature every year. A local strain of wheat that completes its growth in 75 days and barley are the most common crops. Along the terraces of river valleys are found large fields of wheat and barley, and these fields are irrigated by rather primitive contrivances. No fruit trees are grown in the Altai region; wild currants, chokecherry, raspberry, and other wild berries provide fruit.

Animal Life

The fauna of the Altai Mountains is composed of three distinct elements. Animals and birds of the eastern European and Western Siberian forests are common in the region; Eastern Siberian fauna is represented by several animals, such as Siberian wapiti; and Central Asiatic animals and birds, including the gazelle (*Gazella subgutturosa*) and snow partridge (*Tetraogallus altaicus*), are also found in the region. The fauna of the southeastern Altai resembles that of northwestern Mongolia. In the highland steppes are found gazelle, Indian goose (*Anser indicus*), a species of buzzard (*Buteo hemilasius*), Pallas' sand grouse (*Syrrhaptes paradoxus*), which periodically occurs throughout Europe, and ground sparrow (*Montifringilla davidiana*), which in summer is found at about 10,000 feet but during wintering descends to 7000 feet.

In the forest belt are found bear, wolverine, ermine, kolonok (*Mustela sibirica*), moose, muskdeer (*Moschus moschiferus,* called karbargh in Siberia), squirrel (which, as in the Siberian taiga, is the main object of commercial hunting), and wapiti (*Cervus canadensis asiaticus*). Wapiti is locally called maral. This beautiful animal is often killed for its antlers. While in velvet the antlers with a part of the skull are boiled in salt water and shipped to China, where they are used for dubious medicinal purposes. Musk bags, a gland found on the underbelly of male muskdeer, also are usually shipped south of the border. Musk is a favorite perfume of the Orient and a necessary ingredient of all expensive perfumes. At present the demand for musk is not so great as it has been, since the aromatic principle, a ketone, is now manufactured synthetically. Birds of the forest belt include capercaillie (*Tetrao urogallus*) and a small grouse (*Tetrastes bonasia*), a common Eurasian game bird called hazel hen or hazel grouse by the English. The nutcracker (*Nucifraga caryocatactes*), the noisiest inhabitant of dense conifer forests, feeds on the cembra pine nuts (which are also considered a delicacy among the people, who extract the nut oil, as it is commonly called, by rather primitive means and use it in their cooking). In light larch forests occur such birds as pipit (*Anthus trivialis sibiricus*) and thrush (*Turdus viscivorus bonapartei*).

Among the birds of more open habitats are found a beautiful carmine-red long-tailed rose finch (*Uragus sibiricus*), a very widely distributed bird, which occurs from Western Siberia to Kamchatka and as far south as Korea, Japan, and China; a rose-colored grosbeak

(*Erythrina rosea*), several species of crossbills (*Loxia*), thrushes, wood-peckers, owls, and chickadees (*Parus*).

In the alpine habitat is found pika,* or cony (*Ochotona alpina*), an interesting rodent that cuts grass, dries it, and preserves the hay for winter. Siberian ibex, or mountain goat, and mountain sheep (*Ovis ammon*) inhabit highland steppes and rocky summits. In the southern part of the alpine zone are found red wolf (*Cyon alpinus*), occasional snow leopard (*Uncia uncia*), and wild cat (*Otocolobus manul*). The tundra flats are the haunts of wild reindeer, an animal that is usually associated with the arctic region of Eurasia.

Near the snowline lives snow partridge (*Tetraogallus altaicus*), a bird about the size of domestic turkey, red-beaked chough (*Pyrrho-corax pyrrhocorax*), which is common throughout the mountains of central and southern Europe, and alpine chough (*Pyrrhocorax gracu-lus*). At a somewhat lower elevation is the habitat of mountain ptarmigan (*Lagopus mutus*), which in the fall changes its color from brown to white.

In the alpine meadows nest pipit (*Anthus spinoletta altaica*) and Altai brambling (*Leucostice nemoricola altaica*). The alpine finch (*Montifringilla nivalis*) occurs at as high an elevation as 10,000 feet.

In the highland steppes considerable numbers of sheep are main-tained. Yak (*Poephagus grunniens*) is used as a domestic animal and often is crossed with common cattle. The cross is known by a Turkic name, sarlyk. In the southeast domestic camels are found. Horses and common domestic cattle are kept throughout the lower eleva-tions. No domestic reindeer is found in the Altai.

The wapiti or maral is often kept in a semidomesticated state in large corrals. Young wapitis are usually caught in the forest and kept in captivity until their antlers are ready for use. The antlers are then removed and sold to China. The antlers of wild animals killed for this purpose command a much higher price.

Kuznetsk Ala Tau and Kuznetsk Basin

The northern extension of Abakan or Gorbu Range is a range of mountains known to the Russians as Kuznetsk Ala Tau. The range extends from southeast to northwest. Between this range and Salair Range there lies a hilly, rolling land gradually merging into the West-ern Siberian lowlands. It is known as the Kuznetsk coal basin. Ad-

* Pika, a common English name for *Ochotona*, is of Tungus origin.

ministratively the Kuznetsk Basin belongs to Kemerovo Province of Western Siberia. Kuznetsk Ala Tau * is not a well-defined range but rather a group of irregular ancient mountain systems, limited on all sides, with tectonic ruptures. The range is composed of Lower Paleozoic rock. Upon crystalline limestone of the Cambrian period are superimposed sandstone, schist, limestone, and tufa, these latter rocks dating back at least as far as the Low Silurian epoch. Above these layers there are found Devonian deposits. Kuznetsk Ala Tau is a peneplained country that was folded later along lines different from the old Paleozoic folds. The range appears now as a series of watershed-dividing areas of moderate elevations. Alpine landscapes are uncommon, and there are no glaciers at present. Only in the southern part the highest summits are covered with snow almost to the end of the summer. The highest peaks are located near the sources of the Tom and the Bely Yus. In the upper reaches of the latter river lies a narrow rocky ridge with teeth-like pinnacles, known as Teghir Tysh (i.e., Teeth of Heaven) and standing about 6600 feet high. Here is located the highest peak of Kuznetsk Ala Tau, Amzas Taskyl, with an elevation of 7121 feet.

The northern part of the range is covered with typical Siberian taiga of cembra pine, spruce, and fir, with very little of reproduction and with a well-developed moss groundcover. In this mossy cover one may find occasional myrtle whortleberry (*Vaccinium myrtillus*), pyrola, and cowberry (*Vaccinium vitis-idaea*). As the water table is located close to the surface, the ground is generally very damp. On occasional rocky outcrops grows *Rhododendron dahuricum*. Among the conifers birch, aspen, and mountain ash (*Sorbus*) are sometimes found. In the southern part the forests are composed of fir and aspen. After fire they are replaced with herbaceous vegetation. Linden appears sporadically, occupying large hillside areas. It is the only broadleaf European tree that occurs in Siberia, and it grows only in a few isolated localities. With linden are found many relict herbaceous species, which are survivors of the Upper Tertiary period; among them are *Osmorrhiza amurensis, Campanula trachelium,* and *Asarum europeum.*

* This is the easternmost range having the Turkic name Ala Tau. Farther east there are no Ala Taus. Tau in some Turkic dialects is the same as dagh or tagh, i.e., mountain. There is Ary Dagh Mountain in the Sayans. Kuznets is the Russian word for a smith.

Alpine vegetation is found on the rocky summits protruding above the timberline. Such treeless summits are known in southern Siberia as gol'tsy (plural of golets, meaning a bare peak). They may contain subalpine meadows, patches of alpine plants, and stretches of gravelly tundra. The extreme tips of the summits are covered with loose rocks and are practically devoid of any vegetation.

The Kuznetsk coal basin is an undulating area drained by the River Tom and its tributaries. Its lowest point is 354 feet above sea level. During the Low Paleozoic period mountain ranges were formed on the periphery of the basin, and the central part sank. The present basin is separated from the adjacent ranges with steep step-like escarpments, although in places these are replaced by gently descending foothills. Towards the beginning of the Devonian period both Kuznetsk Ala Tau and the Salair Range appeared as stretches of dry land in the large Ural-Siberian sea. After the Lower Carboniferous epoch the basin was changed into a lake. Luxurious riparian vegetation of giant ferns, *Sigillaria*, lepidodendron, and other plants thrived in the warm and moist climate of that period. This vegetation was the source of the enormous coal deposits of the basin. The coal strata go down to a depth of about 6000 feet; the total deposits are estimated to be 450 billion tons; about one-half of this amount of coal is found at depths not exceeding 1600 feet. The Kuznetsk coal fields contain more coal than any other coal-mining center of the Soviet Union.

The vegetation of the Kuznetsk coal basin is of a typical Siberian birch-woodland type. Now, however, almost the whole area is under cultivation. The soil is of a chernozem type suitable for grain growing on a large scale.

South of the Kuznetsk Basin in the drainage of the River Kondoma is located the newly developed iron range of the district of Mountain Shoria. This is a region of medium elevation. The most prominent summit, in Mustagh Range, is 3470 feet high. Iron is mined at Telbess, Temir Tau, and Kondoma, mostly in open pits. The Kondoma deposit is the biggest, amounting to 50 million tons, and the ore is of a relatively high purity, containing 50 to 55 per cent of iron.

Shoria iron is shipped to the Kuznetsk coal basin, where a very important steel manufacturing center has been developed. Originally, iron ore had to be brought by rail from the southern Ural (Magnitogorsk) in exchange for Kuznetsk coal, but now more and more local iron is being used.

Salair Range borders the Kuznetsk Basin on the southwest. Its geological structure is rather complicated. Crystalline limestones of the

Cambrian period alternate with sandstones and shales of the Silurian. The range is rich in zinc, lead, silver, and copper. Prospectors estimated a deposit of 600,000 tons of zinc. Salair is a much peneplained range, and at present it does not look like a mountain chain but rather like rolling country with elevations ranging from 1300 to 1500 feet. The highest point is located in the northern part of Salair. Mt. Pikhtovaia (Russian for Fir Mountain) is 1968 feet high.

The foothills of the Salair are covered with vegetation of the woodland type. On the southern slopes are found patches of prairie with sagebrush (*Artemisia frigida*), cinquefoil, aspen, and birch. Occasionally patches of pine occur in the places where the foothills merge into the Western Siberian woodland region.

People

The native population of the Altai region consists of several Turkic-speaking peoples, formerly referred to as Altai people or as Tatars. At present the Altai aborigines are called the Oirots, and their country is known as the Oirot Autonomous Province. Somewhat north, towards the Kuznetsk Basin in the Shoria district, live Turkic-speaking Shortsi. The predominant population of the region, however, is Russian, including both early agricultural settlers and recent industrial workers.

Chapter 22

Sayan Mountains
and Tuva Region

The Sayan* Mountains are located near the Mongolian border, between the Altai system (Chapter 21), on the west, and the Khamar-Daban Range of the Transbaikal region, on the east. North of the Sayans, and beyond the Minussinsk basin, which is a part of the region, extends the taiga region of Siberia. South of the Sayans is the newly acquired Tuva Region, and beyond it Mongolia.

The Sayan Mountains are divided into the Western Sayan, which extends from the Altai system northeast, and the Eastern Sayan, which extends from southeast to northwest. The two ranges are connected at the sources of the River Kazyr, flowing westward to the Yenisei, and the River Uda, flowing eastward to the Angara (Map 28). The Eastern Sayan, however, extends considerably farther northwest, almost to the city of Krasnoyarsk (i.e., Red Bluff), located where the Trans-Siberian Railway crosses the Yenisei River. As a whole, the Sayan system forms a pattern similar to the Greek letter λ (lambda), in which the left, shorter part corresponds to the Western Sayan and the longer part to the Eastern Sayan.

Topography

The much dissected range of the Western Sayan begins near the sources of the Big Abakan, a tributary of the Yenisei. Here the range is linked by means of the Shapshal Range with the Altai system. From this point the Western Sayan extends northeast for about 400 miles. The Yenisei cuts across the Western Sayan almost midway along its length, forming a narrow and deep gorge. In places where the width of the river is less than 200 feet treacherous rapids are formed, which make downstream navigation by rafts quite a hazardous adventure. The entire main chain of the Western Sayan is composed largely of

---

* In Russian geographic literature the name of the mountains is used both in the singular—Sayan—and in the plural—Sayans.

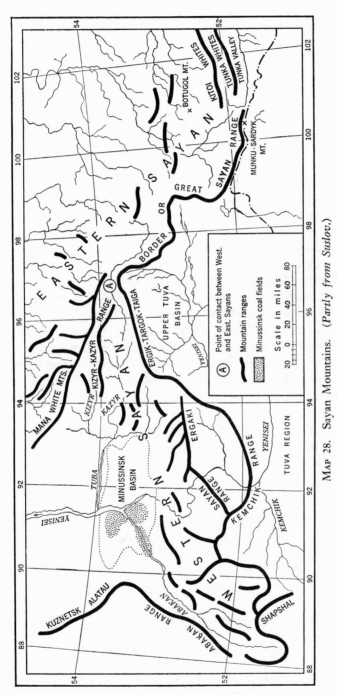

MAP 28. Sayan Mountains. (*Partly from Suslov.*)

granite. In the southwestern part of the range the summits reach 9000 to 9500 feet, well above timberline. Towards the Yenisei elevations drop to 2500 and even to 2000 feet; and near Minussinsk basin the foothills of the Western Sayan average 1600 to 2300 feet.

The Western Sayan east of the Yenisei has not as yet been well studied. Easily eroded metamorphic rocks, such as schist, are found here. The mountains are not very high—5000 to 6000 feet—and are often covered with forests to the crest. In the basin of the River Us, which flows to the Yenisei from the east, the range is known as Ergaki (Russian plural of a Mongol word), and farther northeast it is known as Ergik Torgok Taiga (serrated forest ridge). Extending northward from the western part of the range are several short spurs of considerable elevation—reaching 9600 feet.

Opinions still differ as to which of the several parallel chains of the Western Sayan should be considered the main range. The structure of the Western Sayan is still very poorly known. Generally, the chains of the Western Sayan—except perhaps Ergik Torgok Taiga —do not possess a rugged skyline. The tops of the mountains appear as a moderately hilly plain with occasional rounded summits. These flat tops are the remains of the subsequently uplifted Tertiary peneplain. The crystalline Silurian rocks, at the end of the Upper Silurian epoch, suffered a great deal of dislocation and folding. During the Lower Devonian epoch a part of the Western Sayan (Us Valley) was covered by the sea. After the Middle Devonian the sea retreated, and then considerable faulting and uplifting followed; the latter manifests itself now in river terraces. During the middle of the Tertiary period and especially towards its end there were considerable epeirogenetic movements, faults, and a series of uplifts, as manifested by the ancient terraces. Moreover, the peneplained surface of the Tertiary Western Sayan was later glaciated. The glaciers left numerous signs of their activity, such as moraines and erratics, as far down as 1000 feet above sea level. Some geologists believe that there were two glaciations in the Western Sayan, whereas others maintain that there was only one. At present there are no glaciers in the Western Sayan.

An interesting geological feature of the Sayans, both Western and Eastern, is the rather frequent occurrence of rockfields, locally known as kurums. Often such kurums descend from the summits to the upper ends of valleys as extensive areas covered with loose rocks. The kurums are a product of mechanical disintegration of rocks, caused by the fluctuations in temperature during the early part of the Quaternary period, when the climate was severer than it is at present.

To the north and northwest of the Western Sayan is the Minussinsk basin. West of this basin lie the Abakan Range of the Altai system and the southern part of the Kuznetsk Ala Tau. To the east are branch chains of the Eastern Sayan. In the north the basin is bordered with several ridges that form a connecting link between Kuznetsk Ala Tau and the Eastern Sayan. One such range is known as Batenevski Khrebet. It crosses the Yenisei near the village of Bateni. The Yenisei flows across the middle part of the basin; the lowest points of the country—800 to 1000 feet above sea level—are found along the river. Toward the periphery of the basin, elevations are between 1300 and 2000 feet and even higher. The general topography of the basin is hilly with occasional mountain ridges of medium height. The moderately folded Paleozoic sediments, Devonian and in places Carboniferous and Permian, were covered with loess-like deposits on which rich black soils of a chernozem type developed. In places sandstone has given origin to sands that either are covered with pine forests or, upon destruction of these forests by cutting or fire, have been reconverted into shifting sands. Nearer Kuznetsk Ala Tau and the Western Sayan, the Devonian sediments are more dislocated, predominantly by fault fractures.

The Eastern Sayan is a highland plateau * extending from southeast to northwest. Its southeastern extremity lies between lakes Baikal and Koso Gol (the latter being located in Mongolia), where it is separated by the fault valley of the River Irkut from the mountains of the Transbaikal region, in which the general direction of mountain chains is northeastern rather than northwestern as in Eastern Sayan. In the northwest the range begins on the western bank of the Yenisei, somewhat south of Krasnoyarsk.

The Eastern Sayan descends gently towards the central Siberian plateau, although forming a definite escarpment of about 1300 feet in height. Towards Mongolia the range slopes abruptly. In the southeast the Eastern Sayan is separated by fault valleys of the Selenga River and of Lake Koso Gol (known to Mongols as Khubsugul Dalai) from the Mongolian range of Khangai. Farther west the Tuva basin separates it from the border mountains of Tannu Ola. The Eastern Sayan is much higher than the Western Sayan. The most elevated part of the range is located north of Lake Koso Gol. Here on the boundary line between Russia and Mongolia rises the highest summit

---

* Nagorie, according to the Russian geomorphologic nomenclature. For example, the Mexican Plateau crisscrossed with mountain ranges would be classified by the Russians as a nagorie.

of the range—Munku Sardyk, 11,440 feet. North of the main chain of Eastern Sayan and separated from it by the Irkut Valley extends a high (to 7900 feet) snow-clad parallel range known as the Tunka Whites, or, in Russian, Tunkinskie Bielki (see footnote, p. 229). Still farther north and parallel to the previously mentioned ranges are the Kitoi Whites, up to 9500 feet high, named after the Kitoi River, which separates this chain from the Tunka Whites. At the point where the Eastern and Western Sayans meet, elevations reach above 9000 feet (Mt. Ary Dagh, 9840 feet). From this point farther northwest extends a range of highland mountains that consists of several chains, such as Kanskoie Belogorie and Manskoe Belogorie, meaning Kan (a river) White Highlands (about 6500 feet) and Mana (a river) White Highlands (about 5000 feet), so named because of extensive patches of snow and large areas occupied by whitish lichens.

To the system of Eastern Sayan also belongs Kizyr-Kazyr(ski), or Kryzhin, Range, located between the rivers Kizyr and Kazyr, both flowing into the Tuba River, an eastern tributary of the Yenisei. The highest point of Kryzhin Range is Edelstein Peak,* 8777 feet. Towards the Yenisei the Eastern Sayan decreases in height, and west of the river the range gradually merges into the Western Siberian lowland. The peneplain-like plateaux are preserved along the summits of the Eastern Sayan much more than in the Western Sayan.

In the central part of the range the flat tops of the ancient peneplain are found at elevations of 7500 to 7900 feet and up to 10,000 feet. On the periphery the remnants of the peneplain are located at lower elevations. In some places, however, where the Eastern Sayan has been subjected to intensive glaciation, such as in the Tunka Whites, the topography is more rugged, with sharp peaks and serrated crests.

The most ancient sedimentary and extrusive rocks of the Eastern Sayan are represented chiefly by pre-Cambrian crystalline schist and limestone. Cambrian schist, limestone, conglomerates, and various effusive materials are distributed generally in the central part, also in the outskirts of the region. The occurrence of marine Devonian deposits is rather uncommon. Since the Devonian period the Eastern Sayan has experienced a long continental period, during which the country was almost completely base-leveled, so that by the middle of the Tertiary period the region had the appearance of a peneplain. During the second part of the Tertiary there occurred considerable

* Named after the Russian geologist J. C. Edelstein, who studied the geology of the Sayans and of other Siberian ranges.

faulting and dislocation, accompanied by the effusion of basalts. These effusions apparently continued even during the glacial period.

In the Irkut Valley there are signs of two ancient glaciations. During the first and more extensive glaciation, the sheet of ice descended to the valley to an elevation of about 2700 feet. During the second glaciation, valley-type glaciers predominated. The valley type of glaciers extended for many miles, moving along the valleys of the first glaciation and deepening them considerably. The second Irkut Valley glaciation was about 40 miles long and 1000 feet thick and descended to an elevation of slightly over 4400 feet.

As to the mineral wealth of the Sayan Mountains, the Western Sayan is not very rich. There is some copper, molybdenum, and iron. The Eastern Sayan is rich in gold. The Kizyr Basin is known for the large size of its gold nuggets. Iron deposits north of the confluence of the Kizyr and the Tuba rivers are estimated at 20 million tons, with 60.6 per cent of the metal in the ore. In the sources of the River Biriussa, Muscovite mica is mined. Some of the sheets taken out may be as large as 8 by 12 inches. Nephrite, a kind of jade that is not especially valuable, is found in the form of small boulders along river beds and also embedded in crystalline schists of the Tunka and Kitoi mountains. The Aliber graphite mine on the Botugolski Golets (Botugol summit, elevation 7570 feet) has been in operation intermittently for many years. In the Minussinsk basin are considerable deposits of coal amounting to perhaps 14 billion tons. At present, however, these deposits are used only to a limited extent.

Climate

The climate of the Sayans is little known. Temperature and precipitation records at Minussinsk (elevation 836 feet) differ but little from those of adjacent parts of the Siberian lowlands. Winters are as cold, but summers are somewhat warmer (July mean temperatures at Tomsk, 64°F; at Minussinsk, 68°F).

At Minussinsk the temperature in summer may be as high as 104°F, but in winter it may drop to –58°F. The annual precipitation is a little over 12 inches. Higher in the mountains, of course, climatic conditions are different; precipitation is heavier and temperatures are lower.

At Buibinskoie Lake in the Western Sayan (elevation 4494 feet) the annual precipitation amounts to 48 inches. At this elevation snow begins to fall early in October and stays on the ground until the middle

TABLE 16. TEMPERATURE AND PRECIPITATION AT MINUSSINSK, ELEVATION 836 FEET

Jan.	Feb.	Mar.	Apr.	May	June	July	Aug.	Sept.	Oct.	Nov.	Dec.	Year
Temperature, degrees Fahrenheit												Mean
−4	−0.3	14	36	51	63	68	63	50	34	16	2	32.7
Precipitation, inches												Total
0.4	0.2	0.2	0.5	1.2	2.2	2.1	2.5	1.3	0.8	0.4	0.4	12.2

of June. Winter blizzards pile up snow drifts 8 feet high. Deep snow in mountain valleys in spring and early summer interferes a great deal with travel over the mountain trails. On the other hand, near Minussinsk there is so little snow in winter that wheeled carts are used throughout the year and winter grazing of cattle and horses is quite a common practice.

In the high mountains of the Western Sayan summers are very short. The only frostless month of the year is July; the mean temperature of this month at Buiba, elevation 3444 feet, is 54°F. March is still a winter month with absolute minima reaching –22°F. From October to March temperatures never reach above 32°F; i.e., during that period there is not a single thaw.

The climate of the Eastern Sayan is known even less than the climate of the Western Sayan. Some weather observations have been made only in the Tunka region (Irkut Valley) and at the Aliber Graphite Mine. Generally, the precipitation in the Eastern Sayan region decreases towards the south and southeast, or, more accurately, the summer precipitation increases and the winter precipitation decreases, producing a climate similar to that of Mongolia. At the village of Mondy (elevation 4297 feet) the mean July temperature is 60°F and the mean January temperature is –6°F. During the summer the temperature may reach above 90°F during the day and drop to 60°F in the evening. The precipitation is 12 inches at Mondy and 19 inches at nearby Arshan, which is less than at the same latitudes in the Western Sayan. Seventy per cent of the total precipitation at Mondy occurs during the summer months. At this station summers are cloudy but winters are clear and sunny. The vegetation period is 125 days long. At the Aliber Graphite Mine on the Botugol Summit, summer lasts from the middle of June to the beginning of September. Shortly after August 1, night temperatures may drop to 14°F; snow may fall in the middle of June. There is permanently frozen ground at the summit.

Vegetation

In Minussinsk basin patches of prairie alternate with birch groves and common pine (*Pinus sylvestris*) forests, which grow in narrow strips on pure sand. Generally, the northern slopes are occupied by birch and the southern slopes are prairie-like. At present a great deal of the prairie land is under cultivation. Most of the prairie land, which is a rich chernozem soil developed on loess-like material, is found west of the Yenisei. Among the predominant species here are needlegrass, fescue, and June grass (*Koeleria*). Sagebrush (*Artemisia*) may be found on slopes. The area east of the Yenisei is essentially a woodland type in which prairie alternates with birch groves and pine forests. Continuous fields of flag (*Iris ensata*) are often found on alkaline soils. On the flood plains of the Yenisei and its tributaries, and also on the numerous islands, fertile alluvial soils have developed. These are covered with meadow vegetation with an admixture of some prairie grasses.

South of the main range of the Western Sayan, in the drainage of the River Us, at an elevation of about 2200 feet above sea level stretches the Usinskaia Steppe. The north slopes of deep valleys of the steppe are covered with larch-spruce forests, and on the more gentle slopes with the same northern or western exposure there are park-like stands of Siberian larch with luxurious herbaceous cover. The southern slopes are covered with typical prairie vegetation. The south slopes of the foothills of the Western Sayan are covered with prairie vegetation on chernozem soil up to 1300 feet. On the north slopes where there is more moisture and the soil is more leached, forests develop. These forests are designated by Suslov * as pre-taiga forests. These pre-taiga forests occupy a belt at an elevation of 1300 to 2300 feet. They consist either of patches of the original mountain taiga, somewhat altered by man by burning, cutting, or pasturing, or of secondary birch-aspen forests that replaced the original conifers

* S. P. Suslov, *Physical Geography of the USSR*, Moscow, 1947, p. 247. This author studied the geography of the Sayans in great detail.

which were destroyed by earlier fires. These secondary forests have a considerable admixture of chokecherry (*Prunus padus* *), mountain ash, and alder. The ground is often swampy. On the fringes of the birch-aspen forests are luxurious meadows of onion (*Allium victorialis*), reedgrass (*Calamagrostis langsdorffi*), monkshood (*Aconitum boreale*), and orange-colored globeflower (*Trollius asiaticus*). Peonies (*Paeonia anomala*), roses, and spiraea grow in higher places. Primeval taiga is found above the secondary (pre-taiga) forests and occupies a belt at 2300 feet to 5000 feet or even 6500 feet above sea level. The Western Sayan taiga consists of cembra pine, called here, as everywhere in Siberia, a cedar; spruce; fir; larch (*Larix sibirica*), which here is at almost its eastern limit of distribution (see Map 18, p. 109); common pine (*Pinus sylvestris*); and two birches (*Betula verrucosa* and *B. pubescens*). The understory consists of mountain ash, chokecherry, alder, honeysuckle, and juniper. Occasionally, as in some places in the Abakan drainage, one may find almost pure larch forests. On gentle slopes well irrigated by melting snow or by springs there develops a type of luxurious herbaceous vegetation called, by the natives, elani.† Tall herbs grow here to 16 or 24 inches in height, occasionally reaching 7 feet.

At about 3300 feet above sea level the broadleaf species (birch and aspen) disappear, and conifer taiga in which the fir is dominant prevails above this elevation. Cembra pine occupies a co-dominant position, forming several types of stands, for instance, a stand with an understory of dwarf birch or of badan saxifrage (*Bergenia crassifolia*). Spruce prefers either rocky slopes or deep canyons. The ground under these spruce forests is usually covered with black currant or with honeysuckle.

Uncontrolled fires have ravaged the vegetation of the Sayans for a long time, leaving large burned-over areas. After the forests are gone the countryside is invaded by vegetation consisting of raspberry brambles, reedgrass, and fireweed (*Epilobium angustifolium*), which also grows in North America. Then birch and aspen appear, and these are gradually replaced by fir and spruce developing under the birch-aspen canopy, and eventually cembra pine is established. On the southern slopes, the plant succession after a fire is different. Here

---

* This species of *Prunus* reaches a fairly large size, roughly that of an apricot or a peach tree. The shiny black berries are the size of a pea and are borne in clusters.

† The same term is used for this type of vegetation in the Altai region. See, however, footnote on p. 313.

burned-over larch forests are rapidly reestablished with larch seed-lings.

At about the 4500 to 4600 foot level cembra pine-fir-spruce taiga changes into park-like groves of cembra pine and fir intermingled with subalpine meadows. Here badan saxifrage, *Rhododendron chrysanthum* (locally called cashcara *), and, in low moist localities, rose-colored *Rhododendron fragrans* appear. In places alder clumps (*Alnus fruticosa*, up to 5 feet high) surrounded by dwarf birch may be found. In alpine habitats grow short, brightly colored gentians (*Gentiana altaica*), dragonhead (*Dracocephalum altaiense*), marsh marigold (*Caltha palustris*), and cottonsedge (*Eriophorum alpinum*). A few scattered flowering plants are found on the rocky summits.

The extensive highlands are covered with moss-lichen tundra with a sprinkling of arctic flowers and occasional scrubby arctic willows. In dry places lichen tundra predominates. The highland zone in the Western Sayan, including the subalpine and alpine habitats, occupies elevations of 5000 feet to 8200 feet. The subalpine and alpine vegetation of the Western Sayan is not so luxurious as in the Altai region. Plants are not so tall and the number of arctic species is greater.

The vegetation of the Eastern Sayan is very similar to that of the Western Sayan. There are places in the Tunka district, however, along the Mongolian border where the precipitation amounts to 12 to 16 inches a year. The vegetation here on the exposed slopes is de-cidedly of a steppe type, consisting of bluegrass (*Poa botrioides*), June grass, and crested wheatgrass, with an admixture of such species as yellow flag (*Iris flavissima*) and gentian (*Gentiana macrophylla*). In some localities needlegrass (*Stipa decipiens*) predominates. With it may be found prairie sedge (*Carex stenophylla*), cinquefoil (*Potentilla subacaulis*), and fringed sagebrush (*Artemisia frigida*).

The foothills of the Eastern Sayan, up to 3000–3200 feet elevation, are covered with forests of common pine and Siberian larch. Higher up begins the mountain taiga of cembra pine-fir with or without an admixture of spruce. The broadleaf trees are represented by birch, aspen, and Mongolian poplar or cottonwood (*Populus suaveolens*). At lower altitudes cembra pine forests are widespread. These have a moss ground cover, which higher up is replaced by *Rhododendron chrysanthum*. Near places of habitation the taiga has been badly culled and often replaced with birch-aspen groves.

In the northern part of the region, adjacent to patches of Siberian woodland, at elevations of 2100 to 3300 feet, there are extensive com-

* Not to be confused with western North American cascara, which is *Rhamnus*.

mon pine forests with a ground cover of spiraea, *Rhododendron da-huricum*, reedgrass (*Calamagrostis arundinaceous*), bluegrass (*Poa si-birica*), and hawkweed (*Hieracleum umbellatum*). In Irkut Valley common pine forests do not grow higher than 2600 or 2700 feet above sea level. Above the pine forests, larch begins to dominate. On northern, northeastern, and northwestern slopes are found larch forests with ground covers of *Cetraria* and *Cladonia* lichens. There is an abundance of whortleberry, bog bilberry (*Vaccinium uliginosum*), primula (*Primula farinosa*), *Lloydia serotina*, and *Saxifraga hirculus*. The common shrubs are peashrub (*Caragana jubata*), willow (*Salix ar-buscula*), and dwarf birch. These same shrubs are also found in the flood plains of the Irkut, where they are intermingled with spruce forests, cottonwood groves, and stretches of herbaceous vegetation.

Higher up, the cembra pine, spruce, and fir begin to appear, but the most common type of forest is the cembra pine-larch with a ground cover consisting of cobresia sedge (*Cobresia filifolia*), wild onion (*Allium victorialis*), and needlegrass (*Stipa mongolica*). Between 2600 feet and 5600 feet there is a belt of cembra pine forest with a sprinkling of fir, spruce, and larch and with an abundance of small berry shrubs, such as *Vaccinium myrtillus* and *V. vitis-idaea*. At the upper elevations appears *Rhododendron chrysanthum*. The timberline in the Eastern Sayan is located at 6000 to 6500 feet, with occasional larch and cembra pine trees occurring up to 7600 feet above sea level.

In the cembra pine forests of the lower elevations a recent infestation by a moth (*Dendrolimus sibiricus*) defoliated and, after several years, killed hundreds of square miles of forest. Suslov * describes this infestation as a real calamity; one could hear the sound of millions of caterpillars chewing upon pine foliage; one could not get a drink of water from a stream because its surface would be covered and polluted with a thick layer of dead caterpillars. Wild life—sable and squirrel—left the infested areas, thus depriving the people of hunting revenues. The stench of dead insects in the infested localities was hard to bear. The regeneration of such areas has been very slow and was successful only in places where a few seed trees survived the epidemic and the subsequent fires that ravaged the region.

Above the cembra pine forests, at elevations of 6500 to 7900 feet, are brushfields of birch (*Betula rotundifolia*), willow (*Salix vestita*), alder (*Alnus fruticosa*), black currant (*Ribes graveolens*), and spiraea

* S. P. Suslov, *Physical Geography of the USSR*, Moscow, 1947, p. 262.

(*Spiraea alpina*). Subalpine and alpine meadows are developed to an even lesser extent than in the Western Sayan. The subalpine meadows consist of an extremely palatable reedgrass (*Calamagrostis macilenta*), a wheatgrass (*Agropyron mutabile*), and the usual admixture of showy dicotyledons. These meadows are used very little as summer pastures because of the lack of trails connecting them with inhabited regions.

Alpine meadows are found only in spots; their vegetation consists of some 120 species, among which are *Hierochloe alpina, Koeleria altaica, Allium schoenoprasum, Astragalus alpinus,* and *Papever alpinus.* In places there are moist cobresia meadows. Most of the alpine belt, however, is occupied by tundra, either rocky and almost bare or covered with lichens. The flat highlands of the Eastern Sayan are very similar in appearance to the arctic tundra. Near snowfields one may find badan (*Bergenia crassifolia*), Altai violet, and Altai gentian.

Agriculture of the region is practiced mainly in the Minussinsk basin and in the Us basin. In both these areas almost all suitable land is under cultivation. Minussinsk watermelons are known throughout Eastern Siberia; an extremely sweet variety that is slightly larger than a cantaloupe is especially popular.

The natives and the Russian settlers of the mountainous part of the region, for instance in the upper Irkut Valley, depend for a great deal of their subsistence on wild vegetation. Though staple crops and vegetables are raised in the usual manner, there is a lack of vitamin-supplying fruit, and the people gather in the forest such berries as cowberry, bilberry, whortleberry (*Vaccinium myrtillus*), currant, raspberry, chokecherry; also mushrooms and especially wild onion (*Allium victorialis*), known for its antiscorbutic properties. All this supplementary food is preserved for winter use. The same pattern of partial dependence on wild plants is common, with certain modifications, throughout the forested parts of Siberia.

Animal Life

Animals found in the forests of the Western Sayan near centers of habitation include roebuck (*Capreolus pigargus*), wolf, fox, ermine, and weasel. The principal birds are black cock (*Lyrurus tetrix*), a partridge (*Perdix dahurica*), oriole, and gray-headed green woodpecker (*Picus canus*). The big grouse, or capercaille (*Tetrao urogallus*), and great tit (*Parus major*) live in the patches of intact taiga.

Sable is still plentiful. This valuable predator usually spends all its life in an area of 20 to 25 square miles. Bear lives in the taiga forest. Throughout the taiga of the Sayans the squirrel is, as in all other forest regions of Russia, the most important fur animal. The pika (*Ochotona alpina*) is found in rockfields. Moose is rare if not completely absent. Wapiti elk is found in considerable numbers. Wolverine and lynx also occur in the area but are seldom seen. Common game birds found in the taiga are both the large and the small grouse (*Tetrao urogallus* and *Tetrastes bonasia*).

The highlands of both the Western and Eastern Sayans, with their tundras, offer excellent pasture for reindeer. The habitat of this animal at present is completely isolated from the northern regions of Siberia.* The mountain goat (*Capra sibirica*) is found on the rocky summits; also in the high mountains are muskdeer, bear, and red wolf (*Canis alpinus*). A conspicuous bird is the water pipit (*Anthus spinoletta blakistoni*). Ptarmigan (*Lagopus mutus*) inhabits areas near the snowline.

In Minussinsk basin are such prairie rodents as hamster (*Phodopus songarus*), prairie dog (*Citellus eversmanni*), and steppe lemming (*Lagurus lagurus*) and such prairie birds as bustard (*Otis tarda dybowskii*) and Dahurian partridge (*Perdix dahurica*).

In the patches of prairie in the Eastern Sayan one may find ground squirrels and an abundance of grasshoppers.

The taiga of the Eastern Sayan is inhabited by the same animals as the taiga of the Western Sayan, although moose is quite common here and wild reindeer is more numerous. However, neither the large nor small grouse finds a proper environment here. Wapiti elk, or maral, is hunted for its valuable antlers. Muskdeer, which prefers the highlands just above timberline, is hunted for musk. Both commodities find a ready market in China.

The woods Soyots and Karagas tend domesticated reindeer, which they ride "horseback fashion" by placing the saddle on the middle of the spine rather than above the front legs as the Tungus do. The Sayan reindeer is a much more docile animal than the reindeer of northern Siberia. It is never used as a draft animal. Reindeer milking is practiced both by the Soyots and the Karagas. In some places in the Eastern Sayan both reindeer and Mongolian sheep are grazed in the same pastures. In the patches of prairie near the Mongolian border

---

* For a more detailed description of wild and domesticated reindeer of this region see N. T. Mirov, "Notes on the Domestication of Reindeer," *Am. Anthropologist*, Vol. 47, No. 3, pp. 393–407, 1945.

the inhabitants raise Mongolian sheep, Mongolian cattle, and sarlyk cattle, which is a cross between the Tibet yak and the Mongolian cow.*

People

In the Minussinsk basin live numerous Turkic-speaking people, formerly known as Abakan Tatars, who are probably the Turkicized old Yenisei people. Now they are known as Khakass. Their administrative center is Abakan. Russian settlers are numerous along the Yenisei. The country along the upper reaches of the Yenisei in the vicinity of Minussinsk and in the Tuva Region is rich in remains of older civilizations. There have been found numerous Runic inscriptions, dating back to the beginning of the Christian era, stone images, burial grounds, and remains of irrigation canals and paved roads.

The Sayan Mountains are almost uninhabited by man. Survivors of the Kamasin people live in the northern part of the region; until the middle of the last century they still spoke Samoyed; now they speak only Russian. In the Eastern Sayan Mountains lives a small tribe (200 or 300 people) of woods Soyots, who call themselves Tuva or Tuba.† North of them dwell the Karagas, or Tofalar (the plural of Tofa). Both the woods Soyots and the Karagas speak Turkic.

Tuva Region

The Tuva Region formerly was known as the Uriankhai Territory. It has been under Russian influence for many years but only recently (1945) became a part of the USSR. It is located in the upper reaches of the Yenisei system, between the Western and Eastern Sayans in the north and the Tannu Ola Mountains in the south. In the west it borders the eastern Altai Mountains and in the east it extends to the Bain Ola ridge, which connects the Tannu Ola with the Eastern Sayan.

The geographic center of Asia is located in Tuva. The region is a basin surrounded on all sides with mountains. All the waters drain to the Yenisei, which cuts a narrow gorge in the Western Sayan and rushes to Siberia. Only a few streams flow from the southern slope of the Tannu Ola to the lakes of Mongolia. The Yenisei is formed by the confluence of two large rivers: the Kemchik, which flows from the southwestern mountains belonging to the Altai system, and the Ulu Kem, which in its turn is formed by several rivers originating

---

* Regarding the Sayans and the Minussinsk basin see George Cressey, "Pioneering in Yeniseyland," *J. Sci. Lab. Denison Univ.*, Vol. 24, pp. 103–169, 1939.
† Many Siberian peoples do not differentiate between the sounds *v* and *b*.

in the Eastern Sayan and draining the northeastern part of the region. The Ulu Kem in its lower reaches is over 700 feet wide, about 15 feet deep, and the velocity of its flow is about 6 miles per hour.

The Tuva basin is about 450 miles long and in its central part about 300 miles wide. The total area is equal to 63,700 square miles.* The center of the region is located at 1600 to 2000 feet above sea level; the surrounding mountains reach over 8000 feet.

The Tuva Region is considered one of the richest parts of the Soviet Union. Gold is found here in larger quantity than previously supposed; deposits of silver, asbestos, copper, and coal of fairly good quality have been discovered; there are indications of the presence of oil and of iron. The natural resources of Tuva apparently have not been exploited on a large scale, although gold has been mined for years.

Being located in the middle of Asia, Tuva possesses an extremely continental climate. Winter temperatures may drop to −58°F whereas in summer they may reach 105°F. The region combines features of the climate of the Siberian taiga with those of the Mongolian semideserts. In spite of its relatively small size, its climate is far from being uniform. The northeastern part of the region has relatively abundant precipitation and the snow pack is rather deep. In the southwestern part the precipitation is meager (7 inches at Kyzyl), and irrigation is required there. Traces of ancient irrigation canals are found in this area.

The northeastern part of Tuva is mountainous country covered with taiga. It occupies about one-half of the total area and is located on elevations mainly of 3250 to 6500 feet. The composition of the forests is typically Siberian: larch, fir, spruce, and cembra pine, with admixture of birch and aspen. The common pine is rare. There is no transition woodland type between the taiga and the steppe. The typical taiga extends downward on northern slopes and the steppe stretches upward on southern slopes, thus causing a considerable overlapping of the two types of vegetation. Larch descends lower than any other forest trees, forming park-like groves in the surrounding steppe. The park-like forests in the mountains of the western part of the region in the basin of the Kemchik as well as in the Tannu Ola Mountains are composed of larch. On the southern slope of the Tannu Ola there is not much woody vegetation. Steppes are located along the valleys of the largest rivers and south of the Ulu Kem and

* As a comparison, the area of the state of Washington is 69,127 square miles.

the Kemchik, i.e., in the southwestern part of Tuva. They occupy about one-third of the whole region. This part of Tuva is dissected by numerous branching mountain ridges into separate patches of rolling country covered with steppe or even semidesert vegetation resembling the vegetation of Mongolia. Grass here grows only about 6 inches in height. Herbaceous vegetation in the river bottomlands is more vigorous, consisting mostly of feathergrass and needlegrass (*Stipa*). The percentage of level area suitable for cultivation is estimated at about 2.5 million acres. The yield of grain is considerable, but sometimes the crops suffer from late spring frosts. Livestock raising on the rich bottomland pastures is the main occupation of the natives. Along the Ulu Kem one may find yaks and camels; only about 150 miles northeast the natives tend reindeer. Thus in Tuva the reindeer, a domesticated animal of the tundras of the extreme north of Siberia, is found not very far from places where the camel, a domestic animal of the deserts, is tended by the inhabitants. Above the forest zone, i.e., above 6200–6500 feet, and above a narrow belt of brushfields of rhododendron, birch, alder, and willows, are found alpine meadows. The flat plateaux of high mountains above the alpine meadows, where the precipitation is abundant and the drainage is poor, supports moss and lichen tundra. On rocky slopes a dry type of mountain tundra prevails. Here are the haunts of wild reindeer, which move to the tundra pastures in winter from the taiga where snow piles up too deep.* In the taiga † are found the same animals as in Siberia, i.e., bear, moose, elk, muskdeer. In the steppes live ground squirrel, marmot, wolf, prairie fox, quail, and bustard. In the mountain steppes occurs a very large mountain sheep (*Ovis ammon*). The southern slope of the Tannu Ola Mountains is of a semidesert type. Here are found such semidesert species as an antelope (*Gazella subgutturosa*) and chukar partridge.‡

The Tuva Region is populated by several clans of a mixed people having Mongolian features and generally referred to as Uriankhai, al-

* In the north of Siberia reindeer migrate to the tundra from the taiga in summer. Cf. p. 96.

† Apparently, the word taiga, meaning a primeval forest, originated in this region. In the Tuva territory natives call wooded mountain ridges taigas, such as Djanghis Taiga and Khan Taiga.

‡ An excellent account of Tuva is given in Douglas Carruthers' *Unknown Mongolia*, Vol. 1, London, 1914. This is the best description of the Tuva Region written in English. Several other fundamental works on the region are written in Russian. Of these, *Western Mongolia and the Uriankhai Country*, by

though the tribes living in the mountains of the northeast and east are better known as the Soyots. The new official name of the people is the Tuva. They are much Mongolized but speak Turkic. Russian settlers are numerous.

G. Grumm-Grzhimailo (Vol. 1, 1914; Vols. 2 and 3, 1926), is perhaps the best. In German, besides Leimbach's *Landeskunde von Tuwa* (Pettermanns Mitteilungen, Ergänzungsheft, 222, 1936), an excellent little book on *Reise ins Asiatische Tuwa*, was written by Otto Mänchen-Helfen (Berlin, 1931, 133 pp.).

Chapter 23

Transbaikal Region

The Transbaikal region lies east of Lake Baikal. A narrow strip of land along the northwestern shores of Baikal and the lake itself are included in the region. In the south, Transbaikal borders Mongolia, and on the east it shares a common border with Manchuria. Farther north Transbaikal merges into the Far Eastern Region (Chapter 25), and northeast of it lies the mountainous area of northeastern Siberia (Chapter 24). North and northwest of it is the taiga region of Eastern Siberia (Chapter 10). Transbaikal is occasionally referred to as Dahuria—the land of a now almost extinct Manchurian people, the Dahurs.

Administratively Transbaikal lies partly within the borders of the Buriat-Mongol Republic, a part of Russia proper (see p. 8); the northeastern part belongs to the Chita Province; and a narrow strip along the northwestern shores of Lake Baikal, together with the Vitim Plateau (i.e., the extreme northern part of the region), comprises a part of Irkutsk Province.

Topography

Some geologists consider the Transbaikal region to be composed of a series of broad, flat anticlines, separated by deep, narrow synclines. In places where ruptures and faults occurred the synclines sank, forming deep structural valleys or grabens. Other geologists are of the opinion that, after the ancient foldings had been completed, the region was repeatedly uplifted and peneplained and then broken by tectonic fractures into long stretches of terrain. Some of these stretches of land remained in places as horsts, and others sank, forming deep fault troughs or grabens.

Volcanic activity manifested itself in Transbaikal with basalt intrusions in certain parts, such as in the Borgoi Steppe. On the Vitim Plateau occasional volcanic craters and lava flows are found. Tectonic adjustments in the region have not yet been completed. Earthquakes are frequent, especially in the vicinity of Lake Baikal; occasionally they are destructive.

261

In the higher elevations of the region extensive talus covers the slopes of the barren peaks. This debris is similar to the loose rock fields of the Sayan Mountains. There are many ancient lake deposits, and sands on the river terraces, in the southwestern part of the region. These have led to the development of shifting sands, which later became covered with grass or pine forests. The intrusion of man, fol-

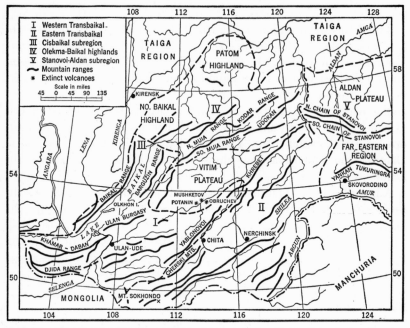

MAP 29. Transbaikal Region. Heavy broken lines denote boundaries between the Transbaikal Region and the adjacent regions. Heavy dash-dot line shows the international border between Russia and China and Mongolia. (*After Suslov.*)

lowed by overgrazing, burning of forests, and cultivation, destroyed a great deal of the vegetative cover and contributed to the reappearance of the shifting sands.

Suslov * divides the whole region into five geomorphological parts, or subregions: (1) western Transbaikal, or Selenga Dahuria; (2) eastern Transbaikal, or Nerchinsk Dahuria; (3) Cisbaikal subregion; (4) Olekma-Baikal highlands; and (5) Stanovoi Mountains and Aldan Plateau. (See Map 29.)

The western Transbaikal subregion is essentially a country of Lower Paleozoic folding. The rocks are predominantly granites and pre-

* S. P. Suslov, *Physical Geography of the USSR*, Moscow, 1947.

Cambrian crystallines. Patches of marine Paleozoic sediments are found in the southern part. There are no Mesozoic rocks. The extreme southwestern corner of the subregion is occupied by four parallel latitudinal ranges, which form a connecting link between the Sayan Mountains and the mountains of Transbaikal. The two northern connecting ranges tower above the timberline; the two southern ranges are fully covered with forests. The topography of these ranges is similar to that of the Eastern Sayan in that their tops also are uplifted ancient peneplains. The ranges have gentle southern slopes and abrupt northern slopes with clearly marked fault lines. Traces of ancient glaciation are present in the form of glacial valleys. Rock debris covering slopes of bare mountain summits (golets) is as common here as in the Sayans.

The Khamar Daban (Mongol for the Nose Pass Mountains) Range extends along the southeastern shores of Lake Baikal. Its summits generally are rounded, reaching altitudes above 6500 feet. In places, however, there are rugged peaks. The northern slope of the range descends abruptly to the lake; the southern step-like slope is rather gentle and easy of access. North of the river Selenga the range changes its name to Ulan Burgasy (Mongol for the Red Willow) and gradually broadens into plateau-like highlands.

Farther northeast, between the River Barguzin and Lake Baikal, is the Barguzin Range (Barguzinski Khrebet of the Russians). The range is composed predominantly of granite. Elevations run to over 8800 feet above sea level. The range descends rather gently towards Baikal, but the southern slope is abrupt and steep. Unlike most of the Transbaikal mountains, the Barguzin Range possesses a rugged alpine appearance, with snow-clad peaks and a serrated crest with towering rock pinnacles. In the northern part there are numerous signs of glaciation in the form of lakes, glacial valleys, and glacial erratics.

The Yablonovoi Khrebet * (a Russian name meaning the Apple Tree Range, probably a corruption of the Mongolian word Yablenni, meaning boulders) cuts the Transbaikal region in two parts, extending diagonally through it from southwest to northeast. The southwestern part of the range serves as the watershed divide between the Arctic and the Pacific drainages, but the northeastern part merely divides drainages of the Lena tributaries. The Karenga, a tributary to the Vitim, cuts through the range, forming a deep and inaccessible gorge. The highest point of the range, Golets (bare peak) Saranakan, 5280

* V. A. Obruchev, "The Yablonovi and Stanovoi Ranges in the Light of the New Data," *Geog. J.*, Vol. 86, pp. 422–440, 1935.

feet, is located about 40 miles northeast of the provincial capital, Chita. The northeastern part of the Yablonovoi Range branches into several bare-topped chains running an average height of about 4500 feet. One of these branches merges into the southern chain of the Stanovoi Range. As a whole, the Yablonovoi Range is not very impressive; its summits appear as broad, wooded plateaux alternating with broad, swampy saddles and elevated above the broad valleys not more than 1000 feet. The Trans-Siberian Railroad crosses the range at an elevation of 3500 feet above sea level, cutting through the post-Tertiary deposits.

Northwest of the Yablonovoi Range lie rolling plains of the Vitim Plateau. Geomorphologically speaking, the plateau is a monotonous alternation of long, low hills and swampy plains. It is composed of granite and gneiss. There is some basalt in the central part. The absolute elevations of the plateau run generally between 3300 and 4400 feet, sometimes dropping to 2800 feet and occasionally reaching almost 4800 feet. On the periphery, however, the terrain is more elevated. Thus, towards the River Barguzin, in the Ikat(ski) Range, elevations may reach 6500 feet.

In the central southern part of Vitim Plateau are several low extinct volcanoes named after the geologists who explored the region: Mushketov, Obruchev, and others. The plateau is drained by the River Vitim and its tributaries.

In the eastern part of the Transbaikal region are found much-dislocated pre-Cambrian rocks; there also occur marine Cambrian, Devonian, Carboniferous, Permian, Triassic, and Jurassic deposits. But essentially the eastern Transbaikal is an area of Mesozoic folds. All Mesozoic folds extend from southwest to northeast, with a tilt towards the northwest. The most intensive folding occurred during the second half of the Cretaceous period. Tertiary folding was milder in character. Later the relief of the land was influenced by the glacial advances. The highest mountains of the region, Mt. Sokhondo (8141 feet) and Mt. Barun-Shebetui (8384 feet), are near the sources of the Ingoda. Mt. Sokhondo is a flat-topped broad summit composed of erupted porphyritic rocks (dacite) with extensive fields of rock debris and traces of ancient glaciation.

In the southern part of eastern Transbaikal, east of the Yablonovoi Range, are several mountain ridges: Dahurski, Cherski,* Borshchev-

* Not to be confused with the Cherski Mountains of northeastern Siberia (Chapter 24).

ochnyi, and others. This is typical eroded country of about 3300 feet above sea level with numerous deep river valleys and canyons.

The southeastern part of eastern Transbaikal is occupied by a series of low, parallel, dry, rocky ridges elevated above the dry valleys only 300 to 500 feet. The area is dotted with depressions without drainage outlets and with numerous brackish lakes.

The Cisbaikal subregion comprises a narrow strip of country located along the northwestern coast of Lake Baikal and bordering the Central Siberian Plateau (see Chapter 10). This strip of land is occupied by several ranges whose flat summits are 2 to 6 miles wide. These ranges form a steep bank 700 to 1300 feet high descending to the Central Siberian Plateau.

Primorski (i.e., By-the-Sea) Range extends from the southwestern end of Baikal to the island of Olkhon. It continues on the island and then extends farther northeast as the submerged Academy Range, 2000 to 3000 feet below the surface of the lake. The Baikal(ski) Range extends from a point opposite Olkhon to the northern end of Baikal. This range is 4000 to 5000 feet above the level of the lake. Its summits rise above the timberline. In the southern part these summits are flat or rounded, with occasional, rather low, rocky crags. Farther north the range with its rocky peaks possesses a more alpine character. In this part of the range on its northwestern slope just a few miles from Baikal is the source of one of the four largest Siberian rivers, the Lena. Still farther northeast the range extends into the north Baikal highland, where elevations increase to 6000 and even to 7000 feet.

Between Lake Baikal and the River Olekma is a system of parallel mountain chains composed of pre-Cambrian schist and gneiss. The general direction of the chains is from southwest to northeast. The country was once peneplained, and the watershed divides are often flat and swampy. There are traces of two ancient glaciations. At present there are no glaciers, although patches of snow lie on the summits all year round.

Between Baikal and the River Vitim lie the Delun Uran, North Muia * (Muiski), and South Muia (Muiski) ranges. The first two are alpine in character, with serrated summits reaching more than 6500 feet high. The South Muia Range, although reaching similar altitudes, has the appearance of a highland with rounded summits. Only in its northeastern part does it have a mountainous character.

* The River Muia is a tributary to the Vitim.

To the northeast, between the Vitim and the Olekma, is the Kodar Range. South of it and parallel to it extends the Udokan Range. Its eastern end, near the Olekma, merges into the northeastern extremity of the Yablonovoi Range. The highest points in the Udokan Range reach over 9800 feet, although accurate figures are not available.

Above the northern end of Baikal stretches the north Baikal highland. Northeast of it, in the basin of the River Patom (a western tributary of the Lena), lies the Patom highland. The highland descends abruptly to the Central Siberian Plateau, with banks 1300 to 2000 feet high.

Stanovoi Khrebet,* a Russian name meaning the main divide, extends from the Olekma to the Maya (a tributary to the River Uda, which flows into the southwestern end of the Okhotsk Sea, and is not to be confused with the Maya that is a nearby tributary to the Aldan and thus to the Lena). On older maps, still used in some classrooms, the Stanovoi Range is shown as a continuous chain of mountains extending from the Transbaikal region to Bering Strait and dividing the Arctic and the Pacific drainages. This idea of a continuous main divide of Eastern Siberia originated at the time of the Russian conquest of the country, when the Russians, in their expansion south from the Yakut country in the seventeenth century, crossed the mountain ranges and reached the shores of the Okhotsk Sea and the River Amur. Although it had been suspected for a long time, only very recently, at the beginning of this century, was it established with certainty that there is no continuous dividing range extending for such a long distance.

At present the name Stanovoi Khrebet is understood to mean a plateau-like highland, bordered both from the north and from the south with high mountain chains. The northern chain, which is higher (up to 8000 feet) than the southern one, is not the watershed dividing chain. Rivers of the Lena system originate on the south slope of this chain. The summits of the southern chain reach a little over 4500 or 4600 feet. Berg † defines the Stanovoi Khrebet as a system of mountain chains extending between the upper reaches of the Aldan and the Maya (tributary of the Aldan) and describes it as a part of the Far Eastern Region, whereas other geographers place it in the Transbaikal region. The Stanovoi Khrebet is located in that

* V. A. Obruchev, "The Yablonovi and Stanovoi Ranges in the Light of the New Data," *Geog. J.*, Vol. 86, pp. 422–440, 1935.

† L. S. Berg, *Priroda SSSR*, 1938, p. 264.

part of Eastern Siberia where Transbaikal, the Far Eastern Region, and the region of the mountains of northeastern Siberia are joined.

The Stanovoi Khrebet is composed of crystalline schist and gneiss of pre-Cambrian age, with extensive granitic intrusions. Tectonically it is similar to all other mountains of northern Transbaikal and the Vitim Plateau. The highest point of the Stanovoi Khrebet is Golets Skalistyi (Rocky Summit), 8131 feet.

Prasolov * makes the following tabulation for the topography of southern Transbaikal:

Large valleys are located at	1600 to 2000 feet
Secondary valleys are located at	2000 to 2600 feet
Mountain passes are located at	3000 to 3300 feet
Summits are located at	3300 to 4000 feet

The western part of the Transbaikal region is rich in placer gold, which is mined on the Vitim Plateau, in the Barguzin country, and along the River Djida. Considerable deposits of iron are found in the Ulan Burgasy Mountains. The estimated amount of the iron ore is 92 million tons, the iron content of the ore averaging 37 per cent. Djida tungsten deposits are of importance to the entire Union. Brown coal is found near Ulan Ude (new name for Verkhne-Udinsk; it means, in Buriat, Red Gate) and near Chita. In eastern Transbaikal also are considerable deposits of tungsten (between the rivers Onon and Argun). Iron deposits of an estimated capacity of 100 million tons are located near Nerchinsk. In the same locality tin, silver, zinc, mercury, antimony, and arsenic are also mined.

The renowned Lena goldfields are located on the Patom highland, the richest part being along the River Bodaibo. In the Stanovoi Mountains, in addition to placer gold deposits, mica is found. Gold is worked on the Aldan Plateau also.

The largest body of fresh water in the Old World, Lake Baikal is located in the southwestern part of the region. It is called Dalai Nor (Ocean Lake) by the Mongols and often referred to by the old Russian settlers as More, the Sea. Lake Baikal is about 400 miles long and 50 miles wide at its widest part. It occupies an area of more than 12,000 square miles. The maximum depth of the lake is 5710 feet. It is thus the deepest fresh-water lake in the world. Baikal is located at an elevation of 1486 feet above sea level, and the surrounding moun-

* L. I. Prasolov, "Southern Transbaikalia," *Materials of the Commission on Investigations of Republics*, Series Buriat-Mongol, Academy of Science Publication, 1927, 422 pp. (In Russian.)

tains tower 6500 feet and more above the surface of the lake. The depression occupied by Lake Baikal consists of three or four tectonic fault troughs formed in the middle of the Tertiary period. Similar troughs, filled with recent deposits, are found both southwest and northeast of Lake Baikal. In addition to the tectonic forces that shaped the Baikal depression, epeirogenic disturbances also contributed to its topography. The southwestern part of the lake contains areas that are still sinking whereas other areas are uplifting. At the settlement of Kultuk the shoreline rises 0.4 inch a year. Seventy-five miles east the shoreline sinks 0.4 inch a year. Earthquakes are common. At the end of the last century the settlement of Kudara in the delta of the Selenga was submerged during an earthquake, forming Kudara Bay.

More than 300 rivers and mountain streams flow into Lake Baikal. The River Selenga, flowing from Lake Koso Gol (Hubsugol Dalai), located in Mongolia near the sources of the Yenisei, and the upper Angara, supply about 85 per cent of all incoming water. The evaporation from the surface of the lake amounts to only 6 per cent of the total loss of water. From the southwestern part of the lake flows the majestic River Angara, which, because of its swift flow and its steady discharge of 60,600 cubic feet of water per second, well regulated by the lake, is an important potential source of water power.

The temperature of Lake Baikal is very low. By the end of summer it may be as warm as 60°F in shallow bays but at the middle of the lake, even in the warmest month, August, the surface temperature averages about 48°F. Below the surface, at 800 feet and deeper, the temperature of the water is pretty nearly constant, 37.6°F.

Baikal is notorious for its strong winds, often reaching the force of hurricanes. Sarma blowing occasionally from the mainland across the southern tip of Olkhon Island may reach a velocity of 90 miles per hour. In its disastrous effects and in its spectacular and sinister force it may be compared with American tornadoes or Japanese typhoons.

Baikal freezes very late in the winter. Only at the beginning of January do its turbulent waters begin to turn to ice. Towards the end of winter the average thickness of the ice reaches 3 feet. There are, however, many treacherous cracks, some of which may be over 3 feet wide, which remain open throughout the winter. At the point where the Angara River flows from Baikal, neither the lake nor the river ever freezes. Lake Baikal remains free of ice from 110 to 248 days a year, depending on the location.

Climate

In the Transbaikal region the climate of the Siberian taiga blends with the climate of the Mongolian steppes. A large body of water, Lake Baikal, also exerts a certain influence on the climate of the region. Temperature and precipitation data for Chita, located in the central part of the region, are given in Table 17. Winter in the region reminds one of the winter of adjacent parts of Eastern Siberia; it is still, sunny, and cold.* The cold is somewhat augmented by the generally high elevations (1600 to 2600 feet) of the region. Absolute minima may be as low at 58°F below zero—as low as in Duluth, Minnesota.

Spring is late, dry, and cold, and its daily ranges in temperature are great, as much as 97°F; i.e., days are very hot, but nights are very cold. Because of the relatively southern location, summer in the region is hot; frosts may occur any time, however, though rarely during July. The vegetative period is about 150 days. After the middle of August frosts become frequent. As early as October the mean monthly temperature is below freezing.

TABLE 17. TEMPERATURE AND PRECIPITATION AT CHITA,
ELEVATION 2240 FEET

Jan.	Feb.	Mar.	Apr.	May	June	July	Aug.	Sept.	Oct.	Nov.	Dec.	Year
				Temperature, degrees Fahrenheit								Mean
−17	−8	11	32	46	60	66	60	47	29	6	−12	26.6
				Precipitation, inches								Total
0.06	0.06	0.12	0.3	1.1	1.7	3.5	3.2	1.3	0.6	0.2	0.2	12.2

The precipitation in Transbaikal is very meager, varying from 8 to 13 inches a year and occasionally dropping to 6 inches, as in the southern part of Olkhon Island in Lake Baikal. Buriat people living on the island irrigate their fenced hayfields (utugs).† On the south-

* January and February are the months with maximum sunshine. Nowhere in the Soviet Union is there as much sunshine as in Transbaikal.
† Hayfields are fenced partly for religious reasons.

western shores of Baikal, however, the annual precipitation is relatively high, amounting to 15 to 20 inches. In the southern part of the region the winter precipitation is practically nil. Summer rains often occur in the form of cloudbursts. Once, at the southern end of Baikal, 9 inches of rain fell in 48 hours.

Because of scanty snow cover and low winter temperatures, permanently frozen ground is widespread. During the summer the surface soil thaws to a depth of about 10 feet. Lack of snow in winter excludes the possibility of floods in the spring.

Winds in the Transbaikal region are predominantly from the northwest throughout the year. In winter there may be some winds from the west, and in July there may also be some from the north.

Lake Baikal exerts a mollifying influence on the surrounding country, but this effect does not extend far from its shores. On the southwestern shores of Baikal temperatures in winter are usually 20°F higher than in Ulan Ude and summer temperatures are 10°F to 15°F lower.

Soils and Vegetation

Transbaikal lies between the Siberian taiga and the Mongolian steppes, and the vegetation of these two areas is intermixed in this region. Conifer forests of the taiga penetrate southward along the mountain ranges, and steppe vegetation, which is predominant in the southern part, penetrates far northward, where it occurs in patches large and small within an essentially forested area. In the northeastern part of Transbaikal the landscape gradually merges into that of the mountains of northeastern Siberia, and east of the Yablonovoi Range there gradually appear trees and shrubs of the Far Eastern Region, such as Manchurian oak, hazelnut, and elm. Steppes usually occur at lower elevations of the region, up to 1600 to 2300 feet. Above them, the vegetation is of the woodland type. Elevations above 4000 feet are covered with the mountain-taiga type of forests, which in southern Transbaikal extend as high as 6300 feet. In the northern part of the region, however, the timberline may be located as low as 4000 feet. Above the forests is the subalpine zone of vegetation.

Grassland vegetation of the region is represented by several different types. In the southern part of Transbaikal, where prairies (or steppes) are rather extensive, the soil is of a chestnut-brown type with a humus content of 3 to 5 per cent. The predominant vegetation here consists of needlegrass, fescue, and June grass. Where the soil

is better, approaching in its humus content that of the southern chernozems of European Russia, the vegetation consists of needlegrass
with an admixture of many dicotyledons. On leached chernozems of
the Transbaikal woodland the vegetation is more diversified, with a
predominance of dicotyledons.

In the basin of the Barguzin the soils are of a chestnut-brown type.
Needlegrass and sagebrush (*Artemisia*) dominate here. In depressions
alkaline and saline patches are common. Mountain ranges, however,
are forest-clad. Dahurian larch is found on the northern slopes and
common pine (*Pinus sylvestris*) on the southern slopes.

Around Nerchinsk, where elevations are lower and the vegetation
resembles the woodland type, grassland areas may be of several types.
In some places a wheatgrass (*Agropyron pseudoagropyrum*) dominates, whereas in others dicotyledons grow in profusion. In still other
places the daylily (*Hemerocallis minor*) adds color to the steppe.

In the southwestern part of the region the countryside is covered
with sagebrush and resembles the Mongolian steppes. The driest
steppes of the region, where only about one-half of the surface is covered with plants, the vegetation consists of a rather short stand (6 to 8
inches) of a grass species (*Diplachne squarrosa*) with an admixture of
Astragalus, Oxytropis, and other xerophytic plants.

Alkaline soils of the solonets type (see description of soils in Chapter 14) support needleleaf sedge (*Carex stenophylla*) and sagebrush
(*Artemisia frigida*). In depressions where the soil is still more alkaline, i.e., of the solonchak type, one may encounter thick, coarse
bunches of chii (*Lasiogrostis splendens*).

In the southern part of Transbaikal dry steppes are common. Siberian tansy (*Tanacetum sibiricum*) is found here, especially on the
upper parts of the hills.

On the island of Olkhon and on the northwestern shores of Lake
Baikal, opposite the island, considerable areas are covered with dry
steppe vegetation developed on coarse chestnut-brown soil. Plants
here never completely cover the ground. By the middle of June this
vegetation is at its best.* Along with the usual fescue, June grass, and
wheatgrass there are astragals, Siberian tansy, *Arenaria capillaris*,†
Sedum aizoon, thyme, *Veronica incana*, asters, many composites, mint
family plants, and the graceful, delicately fragrant *Lilium tenuifolium*.
By the second half of the summer the showy flowering plants dis-

---

* N. T. Mirov, "Distribution of Vegetation of Olhon Island, Lake Baikal,
Eastern Siberia," *Ecology*, Vol. 10, pp. 151–153, 1929.

† This species is also found in the mountains of California.

appear, and one is able to identify only crested wheatgrass, June grass, and fescue, with some sedge (*Carex stenophylla*), feathergrass (*Stipa consanguinea*), and occasional small sagebrush (*Artemisia frigida*).

In some places in southern Transbaikal the landscape is decidedly of a woodland type. Here are found the usual woodland alternations of grassland patches with pine forests, larch groves, patches of birch, and brushfields of *Betula gmelini* and *Betula fruticosa*.

The forests of the taiga type contain, occasionally, along the rivers, swampy meadows with several species of sedge (*Carex*), quackgrass (*Agropyron repens*), and other herbaceous species. In the valleys of large rivers the meadows support a more lush growth. Here we find bluegrass, a species of clover (*Trifolium lupinaster*), a sweet vetch (*Hedysarum sibiricum*), a meadow peavine (*Lathyrus pratensis*), etc.

In the southern part of the region swamps are not common. On the low slopes birch-aspen forests grow mixed with larch and pine. In the higher ranges (such as Sokhondo) the mixed forests are merged into larch park-like groves, and still higher the larch gives way to cembra pine on the northern slopes and in the deep valleys to this pine, fir, and spruce. At about 6200 feet cembra pine forests change rather rapidly to *Pinus pumila* thickets and then to the tundras and barren summits.

The northern part of the region is covered with larch forests resembling the taiga of the Yakut country. In places the larch are admixed with cembra pine and fir. Occasionally there are Mongolian poplar (*Populus suaveolens*), chokecherry (*Prunus padus*), aspen, mountain ash (*Sorbus*), and birch (*Betula platyphylla*). Evidence of forest fires is everywhere, and burned-over areas often extend for many miles. The usual riparian thickets of willow grow along the rivers, and flood meadows are covered with herbaceous vegetation.

Sand areas of the southern part of Transbaikal are covered with pure forests of common pine (*Pinus sylvestris*) with *Rhododendron dahuricum* underneath. A strip of country where the habitats of Siberian larch and Dahurian larch overlap extends across the southwestern part of the region (see Map 18, p. 109). In this strip the two species hybridize so that one may find all gradations from pure Siberian larch to pure Dahurian larch.

In the middle part of the region forests of Dahurian larch predominate. There are many different types of larch forests, such as those with an understory of rhododendron, those with a moss ground cover, and those with cowberry. Sometimes cembra pine and fir are admixed where there is a cooling effect from Lake Baikal, and sometimes on sandy soils common pine may be found growing. On the Khamar-Daban Range dark taiga of cembra pine descends to the shores of Lake Baikal. Common pine forests do not occur in higher elevations; fir and spruce also gradually disappear, as well as the taiga broadleaf trees—aspen and birch. Occasionally high ranges are covered with pure cembra pine forests. On Sokhondo Mountain the timberline of cembra pine is located at about 6500 feet. Thickets of *Pinus pumila*, a species closely related to *Pinus cembra*, are found above the forest belt, usually at 4000 to 4300 feet.

There are no luxurious alpine meadows in Transbaikal. Open grassy patches may be found above the timberline, but generally there will be thickets of *Pinus pumila* and scrub of *Betula exilis* with a ground cover consisting of *Cassiope ericoides* or *Arctostaphylos alpina*. *Juniperus dahurica* occurs occasionally. *Pinus pumila* thickets in many places are severely damaged by insects and destroyed by fire. After fire this pine is replaced by Middendorff birch.

The zone occupied by *Pinus pumila* thickets is rather narrow; in the northern part it is only 150 to 350 feet in width. Above it lie the tundra-like slopes and the rock debris of the summits. *Cladonia alpestris* lichen grows in protected places, together with bilberry and cowberry. In places *Cetraria nivalis* lichen is intermixed with *Arctostaphylos alpina* and crowberry (*Empetrum nigrum*). On the rocky summits one may find another tundra type of lichen, *Alectoria ochroleuca*, with scattered *Cassiope* and sprawling ledum (*Ledum decumbens*). Primula, pedicularis, arctic diapensia (*Diapensia lapponica*), saxifrage, alpine sweetgrass (*Hierochloe alpina*), and other plants also occur on the rocky summits.

Agriculture of the region is restricted to the middle elevations occupied by the woodland type of vegetation where soil is of a chernozem, if slightly podzolized, type. Rye is the main crop, cultivated both by the Russian settlers and by the native Buriats. Occasional patches of grainfields are found in such places as wooded valleys of Olkhon Island.*

In the dry prairies of the south the main occupation of the people is raising cattle, horses, and sheep. Winter grazing is practiced widely. In places where rainfall is not sufficient, as in the steppes of Olkhon Island, the Buriats resort to irrigation of their fenced hayfields. It is possible that religious pilgrimages of the Buriats living near the Mongolian border to the sacred Lake Baikal were responsible for the intro-

* Personal observation.

duction to Transbaikal of many Mongolian species of plants, especially grasses and weeds.

Animal Life

Animal life of the region consists of both prairie and forest species. A shaggy grizzly bear (*Ursus arctos baikalensis*) is found in the Transbaikal taiga. Wolves are common and are menacing to cattle and sheep. They occur both in the prairie-woodland part and in the forest part of the region. Other mammals found include Yakut fox (*Vulpes vulpes jacutensis*), Siberian kolonok (*Mustela sibirica*), ermine (*Mustela erminea*), and weasel (*Mustela nivalis pigmaea*). The much-praised Barguzin sable (*Martes zibellina princeps*) has become almost extinct. Protective measures, including a Barguzin sable preserve, established in 1916, have saved this valuable predator, whose environment is in the *Pinus pumila* thickets and in the rock debris, where it feeds on pika, chipmunk, mice, pine nuts, and berries.

The most important commercial animal, as everywhere in the Siberian taiga, is the squirrel (*Sciurus vulgaris fusconigricans*). This squirrel lives chiefly in larch forests.

Wild reindeer (*Rangifer angustirostris*) live in many mountain ranges, where the tundra vegetation of the high elevation provides suitable fodder. Moose (*Alces alces*) is found in the open forest dales, where swamps and lakes are common. Wapiti elk (*Cervus canadensis sibiricus*) prefers open meadows. Muskdeer and roebuck (*Capreolus pigargus*) occur in the upper forest belt and above the timberline. In the higher part of the Stanovoi Range is found mountain sheep (*Ovis nivicola*). Tarbagan, or marmot (*Marmota kamtschatica doppelmeyeri*), living in meadows along rocky ledges is hunted for its valuable fur.

There are many Siberian taiga birds in Transbaikal. Among the game birds are stone grouse (*Tetrao parvirostis*), a small grouse (*Tetrastes bonasia*), several species of ducks, and other waterfowl. The *Pinus pumila* thickets are the home of the scarlet grosbeak (*Erythrina rosea*) and the pine grosbeak (*Pinicola enucleator*). On the rocky tundra slopes live common ptarmigan (*Lagopus mutus*) and dotterel (*Charadrius morinellus*), a bird related to the plover. The rock thrush (*Monticola saxatilis turkestanica*) is found on the rocky cliffs of northern Baikal. This species also lives in such distant regions as Crimea. It is a common summer visitant to southern and southeastern Europe.

Ground squirrels (*Citellus eversmanni, C. dahuricus*) are found in the prairies and the woodland areas. The former species occurs on Olkhon Island in Lake Baikal. Marmots (*Marmota sibirica, M. kamtschatica*) are common in the steppes of Transbaikal. Marmot, locally called tarbagan, is hunted for its fur. This animal spreads bubonic plague. In nearby Manchuria the Chinese use marmots for food. In addition to ground squirrels and marmots, jumping mouse (*Alactaga saltator*) and field mice of the genera *Microtus* and *Clethrionomys* are found in the steppe.

Among the predators found in the woodland area are badger (*Meles meles raddei*), weasel (*Putorius eversmanni michnoi*), so-called solongoi (*Kolonocus alpinus*), and desert kit fox (*Vulpes korsak*).

The gazelle antelope (*Gazella subgutturosa*) migrates to the region in winter from Mongolia, where it spends the summer.

Birds of the woodland include ducks (*Tadorna tadorna, T. ferruginea*), bustard (*Otis tarda*), crane (*Grus virgo*), Mongolian lark (*Melanocorypha mongolica*), and avocet (*Recurvirostra avocetta*). Black grouse (*Lyrurus tetrix*) is common in forest groves of the Transbaikalian woodland. The same species of bustard and black grouse are also found in the European woodland (see Chapter 12).

The fauna of Lake Baikal is unique. It contains some ancient forms of life of uncertain origin, such as sponges of the family *Lubomirskiidae* and certain fishes and mollusks. There are also relict species of the Tertiary period. The lake is exceptionally rich in small shrimps of the family *Gammaridae*. Out of 66 genera of this family only 5 are found outside of Lake Baikal. Altogether there are about 300 species of *Gammaridae* living in the lake.

Among the fishes that should be noted are 7 genera (12 species) of the family *Cottocomephoridae* and 2 species belonging to the monogeneric family *Comephoridae*. Species of the former family may be found at depths of 3000 to 5000 feet. They are grotesque in appearance, unlike any familiar fish, and are not used for food. *Comephorus baicalensis* (3½ inches long) and *C. dybowski* (about 8 inches long) of the latter family are viviparous, transparent little creatures superficially somewhat resembling the sea horse. There are more than 80 species of mollusks. Two families, *Benedictidae* and *Baikaliidae*, are endemic to Baikal. The endemic Baikal hair seal (*Phoca sibirica*) is related to *Phoca hispida* of the Arctic Ocean.

The most important among the commercial fish is *Coregonus autumnalis migratorius*, locally known as omul. In winter this fish, of the salmon family, stays at depths of 1300 to 2600 feet. In the spring it approaches the shores, where it feeds throughout the summer. At the beginning of October it enters the inflowing rivers (but not the outflowing Angara) for spawning. It ascends the Upper Angara for more than 60 miles. Later in the fall it returns to the lake.

People

The southwestern part of the region and one place in the central part, close to the Mongolian border, is inhabited by the Buriats, who are akin to the Mongols. A few Mongols live along the border. The Buriats are engaged partially in agriculture, but their chief occupation is raising cattle. In the northeastern part of Transbaikal live the reindeer-keeping Tungus. Russians live throughout the region.

Chapter 24

Mountains of Northeastern Siberia *

The northeastern part of Siberia between the River Lena and the Bering Sea, and roughly between the 60th and 70th parallels, includes a territory that differs considerably from the adjacent part of Siberia in its topography, geology, and vegetative cover. (See Map 30.) It is essentially a mountainous country, extensive mountain systems alternating with low swampy areas. Extensive lowlands are also found within the borders of the region. Administratively the region belongs partly to the Yakut Autonomous Republic and partly to the Khabarovsk administrative region of Russia.

Topography

During the Paleozoic and Mesozoic eras this region was a huge geosynclinal basin that extended from the mouth of the Lena to the Bering Sea. It was covered by an ancient sea in which marine sediments were deposited to a thickness of 30,000 to 50,000 feet. The course of the geosyncline development was interrupted by frequent foldings. Only the Kolyma-Yukaghir platform retained a degree of rigidity throughout the whole duration of the formative processes of northeastern Siberia.

The topographic structure of the region is chiefly a product of the early phases of Mesozoic foldings. The most intensive foldings occurred during the Lower Cretaceous period. Because of the great uniformity of sediments of the geosyncline, the foldings also possessed an orderly and uniform character. The Verkhoyansk and Cherski Mountain systems were formed during the Lower Cretaceous period. No foldings occurred in the region after the Lower Cretaceous.

---

* The geomorphology of the region has been studied recently by the outstanding Russian geologist Obruchev. See "The Mountain Systems of Northeastern Asia," by S. V. Obruchev and K. A. Salishchev, *Geog. Rev.*, Vol. 25, pp. 625–642, 1935.

During the time of the Mesozoic foldings the region had already acquired a considerable rigidity and responded to the warping of the earth crust not by acquiring additional folds but rather by epeirogenetic processes. During this time, which extended even into the Quaternary period, a considerable number of faults were formed and considerable areas sank whereas others remained elevated, forming extensive horsts.

Toward the end of the Tertiary period the sea receded and most of the region appeared as land. Tertiary foldings occurred only along the present Pacific coastal area, which at that time was still under water. In this part of the region the Cretaceous and Tertiary deposits were folded forming several meridional chains of mountains.

During the Quaternary period there was considerable glaciation in the region; however, it was confined to the mountains; the valleys were never covered with ice.

At present there are almost no glaciers in the region. Only a few small glaciers have been found and even these are decreasing in size. Tectonic adjustments are still very noticeable in the region. The Chukotski Peninsula is being raised much more energetically than are the Yukaghir Plateau and the adjacent part of the Kolyma Range. The Anadyr depression was repeatedly covered by the sea during Quaternary times. Before the last glaciation the Chukotski Peninsula became separated from North America. In the western part of the region the Verkhoyansk Mountain Range (Russian for the Upper Yana) extends for about 1000 miles, paralleling the Lena River (or in the south its tributary, the Aldan). The Verkhoyansk Range acts as the water divide between the Lena basin, on one hand, and the Yana and (in the southeast) the Indigirka, on the other. To the north the Verkhoyansk Range extends as far as the Arctic Ocean; to the south it extends to the lower Yudoma (a branch of the Maya, which is a tributary to the Aldan). The Verkhoyansk Range descends rather gently to the Yana and the Oimekon plateaux (i.e., towards the east). Its western slope descends towards the Lena and the Aldan rather abruptly, often forming high cliffs up to 1500 feet above the Central Siberian Plateau. In the southern part of the range elevations run to over 8000 feet. Along the Yakutsk-Verkhoyansk highway are encountered altitudes of 6500 feet. Towards the north elevations decrease.

The Verkhoyansk Range is a typical folded system of mountains. It is composed of sandstones and schists of the Upper Carboniferous, Permian, Triassic, and Jurassic periods. After the middle of the

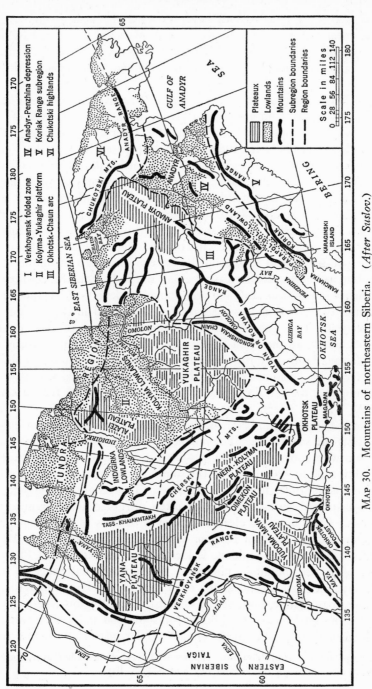

MAP 30. Mountains of northeastern Siberia. (*After Suslov.*)

Jurassic the sea receded and never covered the area again. After the Tertiary period some uplifting took place, as evidenced by the presence of terraces 1000 to 1500 feet above the floor of the valleys. There are indications of two glaciations in the Verkhoyansk Mountains.

The Yana Plateau, Oimekon Plateau, Nera-Kolyma Plateau, and Yudoma-Maya Plateau are located (from north to south) east of the Verkhoyansk Range, between it and the Cherski Mountains. The Yana Plateau lies between the 65th and 70th parallels, with the Verkhoyansk Range to the west and Tass-Khaiakhtakh Range (of the Cherski system) to the east. The plateau is composed of Triassic and Jurassic rocks disrupted by intrusions. The southern part is elevated above sea level 2500 to 3000 feet. Elevations are lower in the north. The Oimekon Plateau stretches southwest of the Yana Plateau and is drained by the upper reaches of the Indigirka and its tributaries. In the southwest and in the northwest elevations are of about 5000 feet, but in the southeastern part, along the Indigirka, the country is somewhat lower—1800 to 2800 feet above sea level. Very low temperatures of −76°F and lower have been recorded in this section of the plateau. The Tass-Kystabyt Range extends east of the plateau, and beyond it lies the Nera-Kolyma Plateau. In the southern part of this plateau, drained by the upper Kolyma River, elevations run above 4000 feet. In the northern part, drained by the Nera, a tributary to the Indigirka, the terrain is lower, barely reaching 2600 feet in some places.

Both the Oimekon and Nera-Kolyma plateaux are composed of Triassic schists and sandstones. The northern portion of the Tass-Kystabyt Range towers above them 2600 to 4200 feet, its absolute altitudes ranging from 6500 to 7200 feet. In the south, however, it becomes lower, reaching about 5000 feet above sea level. The range is composed of much-dislocated Triassic sediments often disrupted with granitic intrusions. Fault lines are clearly seen on both sides of the range.

Southwest of Oimekon Plateau, in the upper reaches of the Maya and its tributary, the Yudoma, is located the Yudoma-Maya Plateau. West of it rise mountain ranges of the southern extremity of the Verkhoyansk system, and south of it extend the Djugdjour Range and the Coast Range, both of the Okhotsk Coast Region (see p. 305). East of the settlement of Okhotsk for some 300 miles there are no mountain ranges parallel to the coast.* Older maps show here a part

* Except for the short and low (up to 4500 feet) range Chutkavar, located near the coast between the Oushki Bay and Nagaev Bay.

of the Stanovoi Khrebet supposedly extending from Transbaikal to
Bering Strait (see Chapter 23, p. 266). The Yudoma-Maya Plateau
is of gentle topography with occasional summits reaching over 4200
feet above sea level and only 1500 to 2000 above the surrounding
country. The plateau is composed of Upper Carboniferous, Permian,
Jurassic, and Triassic rocks. In the northern part of the plateau rivers
flow in deep canyons; in the southern part river valleys are broad
and swampy and the streams are sluggish and meandering.

The Cherski * Range is a complicated mountain system extending
for about 600 miles northeast of the above-described plateaux. In its
widest portion it is about 200 miles wide. The Cherski Range in
northeastern Siberia is not to be confused with the range bearing the
same name and located in the southern part of the Transbaikal region.
The general direction of the mountain chains of the system is the
same as that of the Verkhoyansk Range, that is, from northwest to
southeast. The outer northern chains are composed of Paleozoic
rocks; the inner and western chains are composed of Lower Mesozoic
sediments with frequent granitic intrusions. In the central part of
the system in the Indigirka drainage there are at least nine mountain
chains of rather rugged character and 6500 to 8200 feet high. Northern chains are uniformly flat, peneplained highlands. The southeastern part of the system has the character of an extensive highland
composed of Triassic sediments with occasional granitic intrusions
that form rather high massifs. The northern chains merge in the
northwest into the steep, rocky Tass-Khaiakhtakh Range, which consists of two mountain chains. Elevations here run above 8000 feet,
and snow patches persist on the summits throughout the summer.
The west slope of the range merges into the Yana Plateau. The central chains of the Cherski Range are cut by two mighty rivers, the
Indigirka and Kolyma. These rivers flow in deep gorges with steep
banks towering more than 6500 feet above. The Indigirka gorge
below Tebelakh is 6600 feet deep.

* Named after J. D. Cherski, a Lithuanian, who in his youth was involved in
the Polish uprising of 1863 and exiled by the Russian government to Siberia.
Cherski studied the geology of Lake Baikal and the Eastern Sayan. In 1875 he
returned from exile. Later he was sent to northeastern Siberia by the Academy
of Sciences. He died in 1892 in the Kolyma River region. During this last expedition he discovered the range that was later named after him. Other scientists
exiled to Siberia after the Polish uprising included zoologists Benedict Dybovski
and Victor Godlewski and geologist Alexander Chekanowski. All these men
have contributed a great deal to the knowledge of Siberia.

During the glacial age the Cherski Range was covered with ice. Some glaciers were about 100 miles long, and their terminal moraines are located now at about 1200 feet altitude.

The Yukaghir Plateau is located between the River Kolyma and its tributary the Omolon. The plateau is, for the most part, composed of Mesozoic deposits, i.e., horizontal Triassic sediments with some Jurassic. Among these Mesozoic deposits there are occasional granite and syenite intrusions. In the western portion of the plateau, however, two ridges are formed of Paleozoic rocks. In the northern part of the plateau elevations are from 1000 to 1300 feet; the southern part is higher—from 1300 to 2600 feet.

The Alazei Plateau extends along the eastern shores of the Indigirka. The plateau has the appearance of an undulating plain interrupted by occasional mountain groups composed of crystalline rocks. In the northern part of the Alazei Plateau mountain chains composed of Paleozoic and Mesozoic rocks reach elevations of more than 3000 feet.

Towards the shores of the Arctic the terrain decreases in altitude, forming the Kolyma and Indigirka lowlands. These lowlands are located only about 150 feet above the ocean level, and their deposits are of the Quaternary period. The terrain is swampy and dotted with numerous small, shallow lakes. Local people, Yakuts, as well as Russian settlers, often convert these lakes into excellent hayfields by draining them. Settlements are located above the flood plains on the river terraces, where rich meadows are used for cattle raising.

From Okhotsk to Chaun Bay in the Arctic extends the youngest tectonic subregion of the area, which is designated by Obruchev * as the Okhotsk-Chaun Arc. During the Paleozoic and Mesozoic eras it was divided among different tectonic regions. These divisions became consolidated into one entity only at the time of the Tertiary foldings. The Okhotsk-Chaun subregion includes the Okhotsk Plateau, Gydan Range, Anadyr Plateau, and Anui Ranges.

The Okhotsk Plateau is composed of Mesozoic, much-dislocated sediments, frequently disrupted by massive granitic effusions. The folds of the plateau are parallel to the coastline of the Okhotsk Sea, to which it drops.

Along the Okhotsk coast, from the River Yama northeastward, extends the broad Gydan Range, called by the Russians Kolymski Khrebet. Elevations of the range run between 1600 and 2000 feet. In

* S. V. Obruchev and K. A. Salishchev, "The Mountain Systems of Northeastern Asia," *Geog. Rev.*, Vol. 25, pp. 625–642, 1935.

the north the range just about reaches the Big Anui River. Traces of ancient glaciation have been found in the Gydan Range. The Konginskaia Chain, with summits reaching over 6500 feet, extends from its northern end.

The Anadyr Plateau lies between the Gydan and Chukotski ranges. The Arctic Circle passes across its center. The plateau is 2500 to 3300 feet high, some summits reaching over 3900 feet. The topography of the plateau is very monotonous. The mountains here are of a massif character, with flat summits and gently rolling slopes.

Northwest of the Anadyr Plateau, beyond the Arctic Circle, extends the South Anui Range. Northeast of it, separated by Maly (i.e., the Lesser) Anui River, is located the North Anui Range. Elevations here run from 4200 to 4900 feet, occasionally reaching about 6000 feet. Little is known about the geology of these mountains. The North Anui Range is a rugged chain of mountains with high peaks and steep slopes. Traces of glaciation are evident in the form of moraines. Towards the Anui River the range descends abruptly. The northern slopes are more gradual.

The sunken part of the region between the Chaun Arc, Koriak Range, and Chukotski highlands is known as the Anadyr-Penzhina depression. Until relatively recently it was under water. The depression includes three lowland areas: the Anadyr lowland, Penzhina lowland, and Parapol Dol. The Anadyr lowland stretches along the river of the same name. It is only slightly elevated above sea level and is dotted with numerous small lakes. Its extensive swamps are crossed by sluggish, meandering streams. Only towards the mountains does the lowland assume a slightly undulating character.

The Penzhina lowland is located in the lower reaches of the River Penzhina, which flows into the Okhotsk Sea. Parapol Dol (Dol is Russian for an extensive plain) separates the region from the peninsula of Kamchatka. Both these lowland areas are very similar to the Anadyr lowland. Elevations on Parapol Dol run from 300 to 650 feet. In all these three lowland areas one may find occasional low and not very long ranges where summits may occasionally reach 5250 feet.

Along the coast of the Bering Sea, from Parapol Dol to the northeast, extends the Koriak Range. It consists of several parallel mountain chains separated by valleys. Toward the Anadyr lowland the range descends abruptly, being delineated by a fault line. Its southwestern end breaks up into many branch chains so that its width increases from 60 to 150 miles. Average heights of the Koriak Range vary from 3000 to 5000 feet. In its geological structure the range differs considerably from the inland mountains of northeastern Siberia. Like eastern Kamchatka, it has had very pronounced volcanic activity. The range had no volcanoes in the Quaternary period; its volcanic activity took place in earlier periods.

The Anadyr, or Chukotski (i.e., Chukchi), Range is located on the watershed divide between the rivers flowing into the Arctic and the Anadyr basin. In its center the range reaches elevations of 6500 to 7800 feet. It drops abruptly to the Anadyr Plateau, and its valleys, which are of glacial origin, are deep and in general rather rugged. Near the Gulf of Cross, or Zaliv Cresta (crest means cross), as the Russians call it, Mt. Matachingai is over 8200 feet in height.

The Chukotski Peninsula, i.e., the very end of the Siberian region, separated from North America by Bering Strait, is a highland where not very long chains have the appearance of gently rolling hills, ranging in elevation from 2500 to a little over 3000 feet. Only in the center of the peninsula do summits reach about 5000 feet.

Both the Anadyr Range and the Chukotski highland were folded first during the Paleozoic and then during the Mesozoic era. During the latter period the geomorphological processes were essentially epeirogenetic.

Mineral deposits of the region are considerable. The newly discovered Kolyma goldfields, connected with the new port of Magadan on the Okhotsk coast by a 400-mile automobile road, are perhaps the richest in the country. Lead is mined on the south slope of the Verkhoyansk Range. Tin is found in the sources of the Yana. There are lead-zinc-silver deposits at Endybalsk, which is located also in the Verkhoyansk Range. Coal of good quality is found along the western tributaries of the Kolyma and the eastern tributaries of the Indigirka, also at the northeastern end of the Koriak Range on the shores of the Bering Sea. Notable is the absence of lime, because of a very limited distribution of limestone in the region. Considerable areas of the region, such as the Koriak Range and the Gydan Range, have not yet been explored geologically.

Climate

The climate of the region is little known. Berg quotes some data from weather records taken in 1917–1918 at a mine located at an elevation of 3345 feet at the latitude 64°N: * The January mean tempera-

* L. S. Berg, *Priroda SSSR*, Moscow, 1938, p. 260.

ture was –20°F, as compared with –58°F at Verkhoyansk. The mean July temperature recorded was 47°F. The annual precipitation in that period amounted only to 6.4 inches with a maximum of 1.8 inches in August. Precipitation and temperature data for Verkhoyansk, located at 67°30′ latitude N, in the area where the River Yana emerges from the Yana Plateau to the lowlands, are given in Table 18.

TABLE 18. TEMPERATURE AND PRECIPITATION AT VERKHOYANSK, ELEVATION 328 FEET

Jan.	Feb.	Mar.	Apr.	May	June	July	Aug.	Sept.	Oct.	Nov.	Dec.	Year
				Temperature, degrees Fahrenheit								Mean
−58	−47	−22	8.6	34	54	59	52	36	6.0	−34	−52	3.0
				Precipitation, inches								Total
0.15	0.12	0.12	0.15	0.27	0.89	1.10	1.00	0.50	0.30	0.30	0.15	5.05

Vegetation

The lowland taiga (see Chapter 10) does not cross the Verkhoyansk Mountains. East of them a great deal of the country is covered with scrubby forests of Dahurian larch (*Larix dahurica*). In the Indigirka valley larch extends north as far as 70°15′ latitude. In the foothills of the Verkhoyansk Range larch may be admixed with some poplar or cottonwood (*Populus suaveolens*), and along the streams occasional groves of the same poplar occur—also Korean willow, or chosenia (*Chosenia macrolepis*); larch; and even Siberian spruce, which, however, is absent on the northeastern slope of the range. Along the highway crossing the range from Yakutsk to Verkhoyansk the larch forests disappear at an elevation of about 3000 feet or slightly above. Solitary trees, however, still occur up to 3400 feet. In the Gydan Range, in the upper reaches of the Omolon, the timberline is found at 2600 to 2900 feet. But in the Cherski Mountains the timberline is at 2100 to 2200 feet.

Above the timberline is the tundra with its trailing birches (*Betula subtilis* and *B. middendorffi*) and trailing *Pinus pumila*, the only conifer in the region except for larch. Generally, on the southern slopes of the mountains larch grows comparatively well. On the northern slopes, however, this tree thrives no more than in the forested part of the northern tundra.

In the lowlands of the region larch also is of a scrubby character. Larch suitable for building material is found only in patches where the drainage is fair and where the permafrost recedes deeper than usual. Under a lacy canopy of scattered larch trees one may find blue currant (*Ribes dikuscha*), *Ledum palustre* (a species akin to American Labrador tea), cowberry (*Vaccinium vitis-idaea*), bilberry (*Vaccinium uliginosum*), occasional thickets of Middendorff birch, and an abundance of *Cladonia* lichen (a staple food for wild and domesticated reindeer). Larch forests with an understory of *Pinus pumila* are widely distributed in the Verkhoyansk and Gydan ranges. The summits above the timberline are covered with *Pinus pumila*, which in the lower part of the belt may be as tall as 6 or 7 feet. Higher up it becomes scrubby and trailing. Higher still are extensive rockfields. The ground vegetation of these high elevations is represented either by the lichen tundra or by small patches of higher plants, such as arctic starwort (*Stellaria arctica*), a dryad (*Dryas punctata*), woolly lousewort (*Pedicularis nivea*), sedge, cottonsedge, and *Anemone narcissiflora*. Above 2600 feet stretch extensive rockfields, almost entirely void of vegetation.

Poplar and chosenia grow along the river bottoms of the region. Wood of the former is used for making dugouts, and the latter supplies material for telegraph poles, log cabins, and road bridges.

In the southern part of the region, in addition to poplar and chosenia there may be an admixture of such common Siberian shrubs as mountain ash (*Sorbus*) and chokecherry. Berries of both species are used for food by the inhabitants. Excellent meadows are often found along the rivers on the terraces situated above the flood plains. These are used by the local people as hayfields and pastures.

In the extreme northeastern part of the region, east of the Kolyma drainage, the mountains are bare of forests. Larch is found only in the upper reaches of the Anadyr. The watershed areas are covered here with subalpine shrubs, and the lowlands have the vegetation of scrubby tundra. *Pinus pumila*, scrub alder (*Alnus fruticosa*), and Middendorff birch grow in the mountains of the Anadyr and the Penzhina drainages.

The Chukotski Peninsula is covered with rockfields and patches of lichen tundra. The lowlands of Anadyr, Penzhina, and Parapol are covered with scrubby tundra vegetation. Occasionally along the river courses groves of poplar and chosenia are encountered; underneath grow blue and red (*Ribes triste*) currants, along with rose, groundsel (*Cacalia hastata*, a plant closely related to *Senecio*), and reedgrass (*Calamagrostis langsdorffi*).

The agriculture of the region is very rudimentary. In the southern parts some barley and rye are grown. Hotbeds are necessary for growing vegetables.

Animal Life

The animal life of the region is not very well known. In many respects it differs from the animal life of the adjacent Siberian lowland taiga. Many animals common to the taiga region, such as the kolonok (*Mustela sibirica*), do not cross the Verkhoyansk Mountains. A mountain sheep (*Ovis nivicola*) inhabits the rockfields and barrens above the timberline. In the Verkhoyansk Mountains this animal is not found below an elevation of 5000 feet, but in the northern part of the region (the Anui Mountains) its haunts may be as low as 2000 feet above sea level. Muskdeer is found occasionally in the wooded rocky slopes.

The occurrence of such steppe animals as marmot (*Marmota kamtschatica bungei*) and ground squirrel (*Citellus eversmanni buxtoni*) is of interest. The ground squirrel, however, is absent in the Verkhoyansk Range. Ermine and squirrel are found in the mountain forests; the latter, as elsewhere in Russia, is the most important commercial animal. Other noteworthy rodents are red-back mouse (*Clethrionomys rufocannus kolymensis*); meadow mouse (*Microtus hyperboreus*); and pika, or cony (*Ochotona hyperborea kolymensis*). Numerous rodents, including the Amur lemming (*Lemmus amurensis*) living in the Verkhoyansk Mountains, provide food for predators, such as ermine and sable, and thus contribute to the abundance of these valuable animals. The northeast Siberian moose is closely related to the North American moose.

Among the game birds found in the forests of this region are a large grouse (*Tetrao parvirostris*) and a small grouse (*Tetrastes bonasia kolymensis*), akin to the European hazel hen. Ptarmigan (*Lagopus mutus transbaicalicus*) is found in the rockfields. Geese are abundant along the waterways of the Chukotski Peninsula. For winter they fly as far south as California.

The most important domesticated animals are the reindeer and the sled dog.

People

The sparse population of the region consists of Yakuts, who have settled along the Yana and the Indigirka. The reindeer-keeping Lamuts (Evenes) are found throughout the region, up to the Chukotski Peninsula, where also live some 13,000 Chukchi. The Chukchi are a Paleo-Asiatic people that are now called Luorovetlans. South of them live about 8000 (also Paleo-Asiatic people) Koriaks, or Nymylans. Both these peoples keep reindeer in large herds. The reindeer is used for drawing sledges; watchdogs are used in herding; milking reindeer is not practiced. Yukaghirs (Oduls, a Paleo-Asiatic tribe) live east of the lower Indigirka and in the middle Kolyma region. About 1500 Eskimos (Uits) inhabit the coast of the Bering Sea. Russian settlements, both old and recent, are found along the rivers and in the mining districts of the region.

Chapter 25

Far Eastern Region

It is difficult to define the Far Eastern Region of the Soviet Union (Dalni Vostok, in Russian). Administratively it embraces parts of the country along the River Amur and along the coast of the Pacific, including the Kamchatka Peninsula, Kuril Islands, southwestern part of Okhotsk Sea, and the island of Sakhalin. In this book, however, only the country along the River Amur and a narrow strip of land between the Pacific coast and the River Ussuri from the Korean border to the lower Amur will be included in the Far Eastern Region; Kamchatka, Sakhalin, the Okhotsk coast, and the Kurils will be considered separately. (See Map 31.)

The Far Eastern Region is characterized by (1) a monsoon climate, modified by the influence of the adjacent cold Okhotsk Sea and of the Siberian continent; (2) a wide occurrence of Mesozoic formations; (3) the absence of any evidence of glaciation; and (4) the presence of broadleaf forests not found in the adjacent parts of Siberia.

Topography

Extensive plains are found in the Far Eastern Region along the middle course of the Amur and in the southern part of the Maritime Province, not far from Vladivostok. The region also includes some mountainous country.

The entire Far Eastern Region is drained by the Amur River and its tributaries, except for the short streams running into the Sea of Japan from the Sikhote Alin Mountains and the tributaries of the Tumen River, which separates Russia from Korea. Two navigable rivers, the Zeia and the Bureia, flow into the Amur from the north. The Zeia flows parallel to the Amur for some 300 miles, 60 to 80 miles north of it, and then turns south. The largest tributary flowing from the south, the Sungari, is totally in the Manchurian territory. The Ussuri, which flows into the Amur farther east, almost in a meridional direction, separates the Maritime Province of Russia from Manchuria.

The Amur-Zeia Plateau is located between the Amur and the Zeia and is composed of Tertiary clays and sands underlain with granite,

289

gneiss, and Jurassic sandstone. The plateau is gently rolling, with elevations ranging from 1000 to 1800 feet. Towards the Amur and towards the Zeia and its tributaries, the plateau descends rather abruptly.

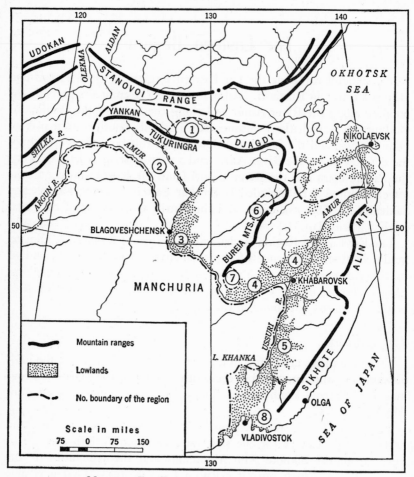

MAP 31. Far Eastern Region. (*After Suslov.*)

1. Upper Zeia plains.
2. Amur-Zeia plateau.
3. Zeia-Bureia lowland.
4. Lower Amur lowland.

5. Khanka-Ussuri lowland.
6. Bureia coal fields.
7. Bureia iron range.
8. Suchan coal mines.

East of the low reaches of the Zeia is the middle Amur lowland, covered with Tertiary deposits and containing some coal. The northeastern and northern parts are about 1000 feet above sea level, but in the south the elevations drop to 300 feet and less. On the east the lowland is bordered by the Bureia Range, sometimes called—especially the section in Manchuria—the Lesser Khingan.

The Bureia Range begins in the upper Selemja River, a tributary of the Zeia which flows into it from the northeast, and extends towards the Amur. The river cuts through the range, forming a 75-mile-long gorge. In the northern part of the range the elevations may exceed 7200 feet, but in the south they decrease rapidly. The Trans-Siberian Railroad crosses the range at about 2300 feet. Near the Amur the elevations are as low as 600 to 700 feet. The range does not appear as a sharply defined mountain chain but rather as highland country located between the middle Amur lowland and the lower Amur low-land. The highland is composed of ancient Paleozoic rocks, which form the core of the mountains. Mesozoic deposits predominate on the slopes. The range was formed during Cretaceous times. It pos-sesses some iron deposits estimated at 5 million tons. The ore is of rather poor quality, containing 37 to 43 per cent of the metal. Coal is found in the upper reaches of the Bureia, in the Jurassic and Cre-taceous deposits. The coal-bearing strata are over 2500 feet thick. The Bureia coal deposits are considered among the largest in the coun-try. Their local importance is augmented by their nearness to the iron deposits of the Bureia Range.

The lower Amur lowland extends from the eastern slopes of the Bureia Range to Lake Bolen-Odjal, and south of the Amur into the area between the Sungari and the Ussuri rivers. It is level country with average elevations little over 150 feet above sea level. There are, however, occasional heights reaching over 2500 feet. The area is a monotonous, treeless stretch of land dotted with numerous small lakes.

A chain of mountains known in different areas by different names extends in a latitudinal direction in the northern part of the region. The western portion, known as the Yankan Range, with elevations up to 3300 feet, merges into the mountains and highlands of the Trans-baikal region. The eastern continuation of the Yankan Range is Tukuringra Range, in which summits are 5000 to 5300 feet high and passes are located at 3000 to 3300 feet. Farther east the range assumes the name Djagdy; elevations here are about 4700 feet.

The Stanovoi Range, which is considered by some geographers, in-cluding Berg, to be a part of the Far Eastern Region, is located north of the above chain of mountains and beyond the upper Zeia plains. It has already been described as a part of the Transbaikal region.

The Khanka-Ussuri lowland extends from the Korean border north to the confluence of the Ussuri and the Amur. Average elevations here are below 100 feet. Quaternary loose sediments predominate. Occasionally, on the east side of the Ussuri valley, rocky outcrops of granite, andesite, and basalt are found. Apparently, not long ago a strait extended from Vladivostok along the Khanka-Ussuri depression to the lower Amur, so that the country between the Ussuri and the Pacific Coast, i.e., the Sikhote Alin Range, appeared as an island.

Sikhote Alin is a corrupted Chinese name, Si-ho Ta-ling (Great Range of Rivers Flowing West), given to the mountains located between Ussuri Valley and the coast of the Sea of Japan. The Sikhote Alin is not a very spectacular range; it consists of several parallel chains, none reaching the line of permanent snow. The alpine zone is almost completely absent. The mountains are much eroded, often appearing as low, rolling hills with average elevations running between 2300 and 3200 feet. The northern summits are rarely over 4200 feet. In the middle part, in the sources of the rivers Bikin and Iman, the summits are as high as 5000 feet, and in the south, in the sources of the Uluhe, summits reach 6000 feet. The highest point in Sikhote Alin is Komarov Golets (peak), 6363 feet.* From Olga Bay northwards the mountains parallel the coastline, and there are very few bays. On the other hand, south of Olga Bay the coast cuts the chains of Sikhote Alin almost at a right angle, forming many bays, inlets, and coves, dotted with numerous islands.

The Sikhote Alin is a folded range composed of metamorphic and sedimentary Paleozoic rocks. Basalt effusions are very common; the most recent ones are of Quaternary times. The most intensive foldings occurred during the Lower Cretaceous epoch. The highest chain of the Sikhote Alin Mountains forms a watershed divide only in the south. In all other places, the upper flows of the streams of both the Ussuri and the ocean drainage often cut through the main chain so that their sources are found on its opposite side.

The only large lake of the Far Eastern Region is Lake Khanka, located not far from Vladivostok. It is a shallow (not over 35 feet) body of fresh water, about 60 miles long, and from 25 to 50 miles wide. Its western shores are rather elevated and covered with forests. On the east, south, and north shores the adjacent country is low and

* Named after V. L. Komarov, 1869–1945, an outstanding botanist and traveler in Middle Asia, Manchuria, and Siberia.

either cultivated or swampy. Sungacha River, a tributary to the Ussuri, flows from Lake Khanka.

Climate

The climate of the Far Eastern Region is of a monsoon type.* In winter high pressure is established over the Siberian mainland, whereas over the Pacific there is low pressure. Dry and cold winter winds in the region are from the north and northwest. Winters in the Far East are almost as severe as in Siberia. In the Khanka region, where in some winters there is no snow at all, the soil freezes to a considerable depth. No permanently frozen ground is found in the region, except in the northwestern part.

In the Zeia-Bureia area the snow cover in the middle of winter may be 10 to 15 inches. Because of the proximity of cold Siberia, the winter climate of the region cannot be called exactly a monsoon type of climate. In summer, high pressure prevails in the Pacific whereas over the mainland the pressure is low. In April the direction of the wind gradually changes, and during the summer months the winds are from the south and southeast. These monsoon winds bring moist and relatively warm masses of air. Summers, especially near the coast, are damp, foggy, and with frequent drizzles and rains. Spring is late, cold, and prolonged. Fall is the best part of the year. It is also the time of frequent forest fires, however. Clear, warm weather extends into October. As a whole, the climate of the region is much colder than one would expect to find at such low latitudes. Temperature and precipitation data for Khabarovsk, located at the confluence of the Amur and the Ussuri, are given in Table 19, p. 294.

The climate of the mountains of the Far East is little known. The Okhotsk Sea, with its almost Arctic climate and slow-melting ice at the beginning of summer, cools the air of the adjacent mountain regions considerably. In the Far Eastern mountains, from June to September, drizzling rain falls almost continuously. Sometimes the weather clears and then oppressive, damp heat follows. Sometimes torrential rains occur which may continue for two, three, or even four

---

* To be more accurate, the Far Eastern Region, as well as the island of Sakhalin and the southeastern part of Kamchatka, is located on the periphery of the region of monsoon climate. These parts of the Soviet Union possess a monsoon-like climate, especially in the summer, but it is not so pronounced as, for instance, in the southern part of India.

TABLE 19. TEMPERATURE AND PRECIPITATION AT KHABAROVSK,
ELEVATION 246 FEET

Jan.	Feb.	Mar.	Apr.	May	June	July	Aug.	Sept.	Oct.	Nov.	Dec.	Year
				Temperature, degrees Fahrenheit								Mean
−9	1	15	37	51	62	68	67	56	40	17	−3	30.4
				Precipitation, inches								Total
0.2	0.2	0.3	1.0	2.5	4.0	5.0	4.8	2.1	1.3	0.6	0.3	22.3

days, causing considerable and often destructive floods of low-lying
agricultural areas.

Soils and Vegetation

Predominantly the Far East is a forest region, but there are, in its
lowlands, extensive grasslands. These are found along the Amur from
the city of Blagoveshchensk (Russian for the Annunciation) to the
confluence with the Ussuri and up the Ussuri, especially in the vicinity
of Lake Khanka. Apparently these open areas originally were covered
with forests. Ancient inhabitants burned the forests, cleared the land,
and cultivated it.

The Amur grasslands, or meadows, or, as they sometimes are called,
steppes, have developed on rich, black soil containing up to 15 per
cent of organic matter and locally known as chernozem. But this soil
is not of a chernozem type. There are no underlying loess deposits
(see Chapter 12, p. 128), and there are no carbonates. The soil lacks
the crumbly structure of chernozem. The Far Eastern black soil developed not under dry climatic conditions but under the monsoon climate. During the summer the grassland soil is often saturated with
water. The soil thus is of a swampy type, possessing bluish lower
horizons—an indication of the prevalence of reduction rather than of
oxidation processes. Because of a high organic content the soil of
the Amur lowlands is very fertile. The type of grassland of the region varies with the amount of moisture in the soil, which in turn depends on the topography of the terrain. With an excess of water,
bogs develop. On more elevated places the vegetation may resemble

that of a dry steppe, with such plants as needlegrass (*Stipa capillata*) and a pungent-smelling tansy (*Tanacetum sibiricum*). Between these two extremes, at least four types of meadows are recognized, as shown in Table 20.

TABLE 20. COMPOSITION OF VEGETATION
(Percentage)

Type of Grassland	Typical Plants	Leg-umes	Sedges	Grasses	Herbace-ous [1] Plants Other Than Legumes
Boggy	*Calamagrostis neglecta, Carex meyeriana*	1	26	54	19
Reedgrass	*Calamagrostis langsdorffi*	3	11	69	17
Herbaceous [1] and grass	*Lilium dahuricum, Hemerocallis minor, Trollius ledebouri, Trifolium lupinaster, Calamagrostis epigeios*	5	8	24	63
Mixed grass	*Agrostis clavata, Poa pratensis, Koeleria gracilis* (occasionally)	2	1	75	22

[1] I.e., composed chiefly of dicotyledons and monocotyledons other than grasses or sedges.

The most common species of the Amur meadows is reedgrass (*Calamagrostis langsdorffi*), which, in admixture with other tall herbaceous species, forms a luxurious stand reaching the height of a man. In places daylily (*Hemerocallis*) covers large areas with a mass of yellow flowers—hence the local name: yellow steppes. Groves of birches (*Betula platyphylla* and *B. dahurica*), Dahurian larch, elm, and chokecherry (*Prunus padus*), with a dense underbrush of *Lespedeza bicolor*, are encountered on more elevated areas of the middle Amur lowlands. Lespedeza, a semitrailing shrub, is very important as a soil-enriching and soil-protecting plant.* Its foliage is palatable to animals. Relatively recently this lespedeza was introduced into the United States. Linden (*Tilia cordata amurensis*), maple (*Acer ginnala*), and hazelnut (*Corylus heterophylla*) also occur in the lowlands.

Park-like larch forests known as mari (plural) are often found in the eastern part of the lower Amur lowland. Mari develop commonly on the gray Tertiary podzolized clay. Larch is mixed here with white birch (*Betula japonica*), and under these trees grow scrubby *Betula*

* Lespedeza, being a legume, possesses nitrogen-fixing nodules attached to the roots.

middendorffi, Ledum palustre, and bog myrtle (*Chamaedaphne caly-culata*). After cutting, the forest areas are often converted into fields.

Luxuriant riparian forests of cottonwood (*Populus suaveolens*), lin-den (*Tilia amurensis*), walnut (*Juglans mandshurica*), *Phellodendron amurense* (locally known as velvet tree because of its soft bark, re-sembling that of cork oak),* ash (*Fraxinus mandshurica*), and elm grow along the rivers of the middle Amur lowlands. The climbing grape (*Vitis amurensis*) is rather common. On the more elevated well-drained stretches along the river one may find forests consisting of black and white birches, Dahurian larch, Aian fir, aspen, and even common pine. Manchurian trees such as *Phellodendron* and oak (*Quercus mongolica*) are also quite common.

Along the River Ussuri forests are of a Manchurian type, consisting of many species of broadleaf trees, such as maple, elm, and velvet tree. Conifers are absent here.

In the southern part of the Ussuri Valley forests are even more luxuriant. The Manchurian broadleaf trees are mingled with Korean pine (*Pinus korajensis*, known to the Russians as Manchurian cedar). There are many climbing woody plants, such as *Actinidia* and *Schi-zandra chinensis*, the latter possessing fruits and bark that have a deli-cate lemon-like flavor. These climbing plants and epiphytic ferns (*Polypodium lineare*) give the broadleaf forests of the Far Eastern Region, especially the southern ones, an almost subtropical aspect not found anywhere else in Russia outside the lowland forests of the Caucasus.

In the southern Ussuri Valley in the swampy lakes and sluggish streams where the water is warm grow a rose-colored lotus (*Nelum-bium nuciferum*, also found in the delta of the Araks and the Volga), *Brasenia purpurea*, a species also found in North America, and a water lily (*Euroyale ferox*) with bluish-purple flowers and leaves reaching 50 inches in diameter. The fruits and rhizomes of all these plants are used by the settlers for food.

The northwestern part of the region is similar to the adjacent parts of Siberia. The climate here is severe; permanently frozen ground is common; the terrain is characterized by low plains and flat plateaux. The drainage is poor, and sphagnum bogs are widespread. The higher

---

* *Phellodendron* is a tall straight-boled tree of the family Rutaceae. Its wood is excellent for furniture making. It contains appreciable amounts of tannin. Its bark is used as a substitute for cork, and its flowers are visited by bees. *Phellodendron* is occasionally grown in parks and botanical gardens of the United States.

vegetation of these bogs consists of *Ledum* and *Cassandra*, with occasional scrubby Middendorff birch and Dahurian larch.

On well-drained sandy stretches along the Amur are forests of *Pinus sylvestris*. East of the Zeia this pine occurs only sporadically, but nevertheless it reaches the shores of the southern part of the Okhotsk Sea. It occupies the largest area of all pines. It grows from Finland to the Armenian Plateau and from Spain to the Siberian shores of the Pacific. Many geographical forms are included within this species. Occasionally it is planted in the United States.

Larch forests are found on the ranges of Yankan and Tukuringra, with a ground cover of trailing *Pinus pumila* * and scrubby birch (*Betula middendorffi*). Above 3000 to 3500 feet the vegetation is of the subalpine type commonly found in the mountains of Transbaikal.

In the mountains of the Far East the soils are either somewhat podzolized or swampy. These soils are intermixed with the poorly developed rocky or gravelly soils commonly found in mountain regions.

In the Bureia Mountains the vegetation is of a rather complicated nature. Here elements of Manchurian, Eastern Siberian, and Okhotsk flora (see Chapter 26) are intermixed. In the northern part of the range the Okhotsk type of forest predominates. Dense gloomy stands of Aian spruce (*Picea ajanensis*) † and whitebark fir (*Abies nephrolepis*), with an occasional admixture of maple (*Acer ukurundense*), are found at elevations of 2000 to 3000 feet. Lichens hang from the trees, and the ground is covered with moss. In the upper parts of river canyons grow larch-spruce-fir forests, which are replaced farther down by pure larch stands. At lower elevations the larch merges into the reedgrass grassland.

Groves of Aian spruce and Ermans birch (*Betula ermani*) mingled with rhododendron and trailing *Pinus pumila* are found in the subalpine zone of the Bureia Mountains. The southern part of the Bureia Mountains is covered with broadleaf forests of oak, ash, maple, *Maakia*, and other Far Eastern deciduous trees, with a considerable admixture of Korean pine (*Pinus korajensis*). The dense underbrush consists of hazelnut, *Euonimus*, *Aralia*, and many other species. Climbing vines of wild grape, *Actinidia*,‡ and *Schizandra* § are common.

* *Pinus pumila* is considered by some botanists to be a stunted, scrubby form of *Pinus cembra*. *P. pumila* is found throughout the mountains of northeastern Siberia and on Hokkaido Island in Japan.

† *Picea ajanensis* or *iezoensis* occurs also in Manchuria, Japan, Korea, Sakhalin, and Kamchatka.

‡ Of the family Dilleniaceae.

§ Of the family Magnoliaceae.

Along the Amur River the broadleaf forests with Korean pine occur as far north as the 50th parallel, where they are found at elevations below 1000 feet. However, the Korean pine penetrates slightly farther north.

The low elevations of the southern part of the Sikhote Alin Mountains, up to 1000 or 2000 feet, are covered with lush forests of the Manchurian type, consisting of many species of broadleaf trees mixed with Korean pine and Manchurian fir (*Abies holophylla*). These two conifers and occasional veteran trees of Manchurian oak form the upperstory of the forest. Somewhat below the main canopy is a second story composed of yellow birch (*Betula costata*), elm (*Ulmus montana*), maple (*Acer mono*), Amur linden, walnut, velvet tree, and dimorphant (*Calopanax ricinifolia* of the family *Araliaceae*). Still lower down are trees such as Manchurian linden, Manchurian maple, a species of cherry (*Cerasus maximowiczi*), lilac (*Syringa amurensis*), and occasional yew (*Taxus cuspidata*). The dense underbrush consists of mock orange (*Philadelphus tenuifolius*), a shrub locally called jasmine that is widely planted in North America, hazelnut (*Corylus mandshurica*), barberry, *Sorbaria*, and *Acanthopanax* or *Eleutherococcus senticosus* (an Aralia family shrub). Woody climbers are at their best in this type of forest, making the dense vegetation even more impenetrable. Some of these climbers are wild grape, *Schizandra*, and two species of *Actinidia* (*Actinidia kolomicta* and *A. arguta*). Actinidias may reach 50 feet in length and 8 inches in diameter. The former species grows rather far north and up to the spruce-fir belt. The latter is found only in the southern part of the region. The epiphytic fern *Polypodium lineare*, growing on the trunks of the trees, adds to the lush, green, exotic appearance of the forest.

The herbaceous vegetation in these forests is rather diversified, but because of the dense canopy of trees it does not form a continuous ground cover. There are found such tall herbs as peony (*Paeonia obovata*), miterwort (*Mitella nuda*), several fern species, and some relict plants such as sweetroot (*Osmorrhiza amurensis*) and yam (*Dioscorea polystachya*), but no moss. There are also such northern plants as beadruby (*Maianthemum bifolium*) and oxalis (*Oxalis acetosella*). Occasionally in the deep canyons occurs the legendary and mysterious ginseng (or zheng-sheng, *Panax ginseng*), whose roots appear to have the form of a man because of their peculiar branching. Hunting for ginseng by the Chinese is accompanied by a great deal of ritual and superstition, and many tragic tales are connected with the plant. A closely related species of *Panax* grows in North America.

After fires the broadleaf-Korean pine forests are replaced by prickly *Aralia mandshurica*. Clearings near places of habitation in low altitudes are usually invaded by hazelnut, but in higher elevations lespedeza usually occupies the areas that formerly were covered by forests. Eventually, however, the climax broadleaf-pine forest is reestablished.

Thickets of willows (among them *Chosenia macrolepis*) and stately cottonwoods (*Populus maximowiczi*) grow along the river courses of the Sikhote Alin Mountains. Herbaceous vegetation is rather scanty, consisting of reedgrass and sedges. Extensive areas along the narrow ridges of southern exposure are covered with oak-Korean pine-broadleaf forests. The most important trees here are oak (*Quercus mongolica*), black birch (*Betula dahurica*), and Korean pine. After clearings and fires, this type of forest is converted either into a scrub oak or into hazelnut-lespedeza stand.

In the middle elevations and the plateaux of the southern Sikhote Alin, and in the northern part of the range too, the Korean pine and the Manchurian broadleaf trees have an admixture of so-called Okhotsk conifers, i.e., Aian spruce (*Picea ajanensis* or *jezoensis*) and the whitebark fir (*Abies nephrolepis*), sometimes referred to in American literature as Khingan fir. Velvet tree, maple, ash, walnut, and other broadleaf trees are also found here. In the river valleys where cold air flows down from the adjacent slopes, spruce and fir dominate.

In the northern part of the Sikhote Alin the Okhotsk conifers descend to the sea level. In the southern part they form forests above the broadleaf belt. Climbing plants so typical of the broadleaf forests are absent in the spruce-fir belt. Groves of Dahurian larch similar to those of the Transbaikal region are found in the higher elevations above the fir-spruce. After a fire, larch is usually replaced by white birch (*Betula japonica*).

The subalpine zone is not very well developed. The vegetation here consists of prostrate *Pinus pumila* and *Rhododendron chrysanthum*. Small patches of stone, or Ermans, birch (*Betula ermani*) occur occasionally. *Cladonia* lichens and some ericaceous species, such as cowberry (*Vaccinium vitis-idaea*) and rhododendron, grow on the rocky summits and slopes. Of interest is the conifer *Microbiota decussata*. This shrub, or small tree, occurs from 1600 feet all the way to 5000 feet above sea level and is endemic to the Sikhote Alin.

In the middle Amur lowlands winters are cold and dry with very little snow. Accordingly, winter cereal crops are not successful here. Rainy summers cause the development of *Fusarium* rust on grain crops.

In addition to spring wheat and spring rye, millet, buckwheat, and sunflower are cultivated along the Amur. At present, most of the lowland is under cultivation, and original grassland appears merely in patches among the fields.

In the southern Ussuri region agriculture was practiced by the early (Manchurian) inhabitants. About one thousand years ago the land fell into disuse, and agriculture was revived only in the middle of the nineteenth century by Chinese, Korean, and Russian colonists. The Chinese grow opium poppy, millet, and vegetables. In the beginning the Russian colonists attempted to grow crops not suitable to the monsoon climate of the region, such as oats, wheat, and rye, and they had a great deal of trouble with these crops. Lately, however, the colonists have turned their attention to rice and soybeans (*Glycine hispida*), which are more suitable for this climate. The main crop, however, is still wheat. Many varieties of millet (*Panicum*) are grown in the region. *Panicum frumentaceum* is considered the best both as a fodder and as food for human beings. *Panicum*, or *Setaria italica*, is a staple crop of Koreans. Proso (*Panicum millaceum*), or broomcorn millet, is rather common. Sorghum (*Andropogon sorghum japonicum*) is sown occasionally as food for human beings and for cattle. The straw is used for thatched roofs and for fuel. Moldavian colonists grow corn.

The culture of fruit trees is almost unknown in the region. Late spring, with frequent frosts, and damp summers, are the chief causes of failure. An unimproved local pear (*Pyrus ussuriensis*) and a small Siberian crabapple (*Malus baccata mandchurica*) are the only fruit trees of the region. The inhabitants of the Far East do not cultivate these trees; they just pick the fruit in the forests. Wild grapes are used for making red wine. Actinidia berries are collected for making preserves. The colonists keep European bees (*Apis mellifera*), not the local *Apis cerana inensis*.*

Animal Life

Animals of both the southern regions and the Siberian taiga are found in the Far East; their distribution is not very well known.†　The raccoon dog (*Nyctereutes procyonoides ussuriensis*), a nocturnal animal, lives in the open meadows of the Far Eastern lowlands. It hibernates in deep burrows and feeds on frogs, mice, fish, acorns, and

* L. S. Berg, *Geographic Zones of the USSR*, 3rd ed., Moscow, 1947, p. 280.
† Bobrinski et al., *Animal Geography*, Moscow, 1946, p. 441.

grapes. The middle Amur is the northernmost limit of its distribution. It is found as far south as Canton, China.

In the Amur lowlands there are also an endemic Manchurian hare (*Allolagus mandshuricus*) and an extremely destructive mouse (*Micromys minutus ussuriensis*). This mouse occurs in large numbers and causes a great deal of damage to the grain crops.

There are numerous birds in the region, among them such game birds as pheasant (*Phasanius torquatus alpheraki*), small grouse (*Tetrastes bonasia*), and waterfowl. Lake Khanka serves as a resting place to the numerous waterfowl in their flight from southern lands to their nesting grounds in the north.

The Manchurian tiger (*Tigris tigris longipilis*) is found in places inhabited by roebuck, wapiti, and wild boar. This tiger can stand temperatures as low as —20°F (but see Chapter 10, p. 112). In summers it migrates to the mountains. This man-eating predator has caused much trouble to the Russians and especially to the Chinese colonists of the region. The latter people have a mortal fear of the animal and call it the great lord of the woods. The tiger's heart and whiskers are used by the Chinese as an internal medicine, or rather as a stimulant for bravery. Occasionally, young tigers are caught in nets and sold to zoological parks.

The leopard (*Pardus pardus orientalis*), although occasionally found in the lowlands, is essentially a mountain animal. Locally it is called bars or panther. It is not so aggressive as the tiger and very seldom molests human beings.

In the middle Amur region are found such prairie inhabitants as quail (*Coturnix japonica ussuriensis*), Eversmann ground squirrel (*Citellus eversmanni*), and bustard (*Otis tarda dybowski*).

The fauna of the broadleaf forests of the Far Eastern mountains is similar to that of the lowlands. It is rich in southern species in the Ussuri region; farther north, taiga inhabitants such as sable, squirrel, and even lemming predominate. There are also badger (*Meles amurensis*) and a large yellow-throated marten (*Martes flavigula*).* In addition to a large Manchurian bear (*Ursus mandchuricus*), there is, in the Ussuri region and the Bureia Mountains, a smaller, black bear (*Selenarctos tibetanus ussuricus*). This climbing bear feeds on roots, berries, and honey. It hibernates in a sitting position in hollow trees. Red wolf (*Cyon alpinus*) occurs in the region; it has been little studied.

---

* This marten, locally known as Kharza, is as large as a domestic cat. Sometimes it attacks such large animals as deer.

A small, curly-haired antelope, locally called goral (*Nemorhaedus crispus*), is found in rocky places in the mountains. The goral is a graceful animal with short horns and a long tail. It is also found in China and the Himalayas.

The Ussuri moose (*Alces americanus bedfordi*) differs from the American moose in that it is smaller, and its antlers, rather than being broad and palmate, resemble those of wapiti. The local wapiti is *Cervus canadensis xanthopygus*.

The spotted, or sika, deer (*Pseudaxis dybowski*, formerly known as *Cervus nippon*), is an inhabitant of the very southern part of the Ussuri region. It is almost extinct. Both wapiti and the spotted deer are occasionally kept in corrals, for, as throughout southern Siberia, their antlers are sold to the Chinese for medicinal purposes. The sika's antlers command the higher price.

The wild boar (*Sus leucomystax continentalis*) is still numerous in the region. It has caused a great deal of trouble to the Russian and Chinese settlers, sometimes destroying completely the cornfields and vegetable gardens.

Muskdeer (*Moschus moschiferus parvipes*) is found occasionally in the region. Roebuck or deer (*Capreolus pigargus blanfordi*) is rather common. All hoofed animals are of considerable commercial importance.

Endemic insectivorous animals of the region are represented by a mole (*Mogera robusta*) and a hedgehog (*Erinaceus amurensis*). There are no marmots.

Birds of the Sikhote Alin include Manchurian pheasant (*Phasanius mongolicus*), whose habitat extends to the River Ussuri. A small black grouse (*Falcipennis falcipennis*), a species closely related to the *Canachites canadensis* of America, is found in the Aian spruce forests. There are many birds, some of which spend their winters in the Philippines, southern China, Indo-China, or India, for instance, the eastern broad-billed roller (*Eurystomus orientalis calonyx*), blue Chinese flycatcher (*Muscicapa cyanomelana cumatilis*), and white wagtail (*Motacilla alba leucopsis*). From India and Indo-China, for the summer, come Chinese black-headed orioles (*Oriolus chinensis diffusus*) and a little Indian blue kingfisher * (*Alcedo atthis bengalensis*). Widely distributed in the broadleaf forests is the azure-winged

* Harry R. Caldwell and John C. Caldwell, *South China Birds*, Hester May Vanderburgh, Shanghai, 1931, 447 pp.

magpie (*Cyanopica cyana*). Other birds of the Ussuri country that should be mentioned are the Ussurian raven (*Corvus corax ussurionus*), golden thrush (*Turdus chrysolaus*), Mandarin teal (*Aix galericulata*), Chinese swan-goose (*Anser cygnoides*), Japanese ibis (*Ibis nippon*), and several species of Chinese cranes.

Turtles, absent in cold Siberia, appear in the warmer climate of the Ussuri valley; *Amida chinensis* is found in Lake Khanka. The reptile fauna is richer than in Siberia. Here one may encounter the Amur or Schrenk coluber (*Elaphe schrenki*), Manchurian rattlesnake or halys (*Ancistrodon halys*), which does not have rattlers, and Chinese tiger snake (*Natrix tigrina*). Among the amphibians that may be mentioned are *Bombinator orientalis*, Ussuri triton (*Geomolge fischeri*), and eastern frog (*Hyla stepheni*).

Insects are abundant. Especially notable are the large, colorful butterflies that give to the region a touch of the subtropics. Among the other insects of importance is the endemic cerambycid beetle (*Callipogon relictus*); three other species of this genus are found in tropical America.

Rivers of the Amur basin are inhabited by northern fish as well as by several Chinese genera. The most important, however, is salmon entering these rivers for spawning. Endemic to the River Amur are a sturgeon (*Acipenser schrenki*) and white sturgeon or kaluga (*Huso dahuricus*).

The pearl oyster (*Margaritana dahurica*) is found in the streams of the Amur basin. In the Amur, the Ussuri, and the Ussuri tributaries is a large mollusk (*Cristaria plicata*), whose shell is a source of mother-of-pearl. Small lobsters of the family Palaemonidae occur in Lake Khanka.

Crawfish, which are absent in Siberia, appear again in the Far East. They belong to the genus *Cambaroides*, closely related to the European genus *Astacus*.

As a whole, the fauna of the Far Eastern Region differs considerably from the faunas of other regions of the Soviet Union and possesses a certain affinity to the fauna of Indo-Malaya.

People

The population of the region includes several Tungus tribes, the most numerous (5000) being the Goldi, now known as the Nanais. The Goldi live on both sides of the lower Amur and the lower Ussuri.

They are hunters, and they grow some crops, such as corn, cabbage, cucumbers, and beans.* The Ude and some lesser tribes live in the Sikhote Alin Mountains. Apparently there has been an influx of Ainu blood from Sakhalin. Survivors of the once numerous Dahurs, after whom the whole region of Transbaikal, or Dahuria, is named, now occur in small numbers in the middle Amur area; some of them live in Manchuria.

Chinese trappers and traders and Korean settlers came to the southern part of the region in the nineteenth century. After the Russians opened the Far East for colonization, people from different parts of Russia settled along the coast of the Sea of Japan and in the Ussuri Valley. One may find there Estonians, Ukrainians, and Moldavians. Apparently most of the Korean settlers have recently been removed to Kazakhstan. (See Chapter 15, p. 162.)

The population along the Amur is predominantly Russian. West of Khabarovsk, the Soviet government established the Jewish Autonomous Region, mainly to accommodate refugees from the western part of European Russia.

The Ukrainian population of the region is considerable.

Efforts have been made recently by the Moscow government to attract more people to the Far East.

* See V. K. Arseniev, *Dersu, The Trapper*, translated from Russian by Malcolm Burr, E. P. Dutton and Co., New York, 1941, 352 pp. Arseniev is a well-known explorer of the Sikhote Alin, and his books are very entertaining.

Chapter 26

Okhotsk Coast and the
Island of Sakhalin

NORTHWESTERN COAST OF OKHOTSK SEA

Along the northwestern shores of the Okhotsk Sea from the low reaches of the River Amur to the settlement of Okhotsk, mountains come closely to the coast, forming a narrow strip of land sloping towards the sea. This strip of land differs considerably in its geographic features from the adjacent parts of Siberia. The western boundary of this so-called Okhotsk coast is the watershed divide between the rivers flowing to the Okhotsk Sea and the rivers of the Lena and the middle Amur drainage, i.e., the Bureia, the Selemja, and eastern tributaries of the Zeia. (See Map 32.)

Topography

In the northern part of the region a range of mountains known as Djugdjour extends parallel to the Okhotsk coast. The northern part of the range merges into the Yudoma-Maya plateau, and the southwestern end reaches another Maya River, a tributary of the River Uda (see p. 266), where it gradually merges into the eastern chains of the Stanovoi Mountains.

Whereas in the Stanovoi Mountains pre-Cambrian crystalline rocks predominate, the Djugdjour Range is composed mainly of Mesozoic extrusives: diabase and andesite. The Djugdjour is a rugged chain of mountains with summits reaching 4000 to 6000 feet above the floor of the valleys and up to 7200 feet above sea level. The eastern slopes of the Djugdjour are abrupt, with deep canyons cut by rushing streams; the western slopes are rather gentle. Occasionally the upper parts of river valleys on opposite slopes come very close to each other, forming rather low passes, elevated over the surrounding country only for 350 to 500 feet.

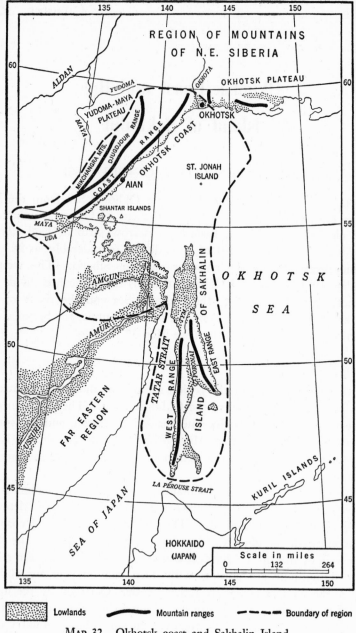

MAP 32. Okhotsk coast and Sakhalin Island.

East of the Djugdjour Range, along the coast of the Okhotsk Sea, extends a mountain chain known as Pribrezhny Khrebet, i.e., Coast Range. Its rounded, bare summits reach above 3200 feet. The Coast Range drops abruptly to the shores of the sea. West of the Djugdjour is a parallel chain, Mikchangra, composed of either crystalline or sedimentary Paleozoic rocks. Elevations of this chain are about 3300 feet.

The southern part of the region is occupied with lowlands, composed mainly of Triassic and Jurassic sediments. Tertiary deposits are found along the rivers Amur and Amgun.

In the southwestern part of the Okhotsk Sea, near the mainland and just opposite the mouth of the River Uda, lies a group of islands known as the Shantar Islands. It consists of a dozen mountainous, large and small islands with abrupt coastlines. The highest summit is about 2000 feet above sea level.

Climate

The climate of the Okhotsk Coast is rather severe. Winters are cold, and summers are cool and foggy with frequent drizzles. Ice melts very late in the spring in the Okhotsk Sea, and this large, almost Arctic body of water exerts a considerable cooling effect on the coast. Table 21 gives temperature and precipitation data for Okhotsk. It is

TABLE 21. TEMPERATURE AND PRECIPITATION AT OKHOTSK, ELEVATION 20 FEET

Jan.	Feb.	Mar.	Apr.	May	June	July	Aug.	Sept.	Oct.	Nov.	Dec.	Year
Temperature, degrees Fahrenheit												Mean
−13	−5	6	21	32	42	53	54	46	28	4	−7	22
Precipitation, inches												Total
0.06	0.06	0.16	0.3	0.8	1.7	2.3	2.4	2.2	0.95	0.15	0.12	11.2

seen from this table that January is the coldest month, with a mean temperature of −13°F. The temperature of the warmest month, August, is 54°F. On the west side of the Djugdjour the climate is more continental: summers are warmer and winters are colder.

The precipitation on the Okhotsk coast is much heavier than in the adjacent parts of Siberia. The annual precipitation at Okhotsk amounts to 11.2 inches; at Nikolaevsk-on-Amur, about 17.5 inches; and at Aian, approximately 35 inches per year. The much greater precipitation at Aian is explained by the position of this town just opposite the Tatar Strait, through which moist air masses penetrate from the Sea of Japan. The relatively high mountains close to the Aian coast catch a considerable amount of the moisture. The maximum precipitation in the region occurs in summer and early fall; the minimum precipitation is recorded in January and February. Fall is the best part of the year. The vegetative period extends well into September, although snow may fall in the mountains during that month. The vegetative period at Okhotsk extends for 109 days, from the beginning of June to the end of September.

Vegetation

The vegetation of the northern part of the region is similar to that of adjacent parts of Transbaikal. The country is covered mostly by larch forests. Farther south, a great predominance is gained by Aian spruce (*Picea jezoensis* or *ajanensis*), with which is admixed whitebark fir (*Abies nephrolepis*). Still farther south, in the lower Amur area, there appear trees generally found in the Far Eastern Region (Chapter 25), such as ash, maple (*Acer ukurundense*), and Manchurian oak.

Narrow bands of willows are usually found along streams. Farther from the streams grassy meadows, the hayfields of the settlers, alternate with groves of cottonwood (*Populus suaveolens*) admixed with alder (*Alnus hirsuta*). White birch (*Betula japonica*) occurs as an understory in such groves; also, the ever-present (as all over Siberia) chokecherry (*Prunus padus*) and mountain ash, and patches of Korean willow (*Chosenia macrolepis*). In the southern part of the region some Far Eastern hardwoods appear.

Great stretches of land in valleys and in occasionally flooded plains are covered with Aian spruce and whitebark fir forests. Dahurian larch sometimes grows in such forests, the understories of which contain white birch, cottonwood, mountain ash (*Sorbus aucuparia*), and, in the southern part, a maple (*Acer ukurundense*).

Noteworthy among the herbaceous vegetation are meadowsweet (*Filipendula kamtschatica*) and woodreed (*Cinna pendula*), a grass species.

In the drainage of the River Uda, on sandy soils where permafrost is found at a depth of about 7 feet, larch-pine forests grow. Here common pine (*Pinus sylvestris*), which is found in patches all over Europe and Siberia, almost reaches the shores of the Pacific.

Mountain slopes are often covered with spruce-fir forests. Whitebark fir holds a subordinate place in these forests. The ground is usually covered with moss. In higher elevations, to the spruce and fir is added Ermans birch, which replaces both conifers on rocky summits, rocky passes, and similar localities exposed to wind. Above these are found thickets of *Pinus pumila*, which in more protected places has the appearance of a shrub 6 to 8 feet high. On exposed sites it assumes a trailing form. Occasionally, in *Pinus pumila* thickets, there are scrubby alder (*Alnus fruticosa*), Middendorff birch, and golden rhododendron (*Rhododendron chrysanthum*).

Rocky summits of the mountains are usually bare. Protected areas where some soil has accumulated may support such plants as snow cinquefoil (*Potentilla nivaea*), sweetvetch (*Hedysarum obscurum*), alpine sweetgrass (*Hierochloe alpina*), and Siberian patrinia (*Patrinia sibirica*). Flat highlands are covered with lichen tundra, used as reindeer pastures. In places one may find sedge swamps and, at higher altitudes, even sphagnum bogs.

Animal Life

Animal life of the Okhotsk coast is, in general, similar to that of the adjacent parts of Siberia. One may find here moose, muskdeer, and reindeer. Mountain sheep is found in the rocky mountains.

Other forest animals of importance include the otter, fox, ermine, and sable.

A typical Okhotsk bird living in the Aian spruce forest is a small black grouse (*Falcipennis falcipennis*). It also penetrates into adjacent parts of the Far Eastern Region.

People

The population of the Okhotsk coast consists chiefly of a few Tungus and some Russian settlers. In the lower Amur live Goldi (Nanais, a Tungus tribe) and a Paleo-Asiatic people, the Giliaks (Nivkhs).

ISLAND OF SAKHALIN

Sakhalin is a long, narrow island located between 54°25' and 45°54' latitude N and separated from the mainland by Tatar Strait, or, as the Russians call it, Tatarski Proliv (i.e., Strait), which is in the narrowest part less than 5 miles wide. From the Japanese island of Hokkaido, or Yezo, Sakhalin is separated by La Pérouse Strait. The northwestern extremity of the island and its entire east coast face the Okhotsk Sea. Sakhalin is about 600 miles long, and at the 45th parallel it is only 17 or 18 miles wide. In its widest part, just above the mouth of the Poronai, it is a little less than 100 miles wide. The Amur discharges its waters into the northern part of Tatar Strait, which freezes in winter, making wheel and sled communication possible between the island and the mainland.

Topography

The island is essentially mountainous. From the mountains of the center of the island two parallel mountain ranges extend north and south. The western range is the watershed-dividing range and consists of several chains. In the central part of the island it is of a rugged character, with deep canyons running towards the coast and abrupt cliffs dropping to the water. The eastern range is higher. The highest mountain, Nevelskoi Mountain, 6603 feet, is located in the eastern range. It is named after a Russian admiral, a navigator and explorer who, in 1848–1849, investigated Tatar Strait and proved that Sakhalin is an island, which fact had been known to the Japanese since the explorations of Mamio Rinso in 1808.*

Apparently the central valley lying between the two ranges is a depression of a fault type. The River Tym flows north in this valley, and the River Poronai flows south. The watershed divide between the two rivers is very low, located at approximately latitude 51°30'. The Tym flows north for some distance and then breaks through the eastern range and empties into Okhotsk Sea. The Poronai flows south into the Gulf of Patience (Zaliv Terpenia). Extensive lowlands are located in the northern part of the island on both the west and east coasts. The rivers flowing towards the east coast form estuaries that are separated from the sea by sand banks which extend along the coast for many miles, affording safe water communication between the coast settlements.

Sakhalin is composed of various intrusive rocks: andesite, porphyry, diabase, basalt, syenite. No granite is found on the island. Paleozoic metamorphics are found only in the southern part of the eastern range. Cretaceous, Tertiary, and post-Pliocene rocks are widely distributed.

* Cf. M. S. Bodnarski, *Essays on the History of Russian Geography*, 1947, p. 239, note 188. (In Russian.)

Most of the Tertiary rocks are found in the western range, in the northern part of the eastern range, and at the northern extremity of the island known as Schmidt Peninsula.* Coal of good quality is found in the Tertiary strata and in the Cretaceous deposits. Oil is restricted to the Tertiary deposits. Most of it is produced at Okha oil field in the northern part of the island on the east coast. Refineries are located on the mainland.

All Cretaceous and Tertiary strata of the island are much dislocated. The main mountain-forming processes occurred in the island between the Pliocene epoch and the time of the advance of the post-Tertiary Sea. Before that period Sakhalin had been connected with the mainland.

Climate

The climate of Sakhalin, as of any northeastern part of the Soviet Union, is very severe. Although the island lies at relatively low latitudes, the proximity of Siberia, with its low winter temperatures, and the extremely cold water of the adjacent Okhotsk Sea contribute to the cold climate of the island. Table 22 † gives a temperature and precipitation record for a station located in the Tym River Valley at 50°44′ latitude N.

TABLE 22. TEMPERATURE AND PRECIPITATION IN THE TYM RIVER VALLEY, ELEVATION 410 FEET

Jan.	Feb.	Mar.	Apr.	May	June	July	Aug.	Sept.	Oct.	Nov.	Dec.	Year
Temperature, degrees Fahrenheit												Mean
−10	−2	12	33	42	52	61	60	51	36	16	−2	29.1
Precipitation, inches												Total
0.7	0.6	0.9	1.3	1.4	1.6	2.8	3.4	3.4	3.2	1.6	1.3	22.2

Most of the precipitation falls during summer and fall. The average monthly minimum temperature in the Tym Valley occurs in Janu-

* Named in honor of Friedrich B. Schmidt (1832–1908), who studied geology of Sakhalin in 1859–1862.
† Taken from L. S. Berg's *Priroda, SSSR*, 2nd ed., Moscow, 1938, p. 272.

ary, −10°F. Farther south, however, winters are warmer. At Point Crillion the mean January temperature is 18°F. The warmest month in the Tym Valley is July (61°F). Summer temperatures at the southern part of the island are not much higher, however; the mean July temperature at Point Crillion is 64°F. Summers on the island are cool with southeastern winds blowing constantly and bringing drizzles, rains, and fogs. Cloudiness is greatest during the summer. Only July and August are free of frost. Fall is rather prolonged, lasting two months, which are relatively warm and rainy.

Winter is severe. Northeastern winds blow over the Okhotsk Sea, bringing a great deal of precipitation, and so there is an abundance of snow. The month of March is still a winter month with frequent blizzards. Although the narrowest part of Tatar Strait freezes, the Okhotsk Sea is often open along the east coast. The Sea of Japan near the southwestern end of the island does not freeze in winter.

Frosts may occur as late as the first half of June. At the beginning of that month, in the inner valley, there may be real summer weather, but in the northwest and on the east coast there may still be some snow on the ground.

Snow lies on the mountain peaks until August, but there are no permanent snowfields, even on the highest summits. Permafrost is rather common on the island, although there may occasionally be patches where it is absent. Floods are frequent on the island. They occur in spring when the valley snow melts. Melting snow in the mountains causes later floods, and towards the beginning of August summer rains again cause the rivers to flood the valleys. Sometimes the flood water level may reach 10 feet or more above normal levels.

Soils and Vegetation

Soils of the island are either a podzol type, in forests, or alluvial, in the flood plains. The latter soils are rich in humus and very fertile. It is said that the fertility of the flood plains is due in considerable degree to the salmon that enter the rivers and, upon their death and decomposition, enrich the soil with organic matter. Swampy soils in which reduction, rather than oxidation, processes prevail are widely distributed on the island.

The vegetation of Sakhalin Island is essentially of the Okhotsk conifer type, i.e., spruce and fir, but even in the northern part of the island one may find an admixture of such Far Eastern—or, as they are commonly called, Manchurian—species as oak, ash, maple, and elm.

Thickets of bamboo, called kamysh * (reeds) by the Russians, are found in the western range. All foothills and mountain slopes are covered with spruce (*Picea ajanensis* or *jezoensis* and *P. glehni*) with an understory of Sakhalin fir (*Abies sakhalinensis*).

Peaty soils covered with larch forests (*Larix dahurica*) are common in the Poronai Valley. In places where the soil is sandy the larch forests have a ground cover of lichen. Occasionally they contain birch and trailing pine also. Larch forests with herbaceous ground cover occur often in valleys. These forests are of considerable commercial value.

Larch forests are common both on the western and eastern coasts, where they are found below the spruce-fir forests. The Schmidt Peninsula also has a great many larch forests, although in the lowland areas they are scrubby.

In the broadleaf forests of the southern part of Sakhalin are such species as maple (*Acer ukurundense*), ash, velvet-tree (*Phellodendron amurense*), Manchurian oak, and Manchurian elm (*Ulmus laciniata*). The last mentioned occurs also in the northern part of the island. Smaller trees and shrubs, such as *Euonimus sachalinensis*, and *Ilex rugosa*, and even climbers, such as *Schizandra chinensis*, grow in these broadleaf forests.

The herbaceous vegetation in the flood plain meadows reaches a height of 10 to 12 feet. It may consist of groundsel (*Senecio cannabifolius*, called nettle by the settlers), Japanese butterbur (*Petasites japonica*), buckwheat (*Polygonum sakhalinense*), and tall umbellifers, such as cow parsnip (*Heracleum barbatum*). In the flood plains are common groves of cottonwood; Korean willow (*Chosenia macrolepis*), which may reach a height of 80 feet; alder; Manchurian elm; and shrubs of chokecherry, mountain ash, and elderberry. Such groves are called elani.†

When spruce-fir forests are cut or destroyed by fire, they are replaced first with luxuriant growths of fireweed (*Epilobium angustifolium*) and later with Japanese birch, Manchurian alder, and occasionally larch. Gradually spruce and fir are reestablished.

* Kamysh is a Turkic word that became a part of the Russian vocabulary.

† In the Altai Mountains the name elani means to the Russian settlers an entirely different type of vegetation. Cf. p. 252, footnote.

At higher elevations in the western range, to spruce and fir are ad-mixed Ermans birch and bamboo (*Sasa kurilensis*), which does not grow very tall, reaching only about 5 feet in height, and forming im-penetrable thickets. Trailing *Pinus pumila* and occasional golden rho-dodendron (*R. chrysanthum*) grow higher in the mountains.

The lowlands of the northern extremity of the island resemble the subarctic tundra. Swampy ground is covered with scrubby larch. Larch of a better quality grows only along the river courses and on better-drained watershed divides. The ground cover here is com-posed of lichen (*Cladonia rangiferina*) and such northern plants as *Poa arctica* and *Arctostaphylos uva-ursi*.

The northern part of the island is not very well suited for agricul-ture. The spring is prolonged and cold, and late killing frosts are common. Moreover, during harvest time the weather is usually rainy. Some spring wheat, spring rye, and oats are cultivated in the central valley and on the west coast but only south of the 52nd parallel. Potatoes and cucumbers are also grown to some extent. Sakhalin pas-tures are luxuriant, and there is a possibility of the development of an intensive livestock industry in the future. Better agricultural condi-tions are found in the southern part of the island.

Animal Life

The fauna of Sakhalin contains species of Siberian taiga mixed with some Okhotsk and Manchurian elements. In the forests there are bear, wolf, wolverine, lynx, sable, squirrel, and hare. A typical in-habitant of the Okhotsk spruce forest, the black grouse (*Falcipennis falcipennis*), is also found on the island. Reindeer is of the Okhotsk variety (*Rangifer tarandus setoni*). There are no moose, roebuck, wapiti, badger, or mountain sheep.

Among the birds of Sakhalin are many Siberian taiga species. Some Himalayan and Chinese species are found in the southern part of the island. The Siberian thrush (*Turdus sibiricus*) leaves the area to winter in southeastern Asia. Ptarmigan (*Lagopus lagopus okadai*) is found in the tundra of the northern part of the island. Multitudes of waterfowl, such as cormorants, auks, guillemots, and puffins, nest on the rocky shores of the Okhotsk Sea.

In the streams are *Cristaria plicata*, which yields mother-of-pearl; a pearl oyster (*Margaritana sakhalinensis*); and another mollusk (*Ano-donta beringiana*). A lizard (*Lacerta vivipara*) and a frog (*Rana amurensis*) are found on the island.

People

Giliaks live on both the east and the west coasts of the island of Sakhalin; Tungus and Goldi live in the inner valleys. Apparently some Japanese have remained in the southern part of the island since it was occupied by the Russians after the end of World War II. There are also found in the southern part of Sakhalin the survivors of old inhabitants of the island, the Paleo-Asiatic people the Ainus. A considerable influx of Russian settlers to Sakhalin has taken place in recent years.

Chapter 27

Peninsula of Kamchatka
and Neighboring Islands

KAMCHATKA

The peninsula of Kamchatka is located between the 51st and 60th parallels. The northeastern part is connected to the mainland by a narrow stretch of tundra-like country known as Parapol(ski) Dol (see Chapter 24). The western shores of Kamchatka face the Okhotsk Sea; the northern part of the east coast, approximately to the 56th parallel, faces the Bering Sea; and the southern part of the east coast is exposed to the Pacific Ocean. Near the eastern shores of Kamchatka are Karaginski Island and the Commander Islands, and from the southern tip of the peninsula, known as Lopatka (that is, the shoulder bone, in Russian), the Kuril Island chain extends toward the Japanese island of Hokkaido (Map 33).

Topography

Kamchatka is about 750 miles long; its widest part, from Point Yuzhny to Point Africa, is a little over 260 miles. Not much is known about the tectonic structure of Kamchatka. There have been some displacements by folding, later supplemented by faults. The general direction of the geologic elements is northeast or north-northeast.

Topographically, Kamchatka consists essentially of two parallel ranges with a depression between * and lowland areas along the west and east coasts. The western, or inner, range consists of uninterrupted chains of mountains with elevations running from 3200 to 5200 feet above sea level. In the south the range is higher so that even the

* L. S. Berg (*Priroda*, 2nd ed., Moscow, 1938, p. 275) points out that this structure of two ranges with a depression between is repeated on Sakhalin, in the extreme northeast of Siberia, in Alaska, and all along the west coast of North America.

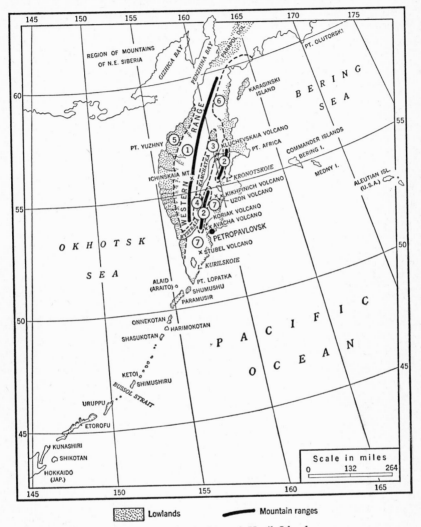

MAP 33. Kamchatka and Kuril Islands.

1. Western range.
2. Eastern range.
3. Kamchatka River Valley.
4. Tundra flatland on the watershed divide between the rivers Kamchatka and Bystraia.

5. West coast.
6. East coast.
7. Area of active volcanoes.

passes there are located at 3000 to 4000 feet. The highest point in the range, an active volcano, Ichinskaia Sopka,* is 11,830 feet high.

The range is composed of crystalline schists and gneiss of the Paleozoic era, with granitic and andesitic intrusions superimposed with volcanic Mesozoic rocks. In the southwestern extremity of the range are dislocated Tertiary sediments. In some places the range possesses a rugged character with sharply protruding peaks. In other places the summits are rather rounded. Towards the northern end the range has the appearance of table mountains. The western slope is gentle, rising gradually from the west coast lowland, but the eastern slope drops steeply towards the central valley.

Between the inner range and the coast of the Okhotsk Sea a flat lowland area extends for a width of about 50 miles, reaching in the foothill region an elevation of 2000 to 2400 feet. This lowland is often referred to as tundra (see p. 88).

The underlying strata of the lowland consist chiefly of dislocated marine Miocene deposits. In places upper Cretaceous rocks are found. On these strata are superimposed layers of peat, and upon these layers stretch immense moss bogs separated by low divides scantily wooded with scrubby Ermans birch.

Rivers and streams flowing from the range, after reaching the seashore, where they meet the resistance of waves and the tide, follow the shoreline for considerable distances until they can break through the sandbars.

There are no active volcanoes along the west coast of Kamchatka. However, there are remains of several ancient disintegrated volcanoes and andesitic laccoliths. Coal deposits are found along the west coast, and there are indications of the presence of oil near the settlement of Tighil.

The eastern range of Kamchatka is not a continuous chain of mountains but rather a series of separate ranges extending in a north-northwest direction. The mountains drop abruptly towards the central valley. The slopes descending to the Bering Sea are often—not always —gentle. The southern part of the eastern range is rather rugged, with picturesque peaks towering 4400 to 4750 feet high.

On the east coast of Kamchatka, especially the northern half, lie open lowlands occupied by peat bogs, meadows, and swamps, with

* Any volcano or high summit of Kamchatka is called by the Russians sopka, i.e., a heavy breather or snorer, in reference to its volcanic activity. Later the name has been incorrectly applied to all bare summits of the Far East and Manchuria.

numerous small lakes and old stream courses. In the southern part of the peninsula, however, some branches of the eastern range reach the coast.

The central depression located between the two ranges and commonly known as Kamchatka River Valley is about 30 miles wide and is delineated by abrupt slopes (fault lines) of the ranges. The valley is drained by the River Kamchatka, which flows north and empties into the Bering Sea just east of Point Africa. The river is navigable by shallow-draft boats as far as the village of Milkovo, located some 200 miles from the mouth.

The watershed divide between the River Kamchatka and the River Bystraia (Russian for swift), flowing into the Okhotsk Sea, is a flat land elevated above sea level about 1500 to 1700 feet. Once it was completely covered with ice. Now it has the appearance of dry tundra, crisscrossed with dry streambeds and with a great deal of alluvial gravel deposits and pebble debris.

Between the eastern range and the Bering Sea, on a hilly, high plain over 1800 feet above sea level, there is located the most spectacular volcanic region of Kamchatka. Of the total number of 127 volcanoes in Kamchatka, both ancient and new, 74 are found on the east side of the peninsula. Thirteen of these are active. Some of the volcanoes, considered for a long time as being dead, have erupted recently. Berg considers 18 volcanoes of Kamchatka to be active. The volcanoes are located in groups around old centers of eruption.

Suslov * divides all Kamchatka volcanoes into four groups: (1) those having a uniform conical shape, (2) those with tops destroyed, (3) those of caldera type, and (4) those whose original shape has been lost and whose badly eroded remains now appear as huge massifs. Kliuchevskaia Sopka, one of the greatest volcanoes of the world, belongs to the group of volcanoes having a perfect conical shape. It is located in the lower reaches of the River Kamchatka and rises from sea level to an elevation of 15,662 feet.† The volcano obtained its name from the nearby village Kluchi (Russian for springs). During the eruption of 1696 the lava flow reached the present site of the settlement, a distance from the crater of about 20 miles. Kliuchevskaia Sopka belches smoke and ashes continuously to a height of more than a mile above its summit. The last major eruption occurred in 1931. In 1935 the crater of the volcano was visited by a group of scientists,

* S. P. Suslov, *Physical Geography of the USSR*, Moscow, 1947.

† L. S. Berg, *Priroda*, 2nd ed., 1938, p. 277, gives the elevation of the Kliuchevskaia Volcano as 15,941 feet.

and Berg describes the event as follows: * "The crater was found to be from 800 to 1000 feet in diameter and 165 feet deep. Masses of ashes and red-hot stones were blown up 650 to 1000 feet in the air and fell back with a crushing sound. The smell of sulfur dioxide and hydrogen chloride gases was suffocating. In the crater there was darkness in which red-hot stones glowed brightly. The whole crater was in a constant tremor. The investigators remained in the crater for 16 hours; once during this time a major explosion occurred: a huge cloud of smoke was thrown in the air with a great force and a shower of red-hot rocks showered the whole area of the crater."

Avachinskaia Sopka (Avacha Volcano), 8938 feet high and located about 20 miles northeast of the capital of Kamchatka, Petropavlovsk (i.e., City of Peter and Paul), belongs to the second group. Its top has been blown off, and in the 2½-mile-wide caldera † a new cone of the now active volcano has been formed.

In the volcanoes of the third group the central part of the ancient crater sinks and a caldera is formed. The caldera may remain dry, as in Uzon ‡ and Moutnaia (muddy) volcanoes, or it may be covered by the sea, such as Tarya Cove in Avacha Bay, or again it may be filled with fresh water forming a lake, like Lake Kronotskoie.

Some Kamchatka volcanoes belong to the fourth group (badly eroded ancient craters that lost their original conical shape long ago). Examples are Ipelka and Shishel volcanoes.

Generally speaking, the volcanoes of Kamchatka are of the Mauna Loa type; the viscous lava often plugs the opening of the crater, causing violent explosions, accompanied by an abundance of ashes in the clouds of emerging smoke. In 1907 Stubel Volcano (2945 feet) erupted; the bottom of its caldera exploded, and the whole peninsula was covered with ashes. Dogsled traffic was stopped by the accumulation of ashes on the surface of the snow, and white partridges and hares could have been detected easily on the black mantle that covered the snow.§

The highest volcanoes on the peninsula are covered with permanent snow; usually the snowline is located at an elevation of about 5250 feet above sea level. Occasionally, volcanic activity causes irregular,

* L. S. Berg, *Priroda*, 2nd ed., 1938, p. 277. More detailed information may be found in *Russian Bull. Geog. Soc.*, Vol. 69, p. 973, 1937.
† Avacha Volcano is not unlike Vesuvius but is twice as high.
‡ The Uzon caldera is 6 miles in diameter.
§ S. P. Suslov, *Physical Geography of the USSR*, Moscow, 1947, p. 367.

patchy melting of snow on the slopes of the volcanoes. Volcanic activity manifests itself also by frequent earthquakes. Since 1790 more than 150 major tremors have been recorded in Kamchatka.

Glaciers are found in some calderas such as that of Avacha Volcano. Slope glaciers are rather common. Six glaciers descend from Shiveliuch Volcano (10,824 feet; "the moving one" is the meaning of its name). The glacier on the north side of the volcano is about 4 miles long. Sometimes, as has already been mentioned, old calderas form lakes. Of the caldera-type lakes, the largest is Lake Kronotskoie, located near the active volcano Kronotskaia Sopka (12,234 feet). The lake is about 400 feet deep.

Lake Kurilskoie, in the southern part of the peninsula and surrounded by volcanoes, is smaller but is 1000 feet deep.

South of Kronotskoie Lake, near Uzon and Kikhpinich volcanoes in the valley of the warm Geyzer River, are numerous geysers ranging in diameter from several feet to a fraction of an inch. Steaming water spurts forth periodically. The largest of these geysers, Velikan (which in Russian means Giant), throws a jet of water higher than 150 feet. The intervals between the eruptions are 2 hours and 46 minutes. The eruption itself lasts 4 minutes. The temperature of the water is between 203 and 207°F.*

Climate

Like the whole Pacific coast of Siberia, Kamchatka is located in the outskirts of the region of monsoon climate with its steady southeastern winds in summer and northern and northwestern winds from the continent in winter. In addition to this general climatic pattern, there are local conditions that influence the climate of Kamchatka. During the winter low pressure dominates over Kamchatka. The pressure decreases both from north to south and from the Okhotsk Sea to the Bering Sea. High pressure is established over Kamchatka in summer. To the south, as well as to the east, the pressure increases. On the east coast the climate is of an oceanic type. Inland, in the central valley, the climate is more continental. The absolute maximum temperature may reach above 80°F and the absolute minimum may be as low as −58°F. The west coast of Kamchatka is much colder than the east coast because of the nearness of the cold Okhotsk Sea. Permafrost is found only in the northern part of the region.

* Ibid., p. 368.

Table 23 gives temperature and precipitation data for Petropavlovsk,* the capital of Kamchatka, located in the southern part of the

TABLE 23.   TEMPERATURE AND PRECIPITATION AT PETROPAVLOVSK,
LIGHTHOUSE, ELEVATION 46 FEET

Jan.	Feb.	Mar.	Apr.	May	June	July	Aug.	Sept.	Oct.	Nov.	Dec.	Year
Temperature, degrees Fahrenheit												Mean
12	12	19	28	36	44	51	53	48	39	27	18	31.7
Precipitation, inches												Total
3.4	2.3	2.3	2.6	1.2	2.0	2.4	2.6	2.8	3.0	2.6	3.2	30.4

east coast of the peninsula.   At Petropavlovsk summers are cool and winters are relatively mild.   The mean temperature of the warmest month, August, is 53°F, although in the daytime the temperature generally reaches 60°F.   The vegetative period, when the average daily temperature is above 41°F, extends from the end of May to the beginning of October.   The precipitation at Petropavlovsk is about 30.4 inches a year.   Most of it is in the form of rain.   The minimum precipitation falls during May.   Snow in winter at Petropavlovsk is, nevertheless, abundant, often piling up to the roofs of the houses and to the tops of telephone poles.   Snow in June is a common sight; but the first snow in winter falls rather late, usually in October and only rarely in September.

Generally, the precipitation decreases from the southeastern coast to the northwestern part of the peninsula, where it amounts only to 14 inches a year.   In the inner valley the precipitation is approximately the same (13.8 inches).   No thunderstorms occur in Kamchatka.

During the summer months there is considerable cloudiness in Kamchatka, especially on the west coast.   The coasts of Kamchatka are notorious for dense summer fogs that conceal the land for days.   Winter months on the coasts are usually clear.

* Officially known as Petropavlovsk-on-Kamchatka to distinguish it from a city of the same name located in Western Siberia.

Soils and Vegetation

The soils of Kamchatka are either, under the conifer forests, podzol type, or where herbaceous vegetation prevails, meadow type. The latter soils develop on ancient alluvial material and are very rich in humus. Swampy soils where aeration is insufficient and oxidation processes are retarded occupy large areas in the lowlands of the peninsula.

The vegetation of Kamchatka is not very rich, amounting to not over 850 species. Ancient glaciation and volcanic activity were detrimental to the preservation of the vegetation of earlier periods, and thus endemic species are rare. One of the relicts of old times is an endemic fir (*Abies gracilis*) found infrequently in the southern part of the peninsula. The isolation of Kamchatka from other regions of northeastern Asia by the tundra stretches of Parapol Dol also has contributed a great deal to the present poor flora of the peninsula.

Noteworthy is the almost complete absence of plants belonging to the families of Compositae (sunflower family) and Leguminosae (pea family); the genera *Oxytropis* and *Astragalus* of the latter family are exceptions. Some plants have been brought by water to southwestern Kamchatka from the Okhotsk coast. Among these are *Swertia tetrapetala* and one of the few legumes of Kamchatka, *Thermopsis fabacea*. Botanically, Kamchatka may be divided into three parts: (1) the east coast, (2) the west coast, and (3) the inner valley. Mountain slopes up to 1000 feet on the east coast of Kamchatka are occupied by parklike open forests of Ermans, or stone, birch, a medium-sized tree (scrubby in places) with shaggy, reddish bark. Growing under the birch are either such shrubs as alder, trailing pine (*Pinus pumila*), scrubby mountain ash or herbaceous species such as sedge, violet, anemone, and, later in the season, northern orchids. July brings milletgrass (*Milium effusum*) and other tall grasses, herbs such as wormwood (*Artemisia vulgaris*), and umbellifers. Ermans birch forests are of considerable economic importance in Kamchatka. They furnish building material, they shelter game, and their herbaceous cover provides food for cattle.

The lower slopes of volcanoes often support groves of aspen of good quality with shrubby ground cover of honeysuckle, rose, and scanty grasses. Black-blue berries of honeysuckle (*Lonicera edulis*) are gathered for winter use late in July or at the beginning of August.

The flat, cold, foggy west coast of Kamchatka is generally covered with swamps, which are found even on the low watershed divides.

Ermans birch does not grow near the coast. It appears farther inland, first in protected places and later on the watershed divides where the terrain is hilly and where the climate is warmer. Here it grows to a fair size. Berg * gives the following scheme of vertical distribution of vegetation, after Pavlov:

1. Forest belt from sea level to 1800 feet. It includes sphagnum bogs, fields of black crowberry (*Empetrum nigrum*), highland meadows, and forests of Ermans birch.
2. Brushfields from 1600 feet to 2600 feet. This area comprises alder thickets and *Pinus pumila* thickets.
3. Alpine belt, 2600 to 4600 feet, including highland tundras, alpine meadows, and patches of alpine vegetation.

Types 2 and 3 are essentially the same as for the upper elevations of Kamchatka Valley, to be described presently.

In Kamchatka Valley, Ermans birch does not grow at low elevations. Here on the alluvial soils of the valley and the adjacent foothills are forests of Dahurian larch with some aspen and white birch (*Betula japonica*), towering over such species as *Pyrola* and cowberry. Spruce (*Picea ajanensis* or *jezoensis*) forests with an admixture of white birch and larch are found on well-drained soil in sheltered situations. The underbrush consists of the usual honeysuckle, rose, aspen, mountain ash, and willow. The north slopes of the ridges are often occupied with spruce forests, whereas larch grows on the south slopes (compare with Altai region). Extensive groves of white birch are found in the valleys.

With increasing altitude the first tree to disappear is spruce, then larch and white birch. The upper limit of spruce and larch is an elevation of a little over 1000 feet. Ermans birch begins to dominate above this elevation. At 2000 to 2400 feet birch is replaced by impenetrable thickets of either trailing pine (*Pinus pumila*), Siberian mountain ash, or alder (*Alnus kamtschatica*). Alder thickets 6 to 10 feet in height appear from a distance as extensive and continuous green fields; they are crisscrossed with tunnels made by bears.

At elevations of 3000 to 3300 feet the thickets disappear and the terrain assumes a subalpine aspect. On the flats and gentle slopes tundralike stretches are found with a few ericaceous species. Subalpine meadow vegetation consists of tall herbs, such as parsnip, aconite, iris,

* L. S. Berg, *Priroda*, 2nd ed., Moscow, 1938, p. 282.

and lily (*Lilium avenaceum*, called by local Russians sarana *). Under these species grow another sarana (*Fritillaria kamtschatcensis*), viviparous bistort (*Polygonum viviparum*), and horsetail. There are neither legumes nor grasses.

Higher up the vegetation is of an alpine type. Short herbaceous species, such as alpine arnica (*Arnica alpina*), arctic diapensia (*Diapensia lapponica*), sweetgrass (*Hierochloe alpina*), and Iceland poppy (*Papaver nudicaule*), form bright patches alternating with attractive ericaceous tundra plants. Extensive alpine meadows on the slopes of the watershed ridges are amply watered by streams running from the nearby snowfields. Here one may find sedges, spike trisetum (*Trisetum spicatum*), fescue (*Festuca rubra alpina*), *Pedicularis aederi*, primrose (*Primula cuneifolia*), and *Oxytropis revolutus*. Tundra vegetation prevails in dry places; here are found low shrubs of *Rhododendron chrysanthum* (called intoxicating herb by the local people), Arctic willow, *Parnassia palustris*, *Gentiana glauca*, and *Campanula lasiocarpa*. On the porous volcanic formations one finds *Cassiope ericoides* and *Rhododendron kamtschaticum* with its large red flowers. On the crests of the mountains the vegetation is scanty, consisting of such inhabitants of dry tundra as willow (*Salix arctica*) and dryad (*Dryas kamtschatica*).

As is usual all over the northeastern part of Siberia, the woody vegetation in the valleys and along the streams consists of willows (*Salix sakhalinensis* being predominant), cottonwood, alder (*Alnus hirsuta*), and the ever-present straight-trunked Korean willow (*Chosenia macrolepis*). Flood plain meadows are covered with herbaceous vegetation, in which one may recognize Siberian burnet (*Sanguisorba tenuifolia*), reedgrass (*Calamagrostis langsdorffi*), meadow peavine (*Lathyrus pratensis*), and sedge. In drier locations among Ermans birch grow tall umbellifers: angelica (*Angelica ursina*), common parsnip (*Heracleum lanatum*), and *Senecio palmatus*. In olden days the Kamchadal people used the parsnip for food. Russian trappers and settlers learned how to make an intoxicating drink from this plant. This practice, however, is not common at present. Early Kamchadals also used roots of meadowsweet (*Filipendula kamtschatica*) for food. Meadowsweet grows extremely fast, reaching 7 feet in height in a couple of weeks. *Fritillaria kamtschatcensis*, or sarana, which grows all the way from the river valleys to the alpine zone, even now is used by the natives for food. Boiled starchy bulbs of this sarana taste like chestnuts.

* This is a common name for martagon lily and other lilies throughout Eastern Siberia.

Local nettle (*Urtica platyphylla*), which may reach a height of 6 feet, formerly provided fiber used by the Kamchadals for cloth and for making fish nets.

Near hot springs, plants are found that do not occur elsewhere in Kamchatka. These are mostly representatives of Sakhalin, Manchuria, and Japan. In March when Kamchatka is still buried under snow, here close to the hot water the violet is already blooming and one may also find the heat-enduring *Fimbristylis ochotensis* (of the sedge family) and flatsedge (*Heleocharis palustris*).

Kamchatka is not a place for agriculture. It is true that in the inner valley summer is warm enough to grow grain, but very often crops do not ripen. Perhaps some cool-climate plants such as flax would be more successful. A suggestion has been made that vegetables be grown near the numerous hot springs.

Animal Life

The animal life of Kamchatka is not very abundant either. The Parapol Dol (see p. 316) acts as a barrier that many Siberian animals cannot cross. Thus there are no moose, muskdeer, kolonok (*Mustela sibirica*), or chipmunk in Kamchatka. The gray squirrel (*Sciurus vulgaris*) appeared in the northern part of the peninsula only in 1910–1911. In 1938 it was recorded in the southern part of the peninsula. Mountain sheep occurs throughout the peninsula, where it inhabits high elevations. Marmot (*Marmota kamtschatica*) and ground squirrel (*Citellus eversmanni stejnegeri*) are found in mountains. Occasionally there is a wild reindeer (*Rangifer tarandus setoni*). Kamchatka sable is large but its fur is not considered to be good. Kamchatka bear (*Ursus piscator*) is a large and fierce animal. It thrives on salmon, which it fishes from the streams with its paws. The Kamchatka population depends on the bear as a source of meat supply.

There are less than 200 species of birds in Kamchatka. Waterfowl is plentiful: there are geese, ducks, snipes, auks, and cormorants. Game birds include the stone grouse (*Tetrao uragalloides kamtschaticus*), but the common small grouse (*Tetrastes bonasia*) and Okhotsk black grouse (*Falcipennis falcipennis*) are absent. In the Ermans birch forests there occur two species of woodpeckers and a variety of Siberian bullfinch (*Pyrrhula pyrrhula cassini*).

The only amphibian represented is a triton (*Hynobius keyserlingi*).

Kamchatka is very poor in fresh-water fish, but there is an abundance of Pacific salmon, which is represented by several species of the genus *Onocorhynchus*. Occasionally a true salmon (genus *Salmo*) is found. The hair seal, following the fish, enters the Kamchatka River and travels upstream for about 120 miles. Fresh-water mollusks are represented by the pearl oyster (*Margaritana middendorffi*).

People

The original inhabitants of Kamchatka were a Paleo-Asiatic people, the Kamchadals. Now they have almost completely disappeared. What remained of them after the conquest of Kamchatka has been Russianized. About 2000 of this people, now known as Itelmen, live on the west coast of the peninsula. A few Lamuts live in the middle western part. The northern, narrow part of Kamchatka is the country of the Koriaks, most of whom live farther north. Some of the Koriaks are settled fishermen; others keep reindeer.

As a whole, the population of Kamchatka region is predominantly Russian.

NEIGHBORING ISLANDS

Karaginski Island is located in the Bering Sea and is separated from Kamchatka by Litke Strait.* It is a mountainous island with elevations over 3100 feet. The coast is abrupt and rocky. The climate and vegetation are similar to those of Kamchatka's east coast. In well-drained elevated situations tundra prevails with occasional fair areas of meadowland. Sphagnum bogs are common. Trailing pine and alder thickets grow on the slopes, and willows grow along the streams. In places there are park-like groves of Ermans birch, together with alder or trailing pine. The openings are occupied with reedgrass. These groves are inhabited by fox, ermine, sable; in the tundra, arctic fox (which the Russians call pesets from pes, meaning dog) and ptarmigan are found.

Migratory birds, including geese and ducks, occasionally stop on the island on their way north. Commercial hunting is the chief occupation of the population of the island, which consists mostly of the Koriaks.

The Commander Islands, consisting of two large islands and two small uninhabited ones, are named for Commander Vitus Bering, who

---

* Named after Admiral Theodor P. Litke (Lütke) (1797–1882), first president of the Russian Geographic Society and an explorer of Kamchatka, the Bering Sea, the Aleutian Islands, and the North American coast.

discovered the largest island (Bering Island) and died there in 1741. The other large island is known as Medny, which in Russian means Copper Island. It was discovered by Bering's companion, Steller. The Commander Islands are located 165 miles east of Kamchatka, from which they are separated by depths of 16,000 feet (measured between Point Kronotski and the islands); from the Aleutian Islands they are separated by depths reaching 11,000 feet. The islands are rocky with an abrupt coast. The highest point on Bering Island is 2200 feet; on Medny Island the highest summit is 1950 feet.

The islands are composed of volcanic rocks (andesite, tufa, basalt, etc.) of the Tertiary period. Earthquakes are common.

The climate of the islands is damp, cool, and foggy. The winter is warmer than, for instance, on Sakhalin. Mean temperatures during the coldest months (January and February) are 25° to 26°F. Summer is cool; the mean temperature of the warmest month, August, is 50°F. Storms are frequent, and the dampness in the air is great. The average relative humidity is 95 per cent. The annual precipitation amounts to about 20 inches.

There are no large trees on the islands. The prevailing type of landscape is the tundra. On the Commander Islands tundra is found farther south (to the 55th parallel) than anywhere else in the world. In protected places, such as in small valleys, there are scrubby willows, mountain ash,* and Ermans birch. These bushes seldom reach more than 6 or 7 feet in height. Parsnip and meadowsweet grow almost as tall as in Kamchatka. In the waters surrounding the islands there are extensive underwater fields of kelp.

Arctic fox and ptarmigan are found on the rocky shores of the islands, and sea otter (*Enhydra lutris*), sea lion (*Eumatopias jubata*, called sivutch by the Russians), and fur seal (*Arctocephalus* or *Callorhinus ursinus*) live in the nearby waters. Steller's sea cow, which was abundant at the time of discovery of the islands, was completely exterminated by the Russian fur hunters as early as 1770. The rocky cliffs of the islands are inhabited by multitudes of sea birds, such as petrels (*Fulmarus gracilis*), kittiwakes (*Rissa tridactyla*), and puffins (*Fratercula cirrata*). Transitory birds, such as sea gulls, geese, ducks, and snipes, are abundant in spring and fall.

The Commander Islands are populated by some 600 Aleuts, who are now called Unangans.

---

* The English name of *Sorbus*, mountain ash, is somewhat inappropriate in describing the scrubby *Sorbus* growing in some parts of Siberia.

The Kuril Islands, although they originally belonged to Russia, were a part of Japan from 1875 until after World War II, when they were returned to Russia. Therefore, relatively little has been done recently by Russian geographers in studying the islands, and our knowledge of this region is dependent either on old Russian descriptions or on secondhand information based on Japanese sources. The present description of the Kuril Islands is based on information gathered by Suslov in his *Physical Geography of the USSR* * and on the author's personal acquaintance with the region.

The Kuril Islands form a long chain extending between the southern tip of Kamchatka and the eastern part of the Japanese island of Hokkaido. The chain consists of 36 large and 20 smaller islands. The islands may be divided into two groups: the main group extends between Kamchatka and Hokkaido for about 750 miles; the lesser group extends from the Nemuro Peninsula of Hokkaido to the island of Shikotan, a distance of only 60 miles.

The total area of all the islands is about 6000 square miles. The largest islands are: Etorofu, Paramushiro, Kunashiri, and Uruppu. These comprise about 40 per cent of the total area.

The Kuril Islands separate the Okhotsk Sea from the Pacific. Surface layers of the Okhotsk Sea are replenished by water flowing from the Pacific, mainly through Bussol † Strait, located south of the island of Shimushiru and having a depth of more than 6500 feet. The outgoing water flows from the Okhotsk Sea through the straits located between the middle islands. West of the chain is the deepest part of the Okhotsk Sea, averaging about 10,000 feet deep. East of the islands, the Pacific is over 26,000 feet deep.

The islands are essentially volcanic cones of lava that broke through the Paleozoic and Mesozoic sediments of an ancient geosyncline. The epeirogenic adjustments and volcanic activity along the Kuril chain have not yet been completed. New islands appear, earthquakes are frequent and violent, and some islands are being uplifted, as demonstrated by the presence of recent young marine terraces. The islands essentially are composed of andesite and tufa; only the Island Shumushu, in the north, and Shikotan, in the south, are composed of sedimentary material. On some islands dislocated Paleozoic and Mesozoic metamorphic rocks protrude from under the lava. In low areas they are covered with Tertiary sediments.

* Moscow, 1947, pp. 382–389.
† The Japanese call it Kitauruppu.

There are, on the islands, more than 50 volcanoes. Eighteen of them are active, among which are Peak Sarychev * on the island of Matsuwa, 4871 feet high, and Peak Prevot on the island of Shimushiru, 4461 feet high.

The Kuril Islands are poor in mineral wealth. Sulfur is mined on Kunashiri Island; silver and iron are found on Paramushiro and Shumushu; and there are indications of zinc and lead on Uruppu Island. Pumice is found in abundance.

Mountains extend along the islands as one longitudinal ridge. Only occasionally are there two or more flat, low, parallel ridges. On many of the islands tall volcanic cones are grouped together. The highest volcanoes are covered with snow. On the volcano on Alaid Island (7655 feet) the snow descends to 2600–1700 feet above sea level.† In 1934, 12 miles from Alaid, where the sea is over 2600 feet deep, a small volcanic island appeared.

Facing the cold Okhotsk Sea, the Kuril Islands have a very severe climate. Winters are long and cold; summers are cool with drizzles and fogs. On Etorofu the mean February temperature is 20°F; the mean August temperature is 60°F. As is to be expected, it is colder on the more northerly islands. The frostless period in the northern part of the chain amounts to 120 days. In the south it is 180 days.

The precipitation along the Kuril chain is abundant: about 30 inches a year in the north, and about 40 inches in the south. The maximum precipitation occurs in August and September; the minimum in January and February. Snow covers the ground by the end of October and remains until the middle of May. Snow does not fall during the period July to September. Blizzards are common. Occasionally in the winter the precipitation falls in the form of rain, although most of the annual precipitation is in the form of snow. Summer rains are mostly long monotonous drizzles. Cloudiness is common. There are approximately 229 cloudy days a year during which time there is no sunshine at all, and there are only 15 fully sunny days in a year. Fogs along the Kurils are very common and during the summer months cover the entire chain almost continuously.

* Named after the Russian captain Gavrila Sarychev, who, with Joseph Billings, explored the northeastern Pacific in 1786–1793. This expedition accomplished very little.

† Alaid Island is located near Kamchatka, in the Okhotsk Sea, somewhat apart from the chain of the Kuril Islands. Alaid is a majestic snow-covered volcano rising from the sea.

During the winter northwestern winds prevail. Temperature may drop then to −15°F. During the summer the air temperature is usually about 54° to 58°F, although occasionally it may be as high as 80° to 88°F or as low as 24°F (in June). Clear, still weather occurs usually in autumn. At that time fogs are less frequent and storms rare.

The Kurils are not well supplied with running fresh water. On some of the islands, such as Raikoke, there is no fresh water at all. Sizable streams flow on the larger islands, but some of them contain water that is not suitable for drinking, either because of the high sulfur content or because of an excess of organic matter.

There are on the islands occasional lakes, mostly of volcanic origin. Water from such lakes is not very palatable. Fresh-water lakes are found occasionally near the estuaries of the rivers. Most of these lakes, however, have either brackish or salty water.

The vegetation of the Kuril Islands consists of about 750 species. Most of these belong to the flora of Japan. Only 45 species are common to both Kamchatka and the islands. Circumpolar species, both of the arctic-alpine type and of the common Eurasian type, are rather numerous. In the surrounding waters are extensive submarine kelp fields. One species of kelp (*Nereocystis lutkeanus*) begins to develop in April, and by July it may reach over 150 feet in length. At that time it rises to the surface. At the end of August the sea currents break the plants loose, and the waves cast enormous quantities of kelp on the shores of the islands.

The northern islands are covered with arctic-alpine vegetation. Here are found dwarf willow, arctic birch, ericaceous species, and dryad. In low places sedge develops. On more elevated locations may be found trailing pine (*Pinus pumila*), alder (*Alnus fruticosa*), crowberry (*Empetrum nigrum*), and *Ledum palustre*. Meadows either with a predominance of reedgrass or with various dicotyledons such as *Cacalia* (or *Senecio*) *hastata* and meadowsweet are found occasionally in the valleys of Paramushiro Island. Vegetation is poorest on the middle islands because these are small and low and well cooled by the cold Okhotsk waters pouring out to the ocean through the straits. Some of these islands, such as Matsuwa, are covered with patches of lichens and are devoid of any other vegetation.

From the Island Ketoi south, there appear more southern species, such as Kuril bamboo (*Sasa kurilensis*) and Japanese yew (*Taxus cuspidata*). Dense birch-alder forests appear on Uruppu Island. On the slopes Ermans birch grows mixed with Kuril cherry (*Prunus kurilensis*).

On the southern islands of Etorofu and Kunashiri there are extensive forests of spruce (*Picea jezoensis*) and fir (*Abies sachalinensis* and *A. glehni*); yew and maple (*Acer ukurundense*) are also present. On the southern slopes one may find groves of oak (*Quercus grosseserrata* and *Q. dentata*), walnut (*Juglans sieboldiana*), hornbeam (*Carpinus cordata*), and hop hornbeam (*Ostrya japonica*).

Above the conifer forests are birch groves (*Betula ulmifolia*) with bamboo and trailing pine underneath. Above the birch are impenetrable thickets of trailing pine with an admixture of alder (*Alnus maximowiczi*).

During their prolonged occupation of the islands, the Japanese have achieved some results in growing barley, rye, and wheat, as well as vegetables, on the southern islands.

The animal life of the Kuril Islands is not very abundant. Most of the mammals are found in the forests. Gray squirrel, bear, wolf, and fox occur on the southern islands. Arctic fox has been introduced by the Japanese and is found on some islands in great numbers.

There are about 170 species of birds, most of them on the southern islands. The rocky cliffs are crowded with auklets, cormorants, kittiwakes, and puffins, and other waterfowl. Ptarmigan is found on the bare summits of the northern and middle islands. Some Japanese birds, such as Japanese quail, blue flycatcher, and Japanese longtail chickadee, live on the southern islands.

Reptiles are found only on the southern islands. The middle islands have almost no insects, but on the southern islands there are many mosquitoes and gnats are numerous and very annoying.

Domestic animals include sheep and cattle, but only in limited numbers.

The original population of the Kuril Islands, the Kurils, who were akin to the Ainus, no longer exist. On Kunashiri and Etorofu live some Japanese and Ainus. Since World War II Russian settlements have been established on several islands.

Chapter 28

Islands of the Arctic

Russia possesses in the Arctic several islands or groups of islands. These have been briefly mentioned in Chapter 1. All Russian Arctic islands are located on the submerged shelf of the Eurasian continent and surrounded with relatively shallow seas. The oceanic depths of the Arctic are encountered only north of the edge of the shelf. Some of the islands of the Arctic belong to the tundra region; others are within the nival,* or the ice, zone where the mean temperature, even of the warmest month, is below or only slightly above 32°F. The northern part of the Taimyr Peninsula is also within the nival zone.

The islands to be considered in this chapter are Franz Josef Land, Novaia Zemlia Islands, Kolguev Island, and Vaigach Island, in the European part of the Arctic; and Severnaia Zemlia, the New Siberian Islands, and Wrangel Island, in the Asiatic part of the Arctic.† (See Map 34.) Besides these large islands there are many small ones that dot the coast of the Arctic. Numerous islands are scattered in the eastern part of Kara Sea, north of the Yenisei estuary.

Kolguev Island

Kolguev Island is located not far from the mainland, north of Bolshezemelskaia Tundra (see p. 91) and east of the Kanin Peninsula. The island is composed of Quaternary deposits. Its area is 1430 square miles. The highest points reach 300 feet. The northern part of the island is covered with moss tundra. In the south are found areas of

---

* According to L. S. Berg's classification. See his *Geographic Zones of the USSR*, 3rd ed., Moscow, 1947.

† In 1916 the Russian Ambassador in London delivered to the Minister of Foreign Affairs a note, stating that the islands of Severnaia Zemlia, discovered in 1913–1914, had been incorporated in the Russian Empire, and added that "The Imperial Government takes this occasion to set forth that it considers as making an integral part of the Empire the islands Henrietta, Jeannette, Bennett, Herald . . . which with the New Siberia Islands, Wrangel and others situated near the Asiatic Coast of the Empire, form an extension toward the North of the continental shelf of Siberia." (Quoted from Stefansson's *The Adventure of Wrangel Island*, The Macmillan Company, New York, 1925, pp. 22–23.)

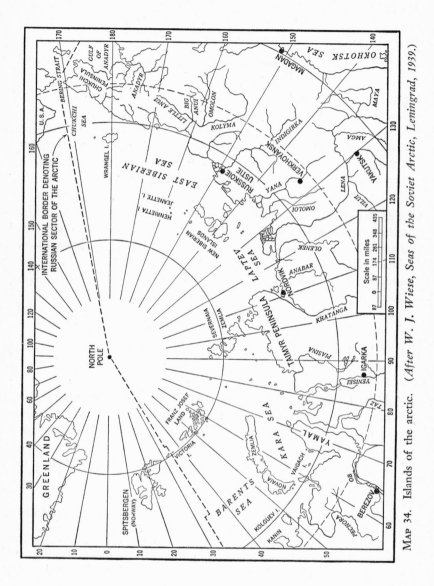

Map 34. Islands of the arctic. (After W. J. Wiese, Seas of the Soviet Arctic, Leningrad, 1939.)

scrub tundra and of hummock tundra. Permanently frozen ground occurs on the island. Kolguev is populated by a few Samoyeds. Russians visit it only for hunting and fishing.

Vaigach Island

The island of Vaigach lies between the mainland and Novaia Zemlia. It is separated from the mainland by Yugorski Shar * (Ugrian Strait), which is only 2.5 miles wide, and from Novaia Zemlia by the much wider Karskie Vorota (Kara Gate) Strait. The area of the island is 1350 square miles. Some zinc, lead, and copper deposits are found on the island. Vaigach is covered with arctic-type tundra; in places the terrain is rocky. The island is frequented by Samoyed hunters. A wireless station is located on the northwestern coast.

Novaia Zemlia

Novaia Zemlia (New Land) consists of two large islands along the coasts of which are scattered numerous small islands. The area of South Island is 15,820 square miles; the area of North Island is 21,250 square miles. The total length of the two islands is about 620 miles, and the widest part of South Island is about 87 miles. The coastline of the two islands is a little over 2900 miles. The two islands are separated by a narrow strait called Matochkin Shar.

The northernmost point of Novaia Zemlia, Mys Zhelaniia (Wish Point), is located at 77° latitude N, which is somewhat south of the tip of the Siberian mainland. There are three Samoyed settlements on the southwestern part of South Island with a total population of a little over 100 people, a weather station, and a radio station. The first mention of Novaia Zemlia appeared in Richard Hakluyt's *The Principal Navigations . . . of the English Nation*, published in 1859, in which he described Willouby's voyage near Novaia Zemlia in 1553.†

Novaia Zemlia is composed of sandstone, dolomite, quartzite, and conglomerates of the Paleozoic era. In the northern part of South Island the elevations are up to about 3300 feet. Twenty or twenty-five

* From the Finnish word saari, meaning an island. Cf. L. S. Berg, *Essays on the History of Russian Geographic Discoveries*, Moscow, 1946, p. 80. (In Russian.)

† Richard Hakluyt, *The Principal Navigations, Voyages, Traffiques and Discoveries of the English Nation*, 8 Vols., London, 1859, F. M. Went & Company; New York, E. P. Dutton & Company, 1907.

miles south of Matochkin Shar glaciers begin to appear. At 74° latitude (on North Island) the inland glaciers reach the shores of fiords, which have cut inland for 20 to 25 miles. At 76° latitude the whole land, with the exception of a narrow strip along the coast, is covered with an ice cap. From here northward lies the nival zone. There is reason to believe that during interglacial times the ice mantle now covering North Island did not exist.

The shores of Novaia Zemlia are gradually being raised. Some stretches of land which at the time of Barents * appeared as peninsulas are, at present, charted as islands. In many places new islands have appeared since the first maps of Novaia Zemlia were made. Narrow and long fiords are numerous on the west coast of South Island. These are original tectonic fissures subsequently enlarged and deepened by the action of water and ice. Most of North Island is covered with ice. Only along the coasts are there strips of bare ground.

Berg describes as follows a crossing of North Island, made by a party of explorers in 1913 at latitude 76.† "On April 4, the temperature at the highest point of the transect (about 3000 feet above sea level) was 0°F. A gentle north-northwest wind was blowing; the sun shone brightly and the weather was perfect. Hoarfrost was settling on the ice throughout the day in enormous quantity; the layer of newly settled hoarfrost measured 1 inch. When the island was recrossed 18 days later, the weather at the same spot was calm with dense fog and rain. The air temperature was 34°F."

At the northern extremity of Novaia Zemlia where weather observations were taken from 1931 to 1936,‡ the mean monthly temperatures, in degrees Fahrenheit, were as follows:

Jan.	Feb.	Mar.	Apr.	May	June	July	Aug.	Sept.	Oct.	Nov.	Dec.	Year
−2	0	−6	4	18	30	29	36	31	24	10	1	14

* Dutch navigator Willem Barents reached Novaia Zemlia in 1594. He died in 1597 and was buried on the South Island.

† L. S. Berg, *Priroda, USSR,* 2nd ed., Moscow, 1938, p. 286. This description was taken from an article of W. J. Wiese, *Bulls. Hydrography,* Vol. 49, 1925, pp. 63–74. (In Russian.)

‡ Z. A. Riazantseva, "Novaia Zemlia and Franz Josef Land," *Trudy Arctic Inst.,* Vol. 79, p. 37, 1937. (In Russian.)

Occasionally in winter temperatures may drop as low as −58° F. The precipitation at Novaia Zemlia is very light, being in the neighborhood of 8 inches a year.

The vegetation of South Island is of an arctic tundra type (see p. 92, Chapter 9). There are no trees; dwarf birch (*Betula nana*) and several species of dwarf willows are found only in exceptionally favorable, well-protected places. There are no sphagnum moss bogs, such as are found in the more southern tundras. Flowering plants include *Crystaltea ledum* (*Ledum palustre*), bog bilberry (*Vaccinium uliginosum*), and cloudberry (*Rubus chamaemorus*).

The vegetation of North Island is even less diversified than that of South Island. It clings to the coastal strip not covered with ice. North of 75° latitude only 80 species of higher plants have been recorded, but the lichen flora consists of more than 200 species. The vegetation of the places where the soil is enriched with droppings of waterfowl develops much better than elsewhere. This fact seems to indicate that, in addition to the low temperatures prevailing during the growing season, lack of nutrients, especially nitrogen, in the tundra soil may be responsible for the poor development of plants. In the cold climate of the tundra nitrogen-fixing bacteria apparently do not develop well and scanty drizzles do not bring much nitrogen oxide to the soil from the atmosphere.

Bird life of Novaia Zemlia is represented chiefly by waterfowl living in large colonies along the coast, a species of guillemot (*Uria lomvia*) being the most common. On the north coast of Novaia Zemlia kittiwake (*Rissa tridactyla*), fulmar petrel (*Fulmarus glacialis*), and auklet (*Alle alle*) are also found in large numbers. In the tundras of South Island are found snowy owl and snow bunting (*Plectrophenax nivalis*). Eider duck (*Somateria molissima*), goose (*Anser fabilis*), and swan (*Cygnus bewicki* and *C. minor*) nest along the coast. Altogether there are 77 species of birds on Novaia Zemlia. There are reported to be over 125 species of insects.

Reindeer and arctic fox occur on South Island. Near the coast are found polar bear, walrus, hair seal, and whale.

Franz Josef Land

Franz Josef Land is an archipelago consisting of some 800 islands located in the northern part of Barents Sea between 79°45′ and 81°50′ latitude N and 42°10′ and 65°00′ longitude E. The archipelago is the northernmost possession of the Soviet Union and is considered an important intermediate base for air travel between Europe and North America.* Franz Josef Land was discovered Aug. 30, 1873, by Weyprecht and Payer's Austrian expedition on the ship *Tegetthoff*.† In 1901 to 1906 the archipelago was explored by two American expeditions sponsored by a manufacturer named William Ziegler. The first expedition was under the command of Evelyn B. Baldwin; the second under Anthony Fiala.‡

In 1926 the archipelago was proclaimed by the Soviet Union to be a part of the country.§ Two years later a research station was established on Hooker Island and systematic weather observations and other research activities were begun. During 1930–1931 the station was visited by the German dirigible *Graf Zeppelin*.

The archipelago may be divided into three groups: the eastern, which includes Graham Bell and Wilczek || islands; the middle group, of many smaller islands; and the western group, which includes the largest islands of the archipelago—Prince George Island and Alexandra Land.¶

Most of the islands consist of an elevated tableland that descends abruptly to the water. Elevations run up to 3000 feet. Alexandra Land, however, is low. The islands are composed of Middle and Upper Jurassic marine sediments capped with basalt more than 60 feet in thickness. In some places Cretaceous rocks containing fossil plants and layers of brown coal are found. About 97 per cent of the archipelago is covered with ice. During the Quaternary period there occurred a dislocation of a fault type which resulted in the formation of the present islands. The fault valleys became straits. These straits are much deeper than the adjacent parts of the Barents Sea, some reaching a depth of over 6500 feet.

The climate of Franz Josef Land is very severe; nevertheless, at Tikhaia (calm) Bay on Hooker Island it is milder than the climate

---

* *Great Soviet Encyclopedia,* Vol. 58, p. 417.

† Julius Payer, "New Lands within the Arctic Circle," *Narrative of the Discoveries of the Austrian Ship Tegetthoff in the Years 1872–1874,* translated from German, D. Appleton & Company, New York, 1877.

‡ Anthony Fiala, *Fighting the Polar Ice,* Doubleday, Page & Company, New York, 1907, 296 pp.

§ Resolution of the Council of People's Commissars of the USSR of Aug. 15, 1926, probably prompted by the activities of the Stefansson expedition on Wrangel Island.

|| An Austrian count.

¶ On Fiala's map it is called Alexander Land.

of the mainland tundra (compare for instance with Russkoie Ustie, p. 90, or Verkhoyansk, p. 285). The mean monthly temperatures for the period 1932 to 1936 are given in Table 24.*

TABLE 24. MEAN MONTHLY TEMPERATURES (DEGREES FAHRENHEIT) FOR THE PERIOD 1932 TO 1936 AT TIKHAIA BAY, HOOKER ISLAND, FRANZ JOSEF LAND

Jan.	Feb.	Mar.	Apr.	May	June	July	Aug.	Sept.	Oct.	Nov.	Dec.	Year, Mean
−2	−3	−8	2	18	30	34	33	28	16	6	2	13

The annual precipitation at Hooker Island is in the neighborhood of 12 inches. In winter blizzards are rather frequent and cloudiness is prevalent. Fogs are common in summer. In summer the temperature may rise occasionally to 54°F.

The vegetation of the archipelago is poor, consisting mostly of lichens. There are only 35 to 40 species of flowering plants. Among these are the saxifrage, poppy, and some grasses. Arctic willow (*Salix polaris*) grows on the southern islands.

Animals, found only occasionally, are the Arctic fox and polar bear.

The ornithofauna is represented by some 30 species of birds. Auklet (*Alle alle*) is the most numerous, living on the coast cliffs in great colonies. Glaucus gull (*Larus hyperboreus*), kittiwake (*Rissa tridactyla*), guillemot (*Uria lomvia*), ivory gull (*Pagophila eburnea*), and fulmar petrel (*Fulmarus glacilis*) also are found. Ptarmigan (*Lagopus mutus*) may be found on the patches of land not covered with ice.

West of Franz Josef Land, not far from the Norwegian archipelago of Spitsbergen, lies lonely Victoria Island. This island is about 4 miles long and is capped with 300 feet of ice. Its geological structure, judging by the occurrence of the Upper Carboniferous pinkish limestone pebbles, is similar to that of Spitsbergen. Victoria Island is the westernmost Arctic possession of the Soviet Union. It was discovered in 1898 by a Norwegian Captain Nielson. The Soviet flag was raised on the island in 1932.†

* Z. A. Riazantseva, "Novaia Zemlia and Franz Josef Land," *Trudy Arctic Inst.*, Vol. 79, p. 37, 1937. (In Russian.)

† M. V. Klenova, "Ostrov Victoria," *Arctica*, No. 3, pp. 79–87, 1935. (In Russian.)

Severnaia Zemlia

Severnaia Zemlia (North Land) is located north of the Taimyr Peninsula, between 78° and 81° latitude N. It consists of four large islands and many small ones. The archipelago separates the Kara Sea from Laptev Sea (see footnote, p. 11). Severnaia Zemlia is separated from the mainland by Vilkitski Strait.* The archipelago was discovered by Captain Vilkitski, who named it Zemlia (Land) of Nicholas the Second. After the Russian Revolution in 1917 this name was changed to the present name. The total area of the islands of Severnaia Zemlia is about 14,200 square miles.

The largest island (now known as the Island of October Revolution) has a rocky, abrupt east coast that is in the process of more intensive uplift than the low west coast. A range that follows a fault line extends along the east coast. The range is composed of green chlorite and of talcum schists of the Cambrian period. A terrace several miles wide and about 160 feet high extends along the seaward side of the range. The slopes of the range are cut by numerous glacial valleys partly filled with ice flows and extending from the inland glaciers towards the coast. Most of these ice flows, however, do not reach the sea. The west coast is low, with numerous inlets, coves, and estuaries. The predominant deposits consist of Silurian reddish marl. Glaciers descend to the coast, often forming walls of ice 15 to 20 feet high. What was once a continuous ice sheet is separated, at present, into four ice caps. The northern one is 2214 feet high. The thickness of the ice on the island is 600 to 800 feet. The island has numerous streams some of which are as much as 20 miles long. These streams either originate at the bases of the ice caps or run from the central part of the island through deeply cut canyons.

Shokalski Strait † separates the Island of October Revolution from South Island, which has abrupt east and west coasts and low north and south coasts. South Island has a gentle, much-leveled topography, with two rather small ice caps.

The third and northernmost of the four large islands of the archipelago is composed chiefly of Quaternary sediments. It is an island

* Boris Vilkitski was a navy officer and explorer of the Arctic. His father, Andrew Vilkitski (1858–1913), was also an explorer of the northern seas and a noted Russian hydrographer.

† Named after a Russian geographer, noted chiefly in the field of limnology and oceanography. One of the past presidents of the Geographical Society. Born 1856; died 1940.

of low hills and lowlands. A large ice cap over 1600 feet in thickness covers about three-quarters of the island. A smaller glacier is located at the northern end, descending into the sea and concealing the shore-line.

Approximately 42 per cent of the total area of the archipelago is covered with ice. There is evidence of two ancient glaciations that were more intensive than the present one.

The structure of the archipelago is rather complicated. The principal folding occurred during the Paleozoic era. Towards the end of the Paleozoic era the area now occupied by Severnaia Zemlia appeared as a mountainous country extending both farther north and farther south, where it was connected with the mainland. The present topography of the islands was formed during Tertiary and Quaternary times. At the end of the ice age the land was broken apart by several tectonic cleavages and separated from the mainland. Because the archipelago was separated from the Taimyr Peninsula of Siberia relatively recently, there is great resemblance between the geology of Severnaia Zemlia and that of the peninsula. The Paleozoic deposits of several-thousand-feet thickness were superimposed with limestone and later with sandstone, marl, and clay of the Upper Silurian epoch. Later, Permian gray sandstones were deposited on top of these rocks.

The climate of Severnaia Zemlia is severer than the climate of any other islands of the Russian Arctic. Table 25 gives temperature data for a group of islands in the western part of the archipelago.* During

TABLE 25. MEAN MONTHLY TEMPERATURES (DEGREES FAHRENHEIT) TAKEN FROM OCTOBER 1930 TO AUGUST 1934 AT A STATION LOCATED ON KAMENEV ISLANDS, SEVERNAIA ZEMLIA

Jan.	Feb.	Mar.	Apr.	May	June	July	Aug.	Sept.	Oct.	Nov.	Dec.
−16	−10	−18	−7	14	31	33	32	28	14	−4	−16

the period of observations no frost occurred for 8 continuous days in July. The absolute maximum temperature recorded during this month was about 41°F. The absolute minimum in winter was −52°F. Blizzards were recorded on an average of 96 days a year. Snow melted

* J. L. Rusinova, "A Short Meteorological Characteristics of the Sergei Kamenev Islands," *Trans. Arctic Inst.*, Vol. 55, pp. 22–36, 1936. (In Russian, English summary.)

near the first of July, and the first winter snow fell at the end of September. The annual precipitation was found to be between 4 and 6 inches.

The vegetation is poorer on Severnaia Zemlia than on any other islands of the Siberian Arctic. Mosses and lichens are found with a sprinkling of higher plants; more of the latter grow on the southern islands. Such plants as *Deschampsia arctica* and *Poa glauca* were found on the western islands. The following species develop especially well near lemmings' burrows: a poppy (*Papaver radicatum*), a saxifrage (*Saxifraga oppositifolia*), a draba (*Draba alpina*), and a sorrel-like plant (*Oxyria digyna*).

The animal life of the islands also is very scarce. On the coastal plains of South Island small herds of reindeer are occasionally encountered. Arctic fox is common. Lemming (*Lemmus obensis*) is found in large numbers. This interesting polar rodent is active throughout the winter. In warm summers lemmings reproduce twice, but if the summer is cold they give birth to only one litter.

There are only 20 species of birds on the islands. Among them are guillemot (*Cepphus grille mandtii*), ivory gull (*Pagophila eburnea*), and Glaucus gull (*Larus hyperboreus*). These few species of birds, as everywhere in the Arctic, live in numerous colonies called, by the Russians, bazaars. Each bazaar may consist of hundreds of thousands of birds, sometimes of several and sometimes of only one species. The noise made by these bird colonies is reminiscent of an oriental market (bazaar) or of a political rally. Snow bunting is found everywhere. It arrives on the islands as early as the beginning of May. Brent goose (*Branta bernicla*) is the only representative of the *Anserinae* family found on Severnaia Zemlia.

Apparently there are no insects on the islands.

New Siberian Islands *

The New Siberian Islands, or, as the Russians call them, Novo-Sibirskie Ostrova, are located north of that portion of the Arctic coast of Siberia which lies between the rivers Yana and Indigirka. The archipelago may be divided into three groups: the De Long Islands, the New Siberian Islands, and the Liakhov (Liakhovski) Islands.

The De Long group consists of five small islands located northeast of New Siberia. The group is named in honor of Lieutenant Com-

* After S. P. Suslov, *Physical Geography of the USSR*, Moscow, 1947. (In Russian.)

mander George W. De Long, U. S. Navy, who explored that part of the Arctic in 1881. The expedition was sponsored by James Gordon Bennett (the son), publisher of the *New York Herald*: De Long's ship, the *Jeannette*, was crushed by ice, and the explorer himself perished in the attempt to reach the Siberian coast. His body and the bodies of some of his companions were found later in the delta region of the Lena.*

The De Long Islands are plateau-like with an abrupt, inaccessible coastline. The islands are small; Henrietta Island, for instance, has an area of about 6 square miles and its highest point is 1033 feet above sea level. Bennett Island is 607 feet higher. The islands are formed of horizontal Cambrian schists (Bennett) or of sandstones, hornblende, and porphyrites (Henrietta). About half of Henrietta Island is covered with an ice cap 500 feet thick. The glacier is fed principally by hoarfrost (cf. p. 336). On Bennett Island a 2.5 mile-wide glacier descends to the south shore, forming a wall of ice ten feet high. There are no streams of any size on De Long Islands.

The New Siberian group proper consists of four main islands: Kotelni (Caldron), the largest; Faddeevski (Thaddeus); Novaia Sibir (New Siberia); and Belkovski, the smallest. Between Kotelni and Faddeevski islands lies a partly submerged sandy lowland known as Zemlia Bunge.†

The Liakhov group consists of two islands: Bolshoi (Large), and Maly (Small). Bolshoi Liakhov Island is separated from the mainland by Dmitri Laptev Strait.‡

The New Siberian and the Liakhov groups differ considerably in their geology and topography from the De Long Islands. Kotelni Island is composed of Paleozoic limestones. Mesozoic schists, sandstones, and effusive rocks are found in low places on Bolshoi Liakhov Island. Spots of Tertiary sediments containing fossil remains of trees such as *Taxodium* and *Sequoia* occur on all islands. Considerable areas on Bolshoi Liakhov Island are covered with ancient Quaternary deposits with a great deal of fossil ice. This fossil ice is the most an-

* Lieutenant Commander George W. De Long, U.S.N., *The Voyage of the Jeannette*, edited by his wife, Emma De Long, Houghton Mifflin & Company, Boston, 1883, 2 vols.

† A. A. Bunge, a Russian botanist and explorer, lived from 1803 to 1890. Visited New Siberian Islands in 1885–1886.

‡ One of the two Laptev brothers, explorers of the Arctic coast of Siberia during the second expedition of Bering, 1733–1743.

cient of all local Quaternary deposits. Large amounts of loose material have accumulated over it, preserving the ice and the remnants of Quaternary animals, such as the mammoth. At present, however, the fossil ice gradually is melting away, leaving behind sinks and caves.

The elevations of the two groups are lower than those of the De Long group. Hoptaghai Tass summit on Bolshoi Liakhov Island is only 951 feet. The highest point of Kotelni Island is Malakatyn Tass, 787 feet. There are no glaciers on the islands.

In tectonics and geology, the New Siberian archipelago is closely related to the northern part of Verkhoyansk Range (see p. 278). But Paleozoic dislocations here are not so prominent as on the mainland. The Mesozoic foldings also are less noticeable than in the Verkhoyansk Mountains. Considerable faults occurred during the late Tertiary period.

The climate of the New Siberian archipelago is characterized by uniformly cold winter months, as seen from the following table:

Month	Mean Monthly Temperature, degrees Fahrenheit
January	−23
February	−24
March	−20

Summers are cool; the mean temperature in July is 38°F and in August 36°F. Frosts may occur any time throughout the year. Cloudiness is common, and fogs are prevalent during August. In winter blizzards are common, and snow falls occasionally during the summer.* The precipitation amounts only to 3 inches a year. The maximum precipitation occurs in August, 0.7 inch, and the minimum in April, 0.04 inch.

The short, cool summers are not conducive to the soil-forming process. Vegetation on the rocky or gravelly ground is scanty and of the tundra type. There are no trees or shrubs. Dry tundras support scattered saxifrages (*Saxifraga caespitosa, S. hiroulus*)—also cinquefoil (*Potentilla fragiformis*); yellow poppy (*Papaver radicatum*); *Luzula hiperborea;* a plant closely related to avens (*Geum*); and several species of grasses. In moist places, such as on Henrietta Island, the ground is covered with moss and lichens, with scattered sorrel-like

* Occasional snow may fall in summertime in any part of Eastern Siberia even as far south as the Mongolian border.

Oxyria digyna. Near the snowfields one may find buttercups (*Ranunculus nivalis*). Where the ground is enriched with bird droppings, scurvyweed (*Cochlearia arctica*) grows. On Bennett Island one may find poppy, dryad, and lichens.

The fauna of the New Siberian Islands is similar to that of the nearby mainland but much scarcer. Sea birds, such as gulls, auks, and guillemots, living on the rocks near the mainland do not like the flat, low islands of the Liakhov and New Siberian groups. There are more sea birds on the cliffs of De Long Islands. Here nest gulls, golden-eye duck (*Clangula hyemalis*), a diver (*Colymbus stellatus*), and king eider (*Somateria spectabilis*). Ptarmigan is found in the stretches of tundra. In winter, when Laptev Strait is covered with solid ice, reindeer, wolves, and arctic foxes migrate from the near-shore islands to the mainland. Toward summer these animals return to the islands. Lemming (*Lemmus obensis novosibiricus*) is found in large numbers throughout the New Siberian Islands.

Wrangel Island

Wrangel Island is the easternmost island of the Russian Arctic, excepting the 1181-foot rock known as Herald Island, located 12 miles east of Wrangel Island. Wrangel Island is about 80 miles long and 18 to 30 miles wide—about 2000 square miles. It is located in the northeastern part of Chukchi Sea, about 85 miles north of Cape Billings,* or North Cape. It was first placed on the map from hearsay by a Russian explorer, Wrangel,† in 1823. In 1849 British Captain Henry Kellett saw it and named it Kellett Land. Wrangel Island was given its present name by an American whaler, Thomas Long, in 1867.

In 1881 American Captain Calvin L. Hooper landed on Wrangel Island and took possession of it for the United States. In the same year Captain R. M. Berry, U. S. Navy, also landed on the island. Russians first visited the island in 1911. In 1921 a small colony was established there by the Canadians, and the British flag was raised over the island. The enterprise, however, met with misfortune. The Russians sent an expedition to the island in 1924 and two years later

---

* Named after an Englishman, Joseph Billings, who participated in the third Cook expedition. He joined the Russian navy in the 1780's. He explored the Arctic coast of Siberia in 1785–1794. Died in 1806.

† Ferdinand von Wrangell, *Narrative of an Expedition to the Polar Sea in the Years 1820, 1821, 1822, and 1823,* edited by Lieut. Col. Edward Sabine, 2nd ed., London, 1844, p. 325.

planted there a small colony of Eskimos and Chukchi. The island is considered to be a convenient air base.*

Central and southern Wrangel Island has two rather high mountain chains. Peak Berry is 2493 feet high. The northern part of the island is occupied by an extensive lowland. There are no glaciers on the island.

The climate of Wrangel Island is of an oceanic type; the temperatures are rather high for the latitude of the island. Winters are relatively warm, the mean February temperature being −14°F. Summers are cool; the mean July temperature is 36°F. In summer the daytime temperature usually is 40° to 41°F. Days when the temperature rises to 43° to 46°F are considered warm. Occasionally a hot spell may occur in which the thermometer may register 50° to 54°F. Thunderstorms are extremely rare.

The precipitation amounts to about 6 inches a year and is mostly in the form of snow. The relative humidity is usually very high; fogs are very common. Winds from the north predominate. Table 26 gives mean monthly temperatures and monthly precipitation data, obtained on Wrangel Island at a station located at 178°23′ longitude W, 70°58′ latitude N.†

TABLE 26. TEMPERATURE AND PRECIPITATION ON WRANGEL ISLAND

Jan.	Feb.	Mar.	Apr.	May	June	July	Aug.	Sept.	Oct.	Nov.	Dec.	Year
				Temperature, degrees Fahrenheit								Mean
−11	−14	−10	2	18	33	36	36	28	18	3	6	13
				Precipitation, inches								Total
0.43	0.24	0.28	0.24	0.31	0.55	0.91	0.93	0.63	0.51	0.28	0.24	5.55

Lowlands and foothills of the island are covered with arctic-type tundra: with moss, lichens, and over 100 species of higher plants. The

* E. Shvede, "History of Discovery and 'Conquest' of Wrangel Island," *Krasni Flot*, Vol. 10, 1924, pp. 111–120. (In Russian.) For details of the history of the island see Vilhjalmur Stefansson, *The Adventure of Wrangel Island*, The Macmillan Company, New York, 1925, 424 pp.

† F. Tikhomirov, "Climate of Wrangel Island," *Meteorologia i Gidrologia*, Vol. 2, No. 12, pp. 64–66, 1936. (In Russian.)

vegetation very seldom forms a continuous cover. Plants grow in small patches in protected places, in cracks of the rocks, and along the streams. Willows are found in the stream valleys of the southern slopes of the mountains. They are not more than 2 feet high, however.

The bird population is considerable; it includes cormorants, geese, ducks, sea gulls, and other waterfowl. Snowy owl and snow bunting also occur on the island.

Lemming, arctic fox, and polar bear are numerous. Hair seal and walrus are abundant near the shores. There may be as many as 10,000 walrus in one herd.

There are about 25 to 30 species of insects on the island. Mosquitoes are seen only occasionally.

The staple food of the Eskimo and the Chukchi colonists is walrus meat; polar bear and seal also are used for food. A small number of pigs and cattle have been recently brought to the island.

West of Wrangel Island lies an unexplored part of the Soviet Arctic. It was believed for a long time that an island of a considerable size, so-called Andreev Land, was located there. Sverdrup's oceanographic investigations * and air reconnaissances, however, have not substantiated this belief.

The waters of the Arctic Ocean and the seas of the northern Pacific adjacent to the Siberian coast are inhabited by several species of whale. In the Barents Sea there is found Greenland seal, which farther east is replaced by several species of hair seal inhabiting the Arctic, the Bering Sea, and the Okhotsk Sea. The walrus is found all over the Arctic coast from the Kanin Peninsula in the Barents Sea to the Bering Straits and farther south into the Pacific to Mys (Point) Olutorski in northern Kamchatka.

* N. U. Sverdrup, "The Waters on the North Siberian Shelf," *The Norwegian North Polar Expedition with the "Maud," 1918–1925, Scientific Results*, Vol. 4, No. 2, p. 107. ·

Index